CW00796727

Variegated Zonal Pelargoniums

Variegated Zonal Pelargoniums

Richard Tilney-Bassett

SERENDIPITY

First published in 2008 by

Serendipity, Darlington, UK

British Library Cataloguing-in-Publication data
A catalogue record for this book is available from the British Library

ISBN 978-1-84394-189-9

Printed and bound in Great Britain by Biddles Ltd, King's Lynn, Norfolk

In memory of Harvey H N Kabwazi

Acknowledgements

I wish to convey my grateful thanks to the editors for their kind permission to include the following publications in my book.

For table 8.2 Annals of Botany 34, 1970, 811-816, table 2. For table 16.14 Crop Science 17, 1977, 667-668, table 1, and also my thanks go to the author Dr J.R. Sedcole. For table 8.3 Genetical Research 16, 1970, 49-61, table 1, and also Cambridge University Press. For several publications in the journal Heredity; they are table 8.1, Heredity 25, 1970a, 89-103, table 1; table 8.4, Heredity 30, 1973, 1-13, tables 1 and 2; again table 8.4, Heredity 33, 1974b, 353-360, tables 2 and 3; tables 9.3a and 9.3b, 9.4 and 9.5 Heredity 37, 1976, 95-107, tables 2, 3 and 4; figures 9.1, 9.2 and 9.3 Heredity 63, 1989, 145-153, figure 1, 2 and 3; figure 8.3 Heredity 72, 1994, 69-77, table 1. For tables 9.6 and 9.7 the Journal of Heredity 85, 1994, 347-354, tables 2 and 3. For figures 11.1 and 11.2 the Journal of Horticultural Science & Biotechnology 70, 1995, 499-508, figure 1 and table V. For table 8.5 Theoretical and Applied Genetics 85, 1992, 317-324, tables 2, 3 and 4, with kind permission of Springer Science and Business Media. Some of the original tables and figures have been modified to suit the present publication. The titles have been given in the lists of references.

I also wish to thank Ms Susan Glen, Deputy Subject Librarian, for undertaking a Web of Science Records on my behalf. I especially wish to thank the Publishing Managers, Charlotte Tarn and Clair Stobbs, and the Managing Director, Kimberley Wheatley, of Serendipity whose enthusiastic encouragement and kind words were most helpful. Many of my older photographs are in black and white, and are published in the many theses quoted. These are all available to the public in the Library of the University of Wales, Swansea. The theses are a source of additional knowledge on pelargoniums, and I am enormously indebted to the many students for them to whom I give my lasting thanks. It has been a great pleasure to work with them.

I also wish to thank all the academic and technical staff of the Department of Genetics, University of Wales, Swansea for their help and for the happy atmosphere they created.

Finally I would like to thank my wife and family for all the help and encouragement they have given me over half a lifetime.

Foreword

Around 180 years ago in a nursery near Paris, the first graft hybrid + Laburnocytisus 'Adamii' was produced. The nature of this accidental marriage between the tissues of Laburnum and Cytisus was, over the ensuing years, the subject of much speculation. It heralded a period of interest and inquiry into the structure and breeding behaviour of other plants with dissimilar layered growing points (now called plant chimeras). By the time that Baur and Bateson had published their papers on chimeras and sports in 1909 and 1916, the chimerical hypothesis was well understood and investigative work at the John Innes Institute further advanced our knowledge of plant oddities of this kind.

The propensity of variegated plants with white leaf margins and green central zones (or the reverse arrangement), to segregate their dissimilar tissues into pure white or green growing points gave the clue to their chimerical structure. Early breeding attempts to create such plants had resulted in many failures and it was not until the publication of Peter Grieve's book in 1868 that the importance of the germ layer, producing pollen or eggs, became apparent. With particular regard to chimerical variegated zonal pelargoniums, Dr Tilney-Bassett has made research into the structure, genetics and plastid physiology of such plants his lifes work. In this volume he draws on the results of his own extensive research, that of his students at the University of Swansea and a wealth of other scientists working in similar fields throughout the world.

A glimpse at the contents pages of this book is sufficient to reveal the range of subjects covered. Much of the research work described is of a highly technical nature and will be understood and appreciated by geneticists, biochemists, mathematicians and those trained in plant anatomy. That said, it will be apparent to practical plant breeders that there is a great deal of information here, in an affordable volume, for those interested in producing new variegated cultivars of Pelargonium zonale. Perhaps only in the genus Hosta has the structure and breeding behaviour of variegated-leaved cultivars been explored in a similar (though less intensive) way. Chapter 5 dealing with **Hybrid Variegation, chapters 6 Plastid Chimeras** and Chapter 8 **Breeding Variegated Plants** all contain information crucial to the successful raising of new cultivars of Pelargonium. Information on cultivars producing a high proportion of variegated progeny, will well reward practical plant breeders prepared to study the case histories of the breeding experiments described. Non-chimerical variegations which, as a result of virus infection, result in net vein leaf-patterns are briefly described. They are few in number, but the information that they are graft transmissible should ensure the future multiplication of new cultivars of this kind.

Peter Grieve would have been astonished at the extent and genetical complexity that his ground breaking breeding work fostered in his beloved variegated pelargoniums. Dr Tilney-Bassett learned his plant genetics under the tutelage of one of worlds foremost geneticists, Professor C.D.Darlington in the University Botany Department at Oxford. He is to be congratulated on drawing together, in the covers of this modest sized book, such a wealth of information of value to scientific and practical plant breeders.

J K Burras, Oxford

March 2006

Preface

In writing this book I have been inspired by the writing of Peter Grieve nearly 140 years ago. For many pelargonium cultivars variegated plants have always been something of a mystery, and I feel it is time to bring the reader up to date. Variegated plants require two kinds of chloroplasts or plastid, the green one and the white, and these have now been investigated extensively. This includes electron-microscope studies at the time of fertilization, and during embryo development, and also biochemical investigation of the very interesting properties of these plastids. The structure of the flowers, and the role of the plastids and of the cultivars in the control of fertilization are important considerations. The shoot is made up of three distinct layers, and when they contain two distinct plastids, we have chimeras. These vary considerably and include both plastids chimeras and nuclear chimeras causing dwarfing, or flower colour changes. In no other plant are chimeras so abundant.

Hybrid variegation arises when different green plants are crossed together, and the two plastids brought together at fertilization do not function equally. This is a relatively unknown phenomenon, which may be exploited in the future.

The main causes of variegation result from genetic differences between the plastids, particularly the mutant plastids, and between the cultivars. The huge differences in the genetic diversity of pelargonium cultivars gives rise to widely varying properties of variegated seedlings. The analysis of such diversity is important for the understanding of variegation. The causes of the many modifications are described.

In all these studies I have referred to the cultivars by name. It is because two seemingly alike cultivars can give rise to quite different results that the real fascination with the genetics really begins. It is not the outward appearance of the cultivar but what lies within that creates the interest. Always remember that I have chosen to work with only a very few of the many cultivars that exist and are continually being produced. There is much more to do.

The zonal pelargonium has horseshoe shaped markings in the leaves; I have recognized several kinds of these and begin to explain their genetic behaviour. Pelargonium cultivars in general have a wide range of flowers forms and colours. The genetic behaviour of the flower colours is quite complex, and many fascinating crosses are discussed. Gradually the various steps are becoming understood. The classification of the many flower colours is detailed and explores new ground. The analysis of the pigments behind the flower colours is again detailed and almost entirely new. Moreover, the methods of measuring these pigments are explained and include exciting new results, which need further development. A few cases of linkage are all we know from over 30 genes; we have much further to go.

I am not going to include the large amount of physiological investigations concerned with the propagation, growth and culture of pelargoniums for commercial reasons. Nor am I going to discuss the many investigations into the causes and treatments of disease, or the many pests. These have been well described before. I am going to discuss the considerable quantity of genetic information, which has till now received rather scant attention. For those readers who are not familiar with genetics I have included a summary of the most relevant sources. Some of this material is not found in basic genetic texts, but is particularly valuable to the plant breeder. I trust the reader will benefit from this.

Finally, I should like to thank all of my students who have contributed so much to the work I describe. They come from China, Egypt, Ghana, India, Indonesia, Iran, Iraq, Malawi, Mauritius, Saudi Arabia, Syria, Uganda and the United Kingdom. All their contributions are written up in theses that they submitted successfully for the Ph.D., the MSc and the BSc of the University of Swansea. I trust that my book does some justice to their endeavours. Also I would like to think that their experience gained in breeding the zonal pelargonium provides a good foundation for breeding their own plant at home. I should like to thank my wife Elisabeth and my children Amanda and Jeremy for their encouragement and patience in writing this book.

Contents

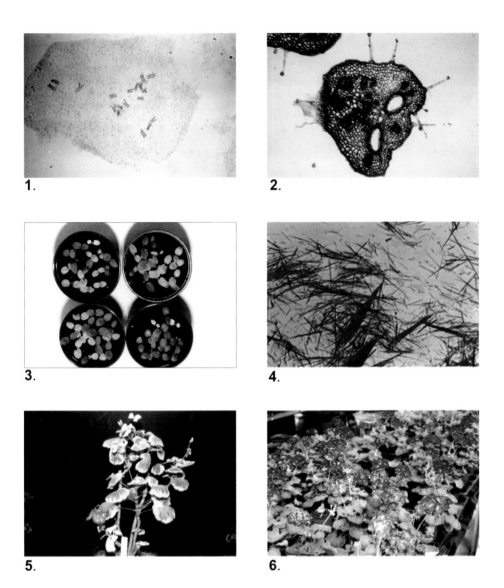

1. The 18 somatic chromosomes of 'Flower of Spring'.
2. A transverse section through the nectary spur showing the twin bore.
3. Segregation into green, golden, and white seedlings of 'Verona'.
4. The anthocyanin crystals of 'Boogy'.
5. The white-over-green chimera of 'Mrs J.C. Mapping' with the whitish flower on the variegated shoot and a red flower on the white shoot.
6. Numerous plants from selfing 'Orange Appeal', some showing the full colour and others the white splash.

7. An inflorescence from 'Single New Life' showing off its striped form of variegation.
8. The strap-like petals of a seedling from 'Fire Dragon'.
9. A light red inflorescence.
10. A light red inflorescence with a broad white splash.
11. The centre pattern of the flowers of a seedling.
12. A pink flower with red spots on the petals and conspicuous feathery veins.

1
Peter Grieve's Vision

It was in 1959 when I first read Peter Grieve's book on "Variegated Zonal Pelargoniums" (1868). I had borrowed a copy from the Bodleian Library, and was surprised to find the pages still uncut. It is a short book filled with pages on sports and seedlings, how to produce variegated pelargoniums, how to propagate and cultivate them, and what properties constitute perfection. It is a classic for pelargonium lovers. What impressed me most of all was the history of the variegated pelargoniums, the rapid changes that occurred, the recognition of the silver margined, the silver tricolors, and the golden tricolors. Pelargoniums were evolving rapidly. The second edition, published a year later, discussed the ways of enjoying pelargoniums through the winter under glass, and it included a list of many cultivars then current (1869, 1977). It pleased me to find that I had in my possession, either thanks to the Oxford Botanic Garden or to Telston's Nurseries, several of the cultivars. These were 'Mrs Pollock', 'Lucy Grieve', 'Sophia Dumaresque', 'Lady Cullum', 'Peter Grieve', 'Happy Thoughts', 'Crystal Palace Gem', 'Miss Burdette-Coutts', 'Lass O'Gowrie', and 'Mangles Variegated' or 'Manglesii'. Some of them were to appear in my future research.

Unknown to Peter Grieve was the cytology of the genus and the extensive taxonomy. The zonal pelargonium is only a small fraction of the whole. Van der Walt (1993) has subdivided the genus *Pelargonium* into 16 sections comprising some 250 species. The chromosome number of at least 177 species has been counted. These include both diploid species and about 26 per cent of polyploid species. The basic chromosome numbers are x = 4, 7, 8, 9, 10, 11, and 17. The most basic chromosome number is 11, and the most primitive species are thought to be the diploid species *P. cucullatum* and *P. betulinum* 2n = 2x = 22, both of the section *Pelargonium*. These two species are closely involved in the ancestry of the Regal pelargoniums. The somatic chromosome numbers are 2n = 8, 16, 18, 20, 22, 32, 34, 36, 38, 40, 44, 58, 60, 62, 84, 88 and 104, and higher numbers are known among artificial polyploids. Miller does not include the sections *Dibrachya* and *Eumorpha* in her book (1996).

She identifies about 230 species, divided into 14 sections. She illustrates many of them, and includes numerous silhouettes with the detailed descriptions of the leaves, which are highly variable in shape and characteristic of individual species. Evidently, the taxonomy of the genus is still being actively researched, including the discovery of new species.

With such a range of chromosome numbers it is no surprise that the chromosomes are studied quite frequently; more details are given in Van der Walt (1993). The taxonomy too is a subject of great interest particularly by the Southern Africa Group where most of the species occur. This has given rise to the three volumes of the Pelargoniums of Southern Africa (1979, 1981 and 1988), in which Ellaphie Ward-Hilhorst illustrates all the species they describe in colour. Other accounts, in varying detail, are given in Knuth (1912), Moore (1955, 1971), Andrews (1969), Clifford (1958,1970), Webb (1984), Clark (1988), Taylor (1989), Key (1993) and Miller (1996), and maybe others. Taylor, for example, offers a complete guide to the cultivation, propagation, and exhibition of geraniums and pelargoniums. In addition, she gives a brief account of the history of the genera she considers, the essentials of the morphology, and the problems of pest and diseases, and much else besides; a really useful and valuable book.

Besides books of this nature, which are written largely for the general reader and grower of pelargoniums, the book by Armitage and Kaczperski (1992) is aimed at the commercial grower. They deal with the propagation, growth and culture of geraniums – zonals, hybrids and regals, for maximising the stock from seed, and cover many of the physiological conditions that are necessary to ensure the production of large crops by the wholesale producers.

Another important area is pests and diseases. Again, I do not wish to give a detailed account in this book, but a brief reminder that they are always present, and can impact the success of the experiments, is worth quite a lot of thought. Disease in pelargoniums is a nuisance to the average gardener, but is a serious menace to the commercial supplier of hundreds of thousands of rooted cuttings a year. They are the root rots and damping-off caused by *Pythium splendens* and related fungi, and the grey moulds of *Botrytis cinerea*. They can be kept down by a number of fungicides, and keeping the glasshouse really clean. The soil mix should be pasteurised, as well as the benches and tools. The glasshouse should be steam sterilized, or treated with a surface disinfectant. The air should be kept dry, and the glasshouse well aerated, especially when the plants are grown under cool, humid conditions. All these requirements are necessary under the rules of good hygiene. In the regals, and to a lesser extent the zonals, the soil borne disease wilt caused by the fungus *Verticillium albo-atrum* is common. The affected plants express symptoms of stunting and slow growth with chlorotic lower leaves. Symptom expression is most acute at flowering. Affected plants are best discarded. In my own experience, plants grown outdoors through the summer and into the autumn often become infected by the rust pustules of the fungus *Puccinia pelargonii-zonalis* on the underside of the leaves, and sometimes the upper leaf surface shows small chlorotic spots. If the attack is severe the affected leaves senesce and die. The urediospores are easily dispersed by air currents and by water splash, and epidemic development can occur in moist, warm conditions. If the plants are brought back into a warm, dry glasshouse and the infected leaves are removed, the disease is gone within a few weeks. Alternatively, if the plants can be spared, they are discarded and not brought back into the glasshouse.

The commercial grower needs the environment to be scroupously clean and free from all sources of contamination. When growing virus free stock, and there are many different viruses that infect pelargoniums, these diseases must first be removed from the plants using tissue culture techniques (Theiler 1977; Hakkart and Hartel 1979; Reuther 1983). When he has done this, and produces his nuclear stock, he may then develop from this clean stock his propagation stock, which he uses for two years, or until random testing shows it to be infected again. From the clean propagation stock he grows the certified stock for onward sale to the public. The cuttings will be free of infection, but should not be propagated from again as they could have easily become re-infected. The methods used to produce disease free nuclear stocks are well described in the section on plant pathology in the Proceedings of the International Geranium Conference for 1992 (Craig 1993). A similar procedure is used to obtain stock free from bacterial infection. The bacterial disease caused by *Xanthomonas campestris pv. pelargonii* is extremely infectious. The symptoms include a black stem rot, and lesions appear above the soil particularly on woody plants. Leaf symptoms appear as small brown circular spots surrounded by a water soaked region. The bacteria are spread by water splash, and through contaminated tools and hands, especially when taking cuttings.

For each cultivar, commercial growers must first obtain a bacterial free nuclear stock, isolated from the public. The process requires frequent testing of the cultivar; shoot tip micro-propagation under sterile conditions, and general precautions of extreme hygiene. From the nuclear stock, the propagation stock and eventually the certified stock are taken. Neither the methods of cleaning the stock, nor the necessary isolation methods of propagation, are available to the amateur grower; the professional only can achieve these.

Of all the pests, one of the most irritating is the leaf curling caterpillar. The larvae of these eat the growing points and parts of flowers. Finally the adults roll up a leaf and after only a few days they emerge. If no action is taken the plants quickly look a ghastly mess. The insects are attracted by light, fly in, and lay their eggs in the soil. The plants may be treated, or else the larvae are picked off and destroyed as part of the daily inspection. For me, an amateur grower, there is no greater menace. With a glasshouse in the Botanical Garden, the windows open, lights sometimes on, the moths are abundant. Careful vigilance is needed throughout the year.

Peat based seed composts are an ideal medium for fungus gnats. These greyish black flies lay their eggs in the growing medium, and the larvae chew on root hairs and organic matter. The larvae are white with black heads. They are often found with newly potted seedlings, particularly if the medium has not been allowed to dry out between waterings. Seedlings are therefore particularly vulnerable. The larvae change to pupae that emerge as an adult fly three or four days later. The compost should be drenched with a suitable chemical to give adequate control.

Aphids are another source of annoyance. They are soft-bodied adults and nymphs, which settle on the plants after having been blown by the wind. They often occur in large numbers and they injure the plant by sucking the sap with their piercing mouthparts. They excrete sticky honeydew, which acts as a medium for the growth of a black, sooty mould. They are also carriers of plant viruses, and so can infect the plant with a virus disease. The aphids may be controlled by chemical spray.

A serious pest is the two-spotted spider mite, *Tetranychus urticae*, which Craig and his colleagues have investigated over many years (1993). There are some pelargonium cultivars that are sensitive while others are resistant. The resistant ones have tall glandular trichomes on their leaves, which produce a high level of ω5 anarcardic acid. This is a dominant character over the recessive susceptible plant, which lacks the glandular trichomes and does not produce the ω5 anarcardic acid. There are many anarcardic acids produced and four types of trichome, so the story is quite complicated and one that I do not wish to pursue.

Seed-grown pelargoniums generally flower within half a year. By contrast, cutting material flowers within a couple of months, depending on the season. Nevertheless, the advantages of seed are numerous (Randolph 1971). Seed-produced pelargoniums are usually free of disease, which is a serious problem with cuttings. Also the benefits of the crossing or selfing programme that went into producing the seeds may be considerable. Seed produced material may produce interesting variations from the cultivar, but cuttings are all genetically identical.

Hybridisation between species of the same section, and between species of different sections, is quite intense. Horn (1993) states that in his investigations his people have made 879 combinations of over 64 species coming from 11 sections. Although an average of eight flowers were pollinated, only 90 crosses resulted in seed set. Among the crosses within sections, only 25 per cent of all the crosses resulted in seed set. Among the crosses between sections, only 6 per cent were successful. There were some exciting successes including *P. peltatum* and *P. zonale*, the ivy-leaf and the zonal pelargonium. Although I notice that Miller (1996) places these two species in the same section *Ciconium*. Horn (1994) gives many examples of species crosses within sections and he reports on the literature. He also reports on the less successful crosses between sections. He gives an account of the influence of different factors – basic chromosome number, sections, and ploidy level – on the success of the crosses. In summary, nearly all their successes were between species having the same chromosome number and the same level of ploidy.

If fertilization is achieved the greatest loss of embryos occurs at the heart stage, mainly 7 – 9 days after pollination. Many workers have developed embryo rescue techniques to overcome the failure to set seed, and eventually to germinate. Kato and Tokumasu (1983) and Kato *et al.* (1988, 1989) reported success with ovule culture of *P.* × *domesticum* hybrids. They combined cultures of *P.* × *domesticum* with *P. quercifolium* and *P. crispum* and obtained fertile progeny. Kakihara *et al.* (1990) succeeded in obtaining plants from ovules after crossing diploid cultivars of zonal and ivy-leaf pelargoniums. Becker-Zens (1983) cultured embryos 14 days old, or older, and obtained plantlets from cultivar crosses. Scemama and Raquin (1990) successfully cultured 13 to 15 day old embryos of a diploid and four cultivars of a tetraploid zonal pelargonium. They also initiated the technique of culturing 5 to 11 day old ovaries under non-sterile conditions, and then transferring the 14 – 15 day old embryos to embryo culture. Bentvelsen *et al.* (1990) cultured 10 – 14 day old embryos from different species of section *Pelargonium* crossed to *P. peltatum* 'Ville de Paris' and obtained fertile hybrid progeny. Horn (1993) and co-workers succeeded in combining zonal and ivy-leaf pelargonium from the heart stage. With these techniques many more successful species crosses will undoubtedly be made, and we may expect to see the results of their efforts in the nurseries and in the garden or glasshouse.

The National Pelargonium Collection is at Fibrex Nurseries in Warwickshire, which they believe is the largest collection of pelargonium species and cultivars anywhere in the world. Their catalogue recognizes the following groups: Single zonal pelargoniums, Double zonal pelargoniums, Irene zonal pelargoniums (American), Stellar pelargoniums, Formosum hybrids (Finger- flowered pelargoniums), Miniature zonal pelargoniums, Dwarf pelargoniums, Cactus pelargoniums, Ivy-leaved pelargoniums, Rosebud pelargoniums (Noisette), Cascade or Balcon-type Ivy-leaved pelargoniums, Variegated and Coloured-leaved pelargoniums, Scented-leaved pelargoniums, Unique pelargoniums, Regal pelargoniums, Dwarf Regal pelargoniums, Decorative pelargoniums, Angel pelargoniums, Species pelargoniums, and Species hybrids. These are the groupings people use; they classify the pelargoniums into various types. Some groups appear separated by a single gene; others have a much greater difference. But it is a logical, sensible grouping. Nevertheless, I shall not closely follow these groups, as I am concerned with differences between individual plants, which often cut across the group. Some plants even belong to two or more groups at the same time such as the variegated ivy-leaved pelargonium 'L'Elegante'. One group that I shall pay a lot of attention to are the variegated plants, but these may also be species hybrids, single or double flowered zonals, ivy-leaved, or of a particular species.

We are interested in plants that may be defined as variegated because they differ from related individuals, races or species, in having a non-uniform development of chlorophyll and related pigments as between plastids, cells or tissues of their leaves, bracts or fruits under normal conditions of nutrient, temperature and illumination. We need to discard a whole group of plants whose variegation does not follow cell lineages. These have figurative patterns, and include many examples of marginal patterns, diffuse spots, prominent veins, stripes and bands, and also restricted or general chlorosis. Many examples of these are given in both editions of "The Plastids" (Kirk and Tilney-Bassett, 1966, 1978). *Pelargonium peltatum* 'Crocodile' is an example of prominent veins in which the surrounding tissue is modified highlighting the leaf veins; this is probably an example of virus infection. Another example of virus infection is the 'Harlequins', in which the striped petals with white and another colour are graft transmissible to other cultivars of the ivy-leaved pelargoniums. The vast majority of variegations in pelargonium belong to the cell lineage variegation, where the leaf consists of a white area against a green background, in which all the cells comprising the white area have a common cell lineage. Of course, this type of variegation may also be combined with coloration, as Peter Grieve indicated was the case for 'Mrs Pollock'. The dark zone entitling it to be considered as a coloured plant, while the green disc, with yellow or white margins, constitutes its variegation.

All gardeners and flower arrangers are well aware of the rich source of material provided by the variegated foliage. There is a whole spectrum of greens, together with, and often in combination with, white, creams and yellows, along with the additional colouring of oranges, reds and purples. In their beautiful book on "Variegated Plants: A gardener's index to patterned foliage", Susan Conder and Andrew Larson (1994) describe nearly 700 examples, including many pelargonium cultivars. The variegated pelargoniums include cultivars still grown a century or more after their origin, others have been fashionable for a while and then lost, but new ones are frequently appearing too. They remain forever popular. With reference to variegation, Peter Grieve writes near the beginning of his first chapter:

"Scientific men do not appear as yet to have given this subject a very great amount of attention, and it would, of course, be like presumption on my part to attempt to offer anything like an elucidation of a matter so mysterious and important. I may, however, be allowed to say that the subject appears to me to offer a very wide and interesting field for scientific inquiry and research".

Today, we have a much better understanding of the subject, and have a good knowledge of how variegation develops and changes, and how to create new variegated plants. It is not, however, such an easy subject that we can simply write out a recipe. Instead, we need to consider a number of different facets which, I believe, would have fascinated Peter Grieve immensely, and which will likewise greatly add to the reader's interest.

Plant breeders always emphasise the improvement of their plants, and the bringing out of new cultivars. The societies stress the attractiveness of the plants and the best way to display them. While both these aims are admirable they are not my main concern. I have been interested in pelargoniums, in particular the zonal pelargonium, for over forty years and my interest is in the examination of the many different facets that make up the final plant. I am therefore interested in all aspects of the pelargonium flower, in the fertilisation process, the growth and development of the embryo and seedling, and especially the role of the normal and mutant white chloroplasts in this. Chimeras are particularly common in zonal pelargoniums and the sorting-out of the green and white plastids are especially relevant, as well as both nuclear and chloroplast mutation. Hybrid variegation is a little known phenomena and perhaps quite an important one for the future of pelargoniums as it necessitates the successful hybridisation of different but closely related species. Embryo culture may prove to be important in this respect. The renewal of variegated plants by breeding is a very interesting topic, again not widely known, and one in which I am closely involved. All these studies have involved a useful examination of the scientific literature, as well as my own endeavours, and that of my students. In the course of this work I have become interested in the many markings on the pelargonium flower, as well as the colour of the flowers themselves, so this area is an exciting topic too. I describe several new methods of looking at flower pigments. Much of my work has involved a number of genetic experiments, which I explain at some length. For the most part I have used named cultivars so that the work should be repeatable. The cultivars again are not the latest combinations of many characters, but are generally the older, less complicated, and single flowers. These cultivars have inflorescences in which two or three flowers tend to be ready each day for pollination over a period of two or three weeks. This suits me better than the inflorescence in which many individual flowers are ready together. Ideally the parents are true breeding, so that by crossing a uniform F1 is produced and only a few are needed. The F2 is then produced by selfing, and now a much larger segregating progeny is required. When more that one pair of characters is to be examined at the same time, the F2 will have to be much larger still in order to accommodate the low frequency of appearance of some of the characters. Sometimes the chosen parents are not true breeding; we must then understand the genetics very well if we are to work out the complicated segregation that may follow.

When we begin to study variegated pelargoniums, we soon find that many cultivars having leaves with white margins and green centres are rather alike, but there are other less common forms with this pattern reversed and a few forms that are truly unique. Underlying these differences in the distribution of the green and white regions are variations in the anatomical structure and development of the plants, and in the origin of the variegation. In turn, these factors may influence the stability of the plants, how they should be propagated, and whether or not they can be useful in breeding new cultivars. The diversity of cultivars also depends on combining the variegated foliage with other characteristics of growth, leaf zonation, and flower colours. A wide and interesting field of study declared Peter Grieve. It is never easy to know where to start, what is the right place to begin for one person, may not be right for another, but I would like to begin with the plant cells and with the plastids, or chloroplasts, because they are the key to understanding variegation itself – why tissues that are normally green are sometimes white.

References

Andrews, M. (1969).
The Marshall Cavendish encyclopedia of gardening. Paul Hamlyn, London.

Armitage, A.M. and Kaczperski, M. (1992).
Seed-propagated geraniums and regal geraniums. Timber Press, Portland, Oregon.

Becker-Zens, R. (1983).
Anther and embryo culture in *Pelargonium zonale* hybrids. Acta Horticulturae 131, 209-213.

Bentvelsen, G.C.M., Stemkens, H.G.W. and Tjeertes, P. (1980).
Interspecific crosses in *Pelargonium* and the application of embryo rescue methods. Proc. Symp. Eucarpia Sect. Ornam., Wageningen, 104-109.

Clark, D. (1990).
The pelargonium guide. Oakleigh Publications, Spain.

Clifford, D. (1958).
Pelargoniums including the popular geranium, a monograph. Blandford Press, London.

Clifford, D. (1970).
Pelargoniums, including the popular geranium, a monograph. 2nd. ed. Blandford Press, London.

Conder, S. and Lawson, A. (1994).
The encyclopedia of patterned foliage. Cassell Publishers Limited, London.

Craig, R. (1993).
Reproduction in pelargoniums – significant advances in physiology, genetics, and technology. In: Proceedings of the third international Geranium Conference. 65-69. Ed. R. Craig. Ball Publishing, Batavia, Illinois, USA.

Grieve, P. (1868).
A history of variegated zonal pelargoniums; with practical hints for their production, propagation, and cultivation. Printed for the author, London.

Grieve, P. (1869).
A history of ornamental-foliaged pelargoniums. 2nd ed.
The British Pelargonium and Geranium Society 1977.

Hakkart, F.A. and Hartel, G. (1979).
Virus eradication from some *Pelargonium* cultivars by meristem-tip culture.
Neth. J. Pl. Path., 85, 39-46.

Horn,W. (1993).
Genetics and crossability of pelargoniums. In: Proceedings of the third
international geranium conference. 33-47. Ed. R. Craig. Ball Publishing,
Batavia, Illinois, U.S.A.

Horn, W. (1994).
Interspecific crossability and inheritance in *Pelargonium*. Plant Breeding 113,
3-17.

Kakihara, F., Kato, M. and Tokomasu,S. (1990).
In vitro cultures in hybridisation between zonal geranium (*Pelargonium
× hortorum* Bailey) and ivy-leaved geranium (*P. peltatum* Ait.) and the
characteristics of hybrid plants. Intern. Hortic. Congr. Florenz, Abst. 3143.

Kato, M. and Tokumasu, S. (1983).
Characteristics of F1 hybrids produced by ovule-culture in ornamental
pelargonium. Acta Horticulturae 131, 247-252.

Kato, M., Fujioka, M., Kakihara, F. and Tokumasu, S. (1988).
Flowering characteristics of hybrids between regal and scented-leaved
geraniums in pelargonium. Mem. Coll. Agric., Ehime Univ. 32, 101-109.

Kato, M., Fujioka, M., Kakihara, F. and Tokumasu, S. (1989).
Improvement of flower color of regal geranium (*Pelargonium × domesticum*) by
means of interspecific hybridisation. Proc. 6th International Congress of Sabrao,
455-458.

Key, H. (1993).
Pelargoniums. The Royal Horticultural Society, 3rd ed. Wing King Tong Co. Ltd.,
Hong Kong.

Kirk, J.T.O. and Tilney-Bassett, R.A.E. (1967).
The Plastids: Their chemistry, structure, growth and inheritance. W.H. Freeman
and Company. London and San Francisco.

Kirk, J.T.O. and Tilney-Bassett, R.A.E. (1978).
The Plastids: Their chemistry, structure, growth and inheritance, 2nd edn.
Elsevier/North-Holland Biomedical Press, Amsterdam.

Knuth, R. (1912).
Das Pfllanzenreich 4, 129. Berlin.

Miller, D. (1996).
Pelargoniums a gardener's guide to the species and their cultivars and hybrids.
B.T. Batsford Ltd. London.

Moore, H.E. (1955).
Pelargoniums in cultivation. Baileya 3, New York.

Moore, H.E. (1971).
Taxonomy of pelargoniums in cultivation. In: Geraniums. A manual on the
culture, disease, insects, economics, taxonomy and breeding of geraniums, 2nd
ed., 14-52. Ed. J.W. Mastalerz. Pennsylvania Flower Growers, USA.

Reuther, G. (1983).
Propagation of disease-free pelargonium cultivars by tissue culture. Acta
Horticulturae 131, 311-319.

Scemama, C. and Raquin, C. (1990).
An improved method for rescuing zygotic embryos of *Pelargonium* × *hortorum*
Bailey. J. Plant Physiol. 135, 763-765.

Taylor, J. (1988).
Geraniums and pelargoniums. The complete guide to cultivation, propagation
and exhibition. The Crowood Press, Ramsbury Marlborough Wiltshire.

Theiler, R. (1977).
In vitro culture of shoot tips of *Pelargonium* species. Acta Horticulturae 78, 403-
409.

Van der Walt, J.J.A. (1979).
Pelargoniums of Southern Africa, 2nd ed. Fischer GmbH and Co. KG, Germany.

Van der Walt, J.J.A. and Vorster, P.J. (1981).
Pelargoniums of Southern Africa. Volume 2. Juta and Co., Ltd. Kenwyn.

Van der Walt, J.J.A. and Vorster, P.J. (1988).
Pelargoniums of Southern Africa. Volume 3. National Botanic Gardens,
Kirstenbosch.

Van der Walt, J.J.A. (1993).
Discovering the world of pelargoniums. In: Proceedings of the third international
geranium conference. 15-27. Ed. R. Craig. Ball Publishing, Batavia, Illinois,
USA.

Webb, W.J. (1984).
The pelargonium family. Croom Helm, Sydney.

2
The Plant Cell

Cells, tissues and organelles

Plants take many forms. A plant like *Arabidopsis thaliana* is really quite small and lives for only a few weeks. At the other extreme are the giant redwood trees, *Sequoiadendron giganteum*, that may live for over a thousand years and reach towards 100m in height. We can make a similar distinction in the size of the leaves from the quite small numerous leaves of *Cotoneaster horizontalis* to the relatively large leaves of *Iris pseudocorus*, and much larger leaves exist like those of the bananas. Or we can compare the shapes of the leaves as simple, compound, palmate, trifoliate and so forth. Whatever form we take, and there are a great many, we see only the surface structure. Beneath the surface, at low magnification with the light microscope, we see that all the varied structures of the plant are made up of numerous cells. Starting with the fertilised egg, growth proceeds by division and expansion through a period of development. Some cells may reach positions in the plant where they are permanently dividing in meristems, but the majority end up as part of the tissues of the stem, root or leaf. The tissues, and the cells of which they are made, are of several kinds, parenchyma, collenchyma, sclerenchyma and schlerids, or they may differentiate further into the conducting tissues of the phloem or xylem.

The parenchyma is the most common type of cell and tissue. The cells are active metabolically. They constitute all the soft parts of a plant, and have many intercellular spaces. They usually remain active when they mature. They have thin walls allowing light and carbon dioxide to pass through to the green chloroplasts or to plant pigments. There are many types including chlorenchyma cells involved in photosynthesis, glandular cells that secrete nectar, fragrances, mucilage, resins and oils, and transfer cells that mediate transport of substances between cells. A parenchyma tissue that conducts nutrients over long distances is the phloem, and is part of the vascular system (Mauseth 1991). Collenchyma cells have a primary wall that remains thin in some areas, but becomes thickened in others, especially the corners allowing no intercellular spaces. A collenchyma tissue is present in elongating shoot tips that must be long and flexible as in grape vines. It is present in the four corners of the square stems of members of the *Labiatae*. In stems, the resistance of the collenchyma counterbalances the tendency for parenchyma to expand, and so the stem becomes rigid. The sclerenchyma has a primary wall and a thick secondary wall that is usually lignified. Sclerenchyma cells develop from parenchyma mainly in organs that have stopped growing and have achieved their proper size and shape. Sclerenchyma supports the plant by its strength alone. Parenchyma and collenchyma cells can absorb so much water that they swell and stretch the walls, thereby growing. Sclerenchyma cells are absent from these growing tips, for their walls are strong enough to prevent the protoplasts from expanding. They are divided into long fibres and short schlerids, both of which have thick walls. The long fibres allow flexibility, and are most often found where strength and elasticity are important as in young trees where the trunk and branches sway in the wind without breaking or becoming permanently bent. The schlerids are short and hard impenetrable surfaces such as the shells of nuts and the pits or stones of fruit; they are responsible for the grittiness of pears. Sclerenchyma that develops for the conduction of water and minerals is the xylem component of the vascular tissue.

Every cell has a highly flexible primary wall consisting of cellulose embedded in a matrix of hemicellulose, pectic substances and protein. In many plant cells, particularly in xylem tissue, there is a much thicker and semi rigid secondary wall consisting of cellulose, hemicellulose and lignin. Connecting the cells is a high density of plasmodesmata, which are extremely thin strands of cytoplasm that extend through the walls of adjacent cells, enabling movement of substances between them.

Internal to the wall is the plasmalemma, the cytoplasm containing the cell organelles, and the large central vacuole. The vacuole contains water, and non-living substances such as gums, oils and resins. The plasmalemma is a lipid bilayer separating the cytoplasm from the cell wall, and it controls the flow of dissolved substances in and out of cells.

The cytoplasm of the higher plant cell is a complex structure. It may be divided into the endomembrane system, the cytoskeleton, the nucleus, and the ribosomes, mitochondria and plastid organelles. Briefly, the endomembrane system is itself divided into the endoplasmic reticulum, a system of narrow tubes and sheets of membrane that form a network through the cytoplasm, the nuclear envelope, the tonoplast, which is the membrane between the cytoplasm and the cell vacuole, the Golgi bodies, the microbodies, and the oleosomes and protein bodies. Microtubules and microfilaments form the cytoskeleton of the plant cell. The nucleus contains the chromosomes, which carry the genes in the DNA that regulate the majority of cell processes. Finally, the ribosomes are the site of protein synthesis where they respond to instructions from the genes in the form of mRNA and tRNA. The two remaining organelles also contain some DNA, and they contain their own ribosomes for synthesising their own proteins. The mitochondria are the organelles associated with respiration in all plant cells, and the chloroplasts are the green organelles charged with the function of photosynthesis. The plastids occur in all living cells, but they develop into green chloroplasts in chlorenchyma tissue, which is the main cell type in green leaves. It is the possession of plastids, and the cellulose cell wall, that distinguishes plant from animal cells. All of these parts are important in the functioning of the cell, but we need to concentrate our attention on the plastids for it is these organelles that determine the variegation of plants.

Because of the large central vacuole of chlorenchyma tissue, the chloroplasts are situated in the cytoplasm close to the cell wall. Each chloroplast is enveloped in a double membrane; it is about 4-6µm long, and roughly elliptical in shape. The two main regions of the chloroplast are the stroma and the thylakoid system. The pigment containing thylakoid system is composed of many grana, ten or more per chloroplast, like stacks of coins. The grana are connected by long stroma thylakoids, there may be as many as 40 thylakoids per granum. The amorphous, gel-like stroma contains from one to five big starch grains, which may squeeze the thylakoid system towards the periphery, or between the grains. There are several small, circular, electron-dense plastoglobuli in between the thylakoids. The ribosomes are also in the stroma, they are small and extremely numerous. The DNA is in regions scattered through the stroma. It occurs in variable number of copies per chloroplast. The number of chloroplasts varies from about eight in meristematic cells to 100 or more in palisade mesophyll cells. The pigments present in the thylakoid membrane consist largely of chlorophyll a and chlorophyll b, which are responsible for the green colour. Also present are yellow to orange pigments known as carotenoids.

By contrast, when the cell is taken from a fully expanded leaf from within the white tissue of the white margined 'Flower of Spring', the plastids look very different. They are slightly smaller, irregular in shape, and quite numerous. They generally contain a prolamellar body, which is a collection of short tubules and vesicles, and these occur also individually or in groups in the stroma. There are no grana. Usually there are one to four vacuoles in the plastid, but no starch is present. The number of the plastoglobuli has increased and mostly they occur in groups of 20 to 30. The ribosomes occur in the stroma of 'Lass O'Gowrie' and 'Miss Burdette-Coutts'.

They were not recognisable in 'Flower of Spring' and 'Foster's Seedling'. Apart from the plastids the cell appeared normal (Khera 1975).

The plastid genome of the average land plant consists of a single, circular chromosome of 150kb (Kilo base pairs). By contrast, the genome of *P. hortorum* 'Irene' is estimated as 217kb (Palmer *et al.* 1987). A pair of duplicated segments, arranged as inverted repeats, being 76kb long instead of the normal 21-26kb, causes this exceptional length. This duplicated region lies between two single copy regions of 7kb and 58kb. Through the increase in this duplicated region at least 10 genes that are present once in most land plants are present twice. Moreover, most land plants have the same gene order, whereas in 'Irene' the order is highly scrambled as the result of at lease six inversions. Furthermore, two short sequences are repeated and dispersed to a number of chromosomal locations, whereas most chloroplast genomes lack any detectable dispersed repeats. The fact that the chloroplast genome is so large makes pelargonium particularly interesting, but this is not thought to have any significant bearing on its mode of inheritance.

Meristems, layers and chimeras

The whole of the flowering plants and gymnosperms are multicellular, built up of millions of cells, each cell having originated by division from a previous cell. These dividing cells are not distributed throughout the plant; they are localised in regions called meristems. The primary meristems are found in the shoot tip, and just behind the tip of the root. The extension of the primary meristems accounts for further elongation of the stem by division of cells in the sub-apical region. In woody plants increase in girth depends upon two lateral intercalary meristems, the vascular cambium and the phellogen, which give rise to the wood and the bark.

The shoot bears two kinds of lateral organs, the leaves and the bud, which grow in the extension of the primary meristems. The leaves develop as outgrowths from the stem at the nodes, and the buds develop in the leaf axils. During vegetative growth buds remain either dormant, or they develop into new shoots. During reproductive growth buds develop into cones, or into inflorescences and flowers.

The structures of apical meristems at the shoot tip are interpreted in a number of ways (Tilney-Bassett 1986). From the point of view of variegated plants, the most useful model is based on the presence or absence of one or two tunica layers overlying the corpus. This has its origins with the theory of Schmidt (1924) and Buder (1928), who divided the apical meristems into two zones. The outer zone, the tunica, consisted of one or more peripheral layers of cells in which divisions were predominantly at right angles or anticlinal to the surface. The inner zone, the corpus, consisted of a central core of cells in which divisions were parallel or periclinal to the surface, and in other planes too. The anticlinal divisions of the tunica allowed for surface growth, and the divisions of the corpus allowed for growth in volume. Each layer of the tunica arose from a small group of initials, an intitial is a dividing cell, and the corpus has its own initials beneath those of the tunica. These layered apices of one, or two, or rarely three, layers overlying the corpus, are readily seen in thin longitudinal sections through the shoot tip.

The way in which the leaves and lateral buds develop from this layered apex is very interesting. The bud repeats the structure of the apical tip. It includes all the tunica layers and the corpus. The divisions initiating a leaf primordium produce a leaf butress at the side of the shoot apex from which the leaf grows upwards and outwards, and finally expands laterally to produce the leaf blade. The pattern of cells within the developing leaf follows the pattern in the apex, just like the bud. The upward growth of the leaf proceeds by extensive cell division, initially in apical regions as the leaf butress elongates, and later through general cell division throughout the primordium in dicots, or by an intercalary meristem at the base of the primordium in most monocots. When the leaf primordium has reached a certain height, lateral outgrowths, which constitute the marginal meristem, appear on either side. The activity of these establishes the number of cell layers in the lamina or leaf blade. They still incorporate cells derived by division from the tunica and corpus layers. Further meristems in the developing leaf contribute to the thickness of the leaf, and the widening of the leaf, followed by cell expansion, until it reaches its full size.

The net result of these changes is that the outer tunica usually remains the outer layer of the leaf; it becomes the epidermis. Peter Grieve (1868) already had this idea of the connection between the leaf and the stem, over fifty years before Schmidt and Buder, when he wrote the following passage:

"The leaves are the natural appendages of the branches, and are, in fact, an extension or continuation of the rind of the stem and the branches, and the thin transparent skin with which the leaf is covered is also an extension of the epidermis, or outer skin, of the plant."

The inner tunica divides and develops a layer of cells all around the leaf blade, and frequently contributes all the marginal cells. The corpus layer produces the tissue at the centre of the leaf. These tissues often extend well into the leaf margins, or are reduced to a small zone around the midrib of the leaf. The overall appearance is, in the case of a variegated plant, a typical chimera structure of a white margin surrounding a green core, or a green margin surrounding a white core, as seen in many pelargoniums. An apparently similar condition is produced by the monocot *Hosta sieboldiana*, or its green margined counterpart. Here there is one tunica outside of the corpus. Instead of producing only the epidermis, it proliferates in the development of the leaf and produces extensive white marginal tissue, while the green tissue of the two-layered apex forms the underlying central tissues of the leaf. If the white outer layer did not proliferate, and remained stable and produced only the epidermis, then no variegated leaf chimera forms, as the epidermis is a thin skin that is not visible to the eye. This is no doubt what happens in the many plants that do not form chimeras, one apical layer and the corpus produces the whole leaf and the outer layer produces the epidermis alone. Thus the visible tissue of the leaf is either wholly green or wholly white, no visible chimera is possible.

When a mutation occurs in nuclear DNA it affects all the plastids of the cell equally. As the plastids remain white, all subsequent cells arising from the original nuclear mutation are white. A white sector appears in the leaf, or in the growing shoot. The single white sector is instantly recognisable. A similar mutation gives rise to a pale green sector, or a golden sector. Whereas when a mutation occurs in the plastid DNA, it affects only that plastid.

With a plastid mutation the first visible signs appear many divisions later after the original mutant plastid has sufficiently multiplied. During the intervening period, the normal and mutant plastids of the mixed cells sort-out from one another by their chance distribution into the daughter cells at cell division. A pure white cell lineage is created when segregation produces a daughter cell that has only mutant plastids. So the tissue becomes a heterogeneous mixture of cells that contain normal plastids, cells that contain mutant plastids, and cells that still contain a mixture of normal and mutant plastids. This mixture continues to sort-out into green and white lineages during all later cell divisions. Thus, as a result of a single plastid mutation, there are within the primary cell lineage, secondary, tertiary, and many more lineages until sorting-out of mixed cells is complete. Hence the overall effect is to produce a characteristic complex multiple cell lineage chequered pattern of green and white areas. This is quite different in appearance from the single sector produced by the nuclear mutation.

During the sorting-out process, the leaf palisade and spongy mesophyll tissue appears as various shades of green, depending upon the proportions of green and white plastids in mixed cells, and the proportions of pure green and white cells. The whole tissue appears as a fine mosaic. Slowly, as sorting-out proceeds, the proportion of mixed cells decreases, and the proportion of green and white cells increases. An increasingly coarse mosaic gradually replaces the fine mosaic; the proportion of new pure lineages from the remaining mixed cells becomes an increasingly rare event. Finally, the last vestige of sorting-out is replaced by pure green or pure white cell lineages. If you are fortunate enough to see such an event in the growing shoot of a young pelargonium plant, you may see these stages unfolding as successive leaves arise from the stem.

Sorting-out in the three layered growing point may give rise to a pure green shoot, or to a pure white shoot. In the former case, the variegation is lost from the growing point. In the latter case, the white shoot eventually dies and new growth arises from non-white areas. If one is to capture the variegation, then the growing point must include both green and white tissue. Sometimes this occurs directly in the apical growing point, but more often the development of lateral shoots is required. This is when the apical shoot is sectorial, green on one side, white on the other side, and often a mixture between the two. The lateral shoot includes tissue derived from only a segment of the apex, and so by encouraging the growth of a suitable lateral bud, one can easily obtain a shoot originating from a mixture of green and white tissue. Also there is a chance that the green and white tissue is derived from cells that occupy different layers. So the lateral shoot may develop straight away as a periclinal chimera. As pelargoniums have three layers contributing to their growth, six kinds of periclinal chimera are possible. They may be green-over-white with a thin skin or a thick skin, GWW or GGW; they may be white-over-green with a thin skin or a thick skin, WGG or WWG; or they may be sandwich chimeras with the middle layer either white or green, GWG or WGW. From any of these periclinal chimeras, propagation of the lateral shoot by cuttings produces a wholly chimeral new plant. A good periclinal chimera is then established as a new cultivar. They are labelled with the outer tunica, L I, first; the inner tunica, L II, next; and the corpus, L III, last. In pelargoniums the two thin-skinned chimeras, GWW and WGG, are easily missed. The ones most commonly seen are the two thick-skinned chimeras, WWG or GGW, and the sandwich chimeras, GWG and WGW. These are the white-over-green chimeras and the green-over-white, involving LII and LIII; these are often abbreviated as W/G and G/W respectively. Several of the more colourful cultivars that are W/G chimeras are illustrated in the article by Burras in Mary Campbell and Others (1990).

Variegated seedlings are predominantly green, or predominantly white, and it is difficult to obtain a periclinal chimera from these. A few variegated seedlings are a more equal mixture of green and white tissue, and these I have known to sort-out into white-over-green or green-over-white periclinal chimeras directly without the need for the lateral buds to sprout. An account of my experiences follows:

I made reciprocal crosses between green 'Flower of Spring' and 'Paul Crampel' with white-over-green 'Flower of Spring', 'Mrs Pollock', 'Dolly Varden' and 'Miss Burdette-Coutts' (Tilney-Bassett 1963). I germinated the seed, and followed the development of 235 variegated seedlings. The sorting-out of pure plastids and pure cells enabled me to divide the seedlings into three groups:

1.   Seedlings that produced green and variegated leaves (G + V).
2.   Seedlings that produced white and variegated leaves (W + V).
3.   Seedlings that produced green, variegated and white leaves (G + V + W).

Periclinal leaves but not shoots occurred in all the groups. The three groups corresponded with a majority of green cells, or a majority of white cells, or a more even proportion of green and white cells. All of the sorting-out of the first two groups into pure green or pure white cells was mostly complete within the first few nodes. About 90 per cent of them had sorted-out into pure shoots by the 8th leaf, counting two for the cotyledons. These seedlings emphasise the fairly rapid rate at which sorting-out proceeds in most cases. In the third group sorting-out progressed gradually and steadily during development, as did the remaining 10 per cent of the first two groups. Since most seedlings of the G + V and the W + V groups completely sort-out into pure shoots within the first few nodes, it is evident that the sorting-out of mixed cells into pure cells is largely completed during the many cell divisions in the development of the embryo. There is still some sorting-out of mixed cells into pure cells, judging by the fine mosaic that occurs in a few leaves. The fine mosaic is seen mostly in the slow 10 per cent of the first two groups, or in the more evenly matched G + V + W group. Where there is roughly equal numbers of green and white cells, these produce roughly equal proportions of green and white tissue. If the two types of cell are equally frequent in the growing point, it is difficult for one type to displace the other and consequently to occupy the whole apex. Hence, sorting-out of pure cells proceeds more slowly than in the first two groups.

Periclinal chimeras were formed intermittently from the 9th leaf onwards, either from the tail of the first two groups, or from the third group. About 2 per cent of the W + V group produced two W/G chimeras. About 7 per cent of the G + V group produced five W/G and eight G/W chimeras. Finally, seven W/G and nine G/W chimeras, about 26 per cent, were produced by the G + V + W group. I did not consider possible chimeras involving the epidermis, as this is largely unseen. The much higher proportion of chimeras from the G + V + W group is clearly related to the more equal proportions of the two types of cell in the growing point of these plants. The inner tunica and the outermost corpus layers become filled with green or white cells. Thus L II is filled with white cells, while L III is filled with green cells, to produce a W/G chimerical growing point. Alternatively, L II becomes filled with green cells, and L III becomes filled with white cells, to produce a G/W chimerical growing point. The periclinal chimera quickly stabilises. When both layers contain an even mix of green and white cells a periclinal chimera does not form, or does so very slowly.

Altogether there were 14 W/G and 17 G/W periclinal chimeras so it appears that the two types were formed in about equal frequency. Furthermore, the two types of chimera appeared to be evenly distributed between the reciprocal crosses:

1.   G x W crosses: out of 210 shoots, 193 completed sorting-out of which eight were W/G and ten were G/W chimeras (9.3%).
2.   W x G crosses: out of 180 shoots, 169 completed sorting-out of which six were W/G and seven G/W chimeras (7.7%).

There were some variegated plants that had reached the 35th leaf stage and still not produced a stable terminal shoot. The growing point contained a mixture of green and white cells in all layers. These plants were discarded at the end of the growing season. The propagation of side shoots might have encouraged the development of periclinal chimeras, but this was not attempted.

Of the seedlings that produced green and variegated leaves, the ratio of green to variegated was about 1: 2. Similarly, in the second group, the ratio of white leaves to variegated leaves was about 1: 2. Finally, in the third group, the ratio of green to variegated to white leaves was about1: 4: 1. It was also noticed that the variegated leaf was frequently sectored one third green to two-thirds white, or one third white to two-thirds green (see Tilney-Bassett 1963). Evidently, the development of the leaf primordium required typically three initial cells. Moreover, the primordium within the meristematic apex of the shoot was typically six cells; these were probably hexagonal cells in transverse section surrounding a single central cell as illustrated in Plant Chimeras (Tilney-Bassett 1986). When the six cells are placed in adjacent groups of three cells green and three cells white, a typical sectorial chimera, and three cells are chosen at a time, the model shows that the ratio of leaves is 1 G: 4V: 1W around the stem. If this sectorial is disturbed so that there are four green to two white cells, or four white to two green cells, and three cells are chosen at a time, the model shows that the ratio of leaves becomes 1G: 2V or 1W: 2V, exactly as found. With the starting ratio of five green to one white, or five white to one green, these are most probably the proportions that give rise to a pure green shoot, or a pure white shoot, very early in seedling development. The two layers, L II and L III, are likely to be the same having their origin in embryo development, but sometimes they will differ when a few of the leaves will show their periclinal structure. Over 8% of the leaves were periclinal in the third group and eventually these developed into 26% periclinal shoots. This frequency clearly demonstrates that the two types of cell, the green and the white, were in a similar proportion, which is most important for the development of periclinal chimeras.

References

Buder, J. (1928).
Der Bau des phanerogamen Sprossvegetationspunktes und seine Bedeutung für die Chimärentheorie. Ber. dtsch. bot. Ges. 46, 20-21.

Campbell, M.E. and others (1990).
Fancy-leaved pelargoniums Peter Grieve and after. (Ed. E.J. Willson). British Pelargonium and Geranium Society.

Grieve, P. (1868).
A history of variegated zonal pelargoniums; with practical hints for their production, propagation, and cultivation. Printed for the author, London.

Khera, P.K. (1975).
Plastid development in zonal pelargoniums. Ph.D. Thesis. University College of Swansea.

Mauseth, J.D. (1991).
Botany: an introduction to plant biology. Saunders College Publishing, Philadelphia.

Palmer, J.D., Nugent, J.M. and Herbon, L.A. (1987).
Unusual structure of geranium chloroplast DNA: A triple-sized inverted repeat, extensive gene duplications, multiple inversions, and two repeat families. Proc. Natl. Acad. Sci. USA 84, 769-773.

Schmidt, A. (1924).
Histologische Studien an phanerogamen Vegetationspunkten. Bot. Arch., 8, 345-404.

Tilney-Bassett, R.A.E. (1963).
Genetics and plastid physiology in *Pelargonium*. Heredity 18, 485-504.

Tilney-Bassett, R.A.E. (1986).
Plant Chimeras. Edward Arnold, London.

3
The Pelargonium Flower

Factors affecting fertility

With such a large number of species, it is difficult to make generalizations, but the pelargoniums have a tendency towards perenniality. They continue to grow for several years, becoming shrubby and woody. They include both erect and scrambling forms. With few exceptions, their leaves, petioles, young stems and flower parts are covered with epidermal hairs. They have an extensive fibrous root system that produces large numbers of small lateral roots that in turn produce the functional root hairs. The efficient root system helps to explain the great success of pelargoniums as pot plants (Adams 1971). They are efficient utilizers of small amounts of soil, but when depleted the plants require extensive feeding to produce good colour and vitality. The stems are erect or decumbent, succulent or sub-succulent, often becoming woody at the base. They are viscid and aromatic, variously hairy, often glandular, sometimes with persistent spine-like stipules or petioles. Each plant has the potential for a greater amount of branching than actually occurs. The leaves are mostly opposite, simple, entire or decompound, stipulate, and the foliage is often scented. The main leaf veins are arranged palmately, radiating from a common basal point. The inflorescences may contain from a very few to as many as two or three hundred flowers depending on the general nutrition and age of the plant, as well as upon the genotype.

The function of the flowers of the zonal pelargonium is to reproduce the species. They are hermaphrodite; each flower has both male and female organs, and consists of the calyx, corolla, stamens and pistil. The calyx is an outer whorl of five green sepals that protect the flower bud, and support the delicate organs within. The sepals are separate most of their length, but joined below as a ring around the receptacle. There is a distinctive nectary tube that opens up from the base of the broadest sepal and adheres to the side of the calyx tube running down the pedicel, it ends as a spur. The nectary tubes are either single or twin bored (Almouslem 1988). The corolla represents the element of beauty in the flower and attracts pollinators to it. It is zygomorphic and consists of five petals; the two uppermost ones are usually larger and more prominently coloured than the lower three petals. There is a wide range of attractive colours. Selective breeding has changed the appearance of the petals in some sections, so they often look more symmetrical with petals overlapping.

The stamens are the male organs. They surround the pistil. Each stamen consists of a filament, which ends in an anther. Two of the stamens are short and five long. The anthers contain the male pollen that is transported to the female at pollination. In the centre of the flower is a single long style, which divides when it is ready to receive the pollen, into a five lobed stigma. The style leads down to the ovary, which consists of five carpels lightly fused to give five distinct valves. At fertilisation, each valve contains two superposed ovules. One ovule, usually the lower, does not get fertilized as a rule or aborts, so there is one seed per valve, giving five seeds per flower. Twinning occurs rarely (Kubba and Tilney-Bassett 1980) when both ovules are fertilized and grow to maturity giving two superposed seeds per valve. The valves separate from the ripened stylar apex by coiling and twisting in response to hygrometric conditions. The seed is shed attached to the style that finally becomes feathery to aid dispersal by wind.

Twin embryos were recorded in *P. crispum* and *P. quercifolium*, but not in five other species including *P. × hortorum* (Yano *et al.* 1975). We found a low frequency of twinning of between 0.5 and 4.3 per cent in all six cultivars examined (Kubba and Tilney-Bassett 1980). The analysis of variance showed that the frequency of twins in 'Dolly Varden', at 4.3 per cent, was significantly higher than the other five cultivars, at 0.5 to 1.8 per cent; none of these was significantly different from each other. We have seen very rarely all ten ovules developing into ten embryos in 'Dolly Varden'; six embryos developing are quite common. Among hybrids between 'Dolly Varden' and 'Flower of Spring' there were some families with much higher values than either parent. This suggested to us that there were a number of genes affecting twinning frequency.

In order to observe how well pollen tubes grow down the style, I removed the flowers 12 hours after pollination, and boiled in a 4 per cent solution of sodium sulphite for 10 minutes (Tilney-Bassett 1963). I next dissected out the central strands or transmitting tissue from the style, stained with acid fuchsin and light green, mounted on a slide under a cover slip, and heated in an oven at 55°C for 6 hours. The darkly stained pollen tubes were easily visible with a microscope (Kubba 1980). I observed four to eight pollen tubes in 'Paul Crampel', and the green forms of 'Dolly Varden', 'Mrs J.C. Mapping' and 'Flower of Spring' (Tilney-Bassett 1963), which is in accord with that of Philippi (1961) for 'Meteor'. Tsai *et al.* (1973) recorded a mean of 27.3 pollen tubes in the style of 'Purple Heart'. Yano *et al.* (1975) recorded a range of five to ten for *P. roseum* 'Bourbon' and 20 to 25 for *P. crispum* 'Prince Rupert'. In all cases less than half of the ovules were fertilised, which suggests that these contrasting values reflected how far the pollen tubes proceeded down the style before the growth of some was inhibited, rather than of their relative effectiveness in achieving fertilization. The transmitting tissue, through which the pollen tubes grow down the style until they enter each ovule, was recognized by Glicenstein and Craig (1989) and Craig (1993) using safranin O as a fluorescent stain, and using a microscope fitted with a fluorescent filter system with a range of 355-425nm. When sections of pollinated styles were stained first with resorcinol blue, followed by a 10-15 minute staining with safranin O, the blue-black pollen tubes were distinctly visible against the background of the fluorescent orange yellow transmitting tissue. They did not count the pollen tubes.

To determine what is the effect of variegated plants compared with green plants, we combined crossing experiments with statistical analysis. We made use of the analysis of variance methods that are fundamental to much of the application of statistics to biology. The method enables us to test what is the likelihood that two or more samples belong to the same population. We chose six variegated cultivars: 'Miss Burdette-Coutts', 'Lass O'Gowrie', 'Dolly Varden', 'Flower of Spring', 'Foster's Seedling' and 'Mrs J.C. Mappin', and the isogenic bud variations derived from them. The green bud variations were obtained by waiting until a green shoot arose on each variegated plant; we then propagated from the green shoots until we achieved sufficient in number. In this way we obtained six green clones of the six variegated cultivars. They are referred to as isogenic because the variegated plant and the green clone derived from it have an identical nucleus; only the plastids differ as the green clone contains green chloroplasts and the variegated parent contains mutant white plastids in their germ layers. We then selfed and crossed the green and the variegated parent in four different ways G × G, G × W, W × G, and W × W, where G and W stand for the two parents. Within the same cultivar these are the same as selfing the nucleus four times, but there are four plastid combinations. The result with all six cultivars is that we made 6 × 6 × 4 = 144 crosses, of which we scored an average of 78 flowers per cross. All selfs and crosses were performed during the summer in the same greenhouse with no other environmental control. The pollen was applied by gently rubbing the anthers on the stigmas using a pair of forceps to hold each detached anther. All selfs were purposely hand pollinated, as there is only a little natural self-pollination. Cross-pollinations were applied in the same way only after all the anthers were emasculated with the forceps. The emasculation was done one to three days in advance of pollination owing to the fact that the male stamens were protandrous, that is they ripened before the stigma. The female was pollinated after the young style opened up as a five lobed stigma. Examination of the surface of the stigma was made with an x 10-hand lens to check for accidental self-pollination. The embryos were dissected out of the seed coats three weeks after pollination, and the number of embryos within each flower scored for a variety of characters. The character, total fertilization, involved scoring all embryos, including dead or dying ones as well as healthy, that had shown any sign of development after fertilization. As each flower contains, with rare exceptions, five carpels each with two superposed ovules, we can assume a theoretical maximum of ten embryos per flower that we use as a standard with which to compare all fertilization data.

Thus, for example, a mean of three embryos per flower is equivalent to 30 per cent fertilization. With this experimental procedure we were able to partition the variance, and so we were able to calculate the effect of the plastids, the females, the males, interactions between them, and an error term. We used the same six cultivars to measure several different events, but I shall only highlight the main effects. We also used the same cultivars to determine the frequency of embryos maturing in the upper and lower positions.

In 'Flower of Spring' and 'Paul Crampel' a minority of 20.6 per cent and 3.5 per cent of the developing embryos were in the lower position of each carpel (Tilney-Bassett 1963). Tsai *et al.* (1973) observed 8.0 per cent lower embryos in 'Purple Heart'. In cultivars and F1 hybrids between cultivars of *P. crispum* Yano *et al.* (1975) observed a range from 51.6 to 97.6 per cent upper embryos. In *P. roseum* they made a distinction between a diploid cultivar with 84.0 per cent upper and its tetraploid derivative with 100 per cent upper embryos. Samples from *P. denticulatum, P. domesticum, P. hortorum, P. peltatum* and *P. quercifolium* varied from 67.6 to 97.7 per cent upper embryos. Kubba and Tilney-Bassett (1981b) decided to examine these differences further by analysing their variance. The analysis enabled them to rank the six cultivars in descending order of the frequency of upper embryos as follows:

Female cultivars   LG > MBC > FS ≈ DV ≈ FOS > JCM
Mean percentage   95.6 84.0 79.7 78.7 78.5 68.1

The huge female effect, accounting for 71% of the variance with 'Miss Burdette-Coutts' included and 89% of the variance with this cultivar excluded, against the much smaller male item, accounting for less than one per cent of the variance, demonstrated a highly significant maternal effect. So like many characters determined in early development, the genetic control lies almost entirely in the maternal genotype. The significant difference between four of the cultivars suggested that the control operated through a polygenic system of many genes having small effects, rather than a simple Mendelian control by one or more major genes. Further analysis showed that the likelihood of an upper ovule being fertilized is dependent solely on the overall frequency of this event in any cultivar; therefore each carpel is behaving independently of other carpels within the same flower.

When we studied fertility, we looked at the results of the 6 × 6 × 4 analysis of variance at two stages (Kubba and Tilney-Bassett 1981a). We looked at the total of all the embryos including the dead or dying ones. These are usually much smaller than the full embryos and have stopped growing beyond the heart stage, or they have grown further but are translucent, misshapen, and lack any turgidity in the tissues. The full embryos are turgid and have cotyledons well formed. The sum of all embryos reflects the total fertilization, while the embryos surviving are the ones that go on to form good seeds at maturity. These two stages are compared with each other in respect of the plastid combinations (Fig. 3.1), and in respect of the six cultivars (Fig. 3.2). The analysis of variance shows that there is a significant effect of the plastids, with the green females achieving a higher rate of fertilization than the white females, and the trends continue when the embryo survival is assessed (Fig. 3.2). There is only a minor difference between the corresponding male parents. We see that in comparison with G × G selfs and crosses, the overall fertility is reduced by about 10 per cent for a white male, 20 per cent for a white female, and 30 per cent for both white male and white female together. Although the fall in fertility owing to the combination of white embryos with white mothers is clearly significant, it is noteworthy that the overall fertility can be depressed as much by the genotype of some cultivars as by the effect of mutant plastids.

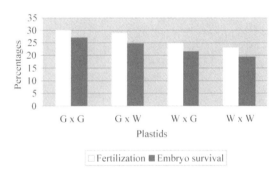

Fig. 3.1. The percentage fertilization and percentage embryo survival at three weeks is compared for four plastid combinations.

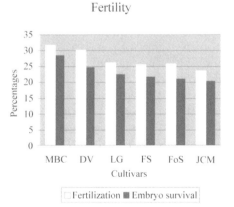

Fig. 3.2. Comparison of fertility for different cultivars; the left of each cultivar is the percentage fertilization; the right is the percentage survival at three weeks.

The analysis of variance shows that there are significant differences amongst the cultivars in respect of total fertilization and embryo survival, but the variance is only half that shown by the plastids (Kubba and Tilney-Bassett 1981c). The heterogeneity among female cultivars is rather more significant than among male cultivars. The cultivar plastid interactions are much less significant and there are no maternal effects. The differences between cultivars and between plastids are attributed to additive effects corresponding to additive gene action. The net fertilization achieved for each cultivar is thought to effect small differences in the balance between the drive of pollen tubes down the style and the strength of their inhibition by already fertilized ovules.

The action of white plastids in depressing both fertilization and embryo survival is likely to be a physiological effect related to the inability of white plastids, and white tissues, whether in the female parent or in the embryo itself, to provide adequate nourishment that has to be supplied by neighbouring, or maternal, green tissues. These studies therefore agree with the fine structural observations in which the cellular development of most white embryos appears normal, apart from the plastids themselves. The poorer overall viability of white embryos, with a variegated mother, appears to be related to inconspicuous quantitative differences, resulting from the poorer nutrition of these embryos throughout development, rather than to any specific effect as a single stage.

The failure of many male sporogenous cells to form bivalents during meiosis is a potential cause of unbalanced gametes and subsequent embryo breakdown. Badr and Horn (1971) examined six normal diploid cultivars and found an average chiasma frequency of 7.50 – 8.95. This is just under one chiasma per bivalent ($2n = 2x = 18$). They found individual cells with 5 – 9 bivalents and 0 – 8 univalents, so we may suppose that some pollen grains were unbalanced with less than, or more than, the normal haploid number of nine chromosomes. As there is a surplus of pollen grains many are wasted, and it may be that these include all the unbalanced ones. Nevertheless, the possibility that they are not excluded from the fertilization process remains. Abdel-Wahab et al. (1979) examined the green and white clones of two cultivars. 'Dolly Varden' had an average of 9.2 and 9.7 chiasmata per cell, and 'Lass O'Gowrie' had an average of 12.6 and 12.7. The effect of the white plastids did not lower the chiasma frequency. Two univalent pairs were found in 'Dolly Varden' cells out of 59 cells counted, and none in 'Lass O'Gowrie'. A few cells scored in 'Mrs J.C. Mappin' and 'Flower of Spring' had chiasmata frequencies similar to 'Lass O' Gowrie'. The proportion of cells with unbalanced gametes is clearly quite low.

More interesting is the difference between cultivars in the average chiasma frequency, which is almost certainly attributable to genetic differences.

'Dolly Varden' has nearly all rod bivalents, whereas 'Lass O' Gowrie' had at least three and sometimes five ring bivalents. 'Dolly Varden', on the other hand, had two cases of a ring bivalent with three chiasmata, one in one arm and two in the other. The presence of rod or ring bivalents with mostly terminal chiasmata makes it unlikely that there is much recombination between the genes, except at the ends of the chromosome arms. This means that any genes situated in these non-recombining regions are likely to be tightly linked, and therefore traits dependent on these genes will also remain together and segregate together. They may recombine only rarely, but the genetic control of chiasma frequency and chiasma position along the chromosome may allow some cultivars to exist that have a higher chiasma frequency and a more random distribution of chiasmata. Indeed, we should expect more variation than we have seen so far in only a very small sample of the huge number of cultivars that occur. It would be very useful to find cultivars with higher chiasma frequencies because they would recombine the characters more frequently, and this would be sure to create more variation and hence more combinations of characters from which to select.

The absence of an effect of mutant white plastids upon chiasma frequency and hence the chromosomal balance of white embryos, supports the view of Khera and Tilney-Bassett (1976b) that the poor survival of white embryos after W × W crosses is a physiological effect related to the inability of a variegated mother adequately to nourish all white embryos.

Male sterility

The origin of many instances of male sterility, which is the failure of the anthers to form pollen, is caused by the consequences of polyploidy. The section Pelargonium has many species with a basic chromosome number of x = 11, and multiples 2n = 22 diploid, 2n = 44 tetraploid, 2n = 66 sextaploid, and 2n = 88 octaploid, all of which are male fertile (Albers and van der Walt 1984). The septaploid form of P. roseum, 2n = 77, is unbalanced because its chromosomes cannot all find partners with which to pair. The unpaired chromosomes usually result in some univalents being produced at meiosis, which lead to sterility. This can be restored to fertility by the doubling of the chromosome complement, 2n = 154, through treatment of the plant with colchicine (Tamai et al. 1958). Similar failure of the process of reduction division leading to poor fertility has been recorded for the artificially induced tetraploid P. denticulatum, 2n = 4x = 44 (Tamai et al. 1963), and hybrids between the higher polyploidy forms of P. roseum × P. denticulatum, which nevertheless showed some fertility (Tamai and Tokumasu 1969). Even at the diploid level there may be some chromosome failure to pair as in hybrids between P. crispum 'Prince Rupert' and 'Lemon Crispum', 2n = 2x = 22; Tokumasu (1974) observed eight to ten bivalents instead of the expected eleven bivalents at meiosis.

There is nothing unusual in plants, which have a wide range of polyploid forms, but which can be propagated and kept alive by cuttings, showing such varying degrees of male sterility. Correct pairing of chromosomes, giving a balanced separation at meiosis, may be essential to maintain a high degree of fertility, but this is often not essential for a healthy and vigorous plant.

The section *Cichonium* contains diploid species, 2n = 2x = 18, and the cultivated zonal pelargonium contains tetraploid species, 2n = 4x = 36, as well. Indeed, these are very common, accounting for many fine specimens. Unfortunately, these are often characterised by shrunken brown anthers following the chromosomes not pairing successfully at meiosis (Philippi 1961; Knicely 1984; Harney and Kung 1967; Badr and Horn 1971). These newly arisen tetraploids have not had sufficient time for selection to ensure that their chromosomes pair regularly at meiosis.

Aneuploidy, with the loss of one or more chromosomes, is another cause for sterility. The monsomic, with the loss of one chromosome, causes the chimera 'Madame Salleron', 2n = 2x = 17, never to flower (Gauger 1939; Daker 1969a). In fact the roots, whose tissue is derived from L III, have 17 chromosomes and this layer is sterile as proven by green shoots that arise adventitiously from it. Whereas tissues derived from L I or L II have 18 chromosomes as these layers produce flowering shoots. 'Madame Salleron' is therefore a trichimera, a mixture of a variegated leaf and a chromosomal chimera (Bergann and Bergann 1959).

Another plant of particular interest to us is the variegated 'Kleine Liebling', which is a haploid, 2n = x = 9 (Daker 1966, 1967, 1969b). The loss of a whole chromosome complement is not sufficient to kill the plant, but it completely upsets the chromosome pairing at meiosis. This attractive little plant is completely dependent on vegetative propagation.

Besides polyploidy and aneuploidy as a cause for male sterility, interspecific hybridisation is also likely to be traced to irregularities in chromosome pairing. When *P. × hortorum* 'Mme Buchner' was crossed with some of its putative ancestral species *P. inquinans, P. scandens, P. stenopetalum*, and *P. zonale*, Chow and Harney (1970) found evidence of male sterility in some hybrids of all crosses, and in hybrids between the species (Harney and Chow 1971). The male sterility took the form of complete indehiscence, to dehiscence of some anthers in a flower, to dehiscence or non-dehiscence depending on environmental conditions. Cohan (1969) stressed the importance of temperature for the expression of male sterility, and he described the anatomical changes that occur during developmental breakdown in male sterile anthers. It is our experience that the anthers of some variegated cultivars, like 'Miss Burdette-Coutts', are infertile except during the summer months. In other words, they are sterile in April and May and again in August and September give or take a week or two allowing for the weather. The presence of flowers does not necessarily mean that the pollen is good. Good cultivars are 'Flower of Spring' or 'Dolly Varden' that always produce good pollen, even as late as November or as early as March.

Partial male sterility is often present in semi-double or double flowers, as they have good as well as non-functional anthers (Chow and Harney 1970). Double flowers often make extra petals at the expense of the stamens, some of which may have functional anthers at the tips of the petals (Meyer 1966; Clifford 1970). Functional anthers may be difficult to find, making double flowers at least risky as a source of pollen, and sometimes useless.

Dale (1968) and Dale and Rogers (1971) identified two genes, Ms1/ms1 and Ms2/ms2, responsible for male sterility. They found that male sterility was expressed by the homozygous recessive condition of mutant, ms1ms1 or ms2ms2. On selfing a double heterozygote, they found that Ms2/ms2 interacted in a complementary manner with a third gene to give a ratio of 9 male fertile: 7 male sterile.

When we investigated male sterility in our stocks we found four cultivars that were homozygous male fertile; these were 'Alde', 'Dolly Varden', 'Lass O'Gowrie' and the green form of 'Miss Burdette-Coutts'. After ten selfs and nineteen crosses 'Fleurette', 'Flower of Spring', the variegated form of 'Miss Burdette-Coutts', 'Foster's Seedling', 'Hills of Snow', 'Mrs J.C. Mapping', 'Verona' and six hybrids produced 915 male fertile and 285 male sterile progeny ($\chi^2 = 1.000$, P = 0.5 – 0.1). The overall agreement with a Mendelian monohybrid ratio suggested that these plants were heterozygous for a single gene controlling male fertility versus male sterility (Almouslem 1988). He symbolised the gene as Ms3/ms3, in which the male fertility allele was dominant and the male sterility allele was recessive. Crosses between plants of the two groups produced only male fertile progeny as we expected from crosses between homozygous dominant and heterozygous male fertile. We tested the homozygous state of the first group by crossing with a male sterile tester 'MS1H'. This plant was the result of earlier hybridisation between variegated 'Miss Burdette-Coutts' and green 'Flower of Spring'. We had kept this plant because it was a perfect example of male sterility. It was a medium sized plant, not too vigorous, and had pink flowers, and it had remained completely male sterile throughout the year. Moreover, after vegetative propagation each year, it was as sterile as ever. It remained male sterile for about 25 years after propagation by cuttings. All of the 190 F1 progeny were fertile. On selfing six of these, the F2 segregated 229 male fertile and 85 male sterile in good agreement with a 3: 1 ratio ($\chi^2 = 0.718$, P = 0.5 – 0.1). On backcrossing four of these six F1 plants with the male sterile tester, the progeny segregated

47 male fertile and 58 male sterile in good agreement with a 1: 1 ratio (χ^2 = 1.152, P = 0.5 – 0.1). There was no significant heterogeneity. The 3: 1 and the 1: 1 ratios prove that the F1 plants were heterozygous for male sterility and so had the genotype Ms3ms3. This was confirmed by making the backcross between three heterozygous cultivars 'Flower of Spring', 'Mrs J.C. Mapping' and 'Verona' and the male sterile tester. Their progeny segregated 101 male fertile and 87 male sterile in good agreement with the 1: 1 ratio (χ^2 = 1.043, P = 0.5 – 0.1), which confirmed the genotype of the three cultivars as Ms3ms3. It came as a surprise to us that over half the cultivars we had tested were heterozygous carriers of male sterility. The breeders of new cultivars were presumably unaware that they were propagating from this potentially difficult stock, and if they had known it would not have mattered too much as any good specimen could be easily propagated by cuttings.

References

Abdel-Wahab, O.A.L., Evans, E.A. and Tilney-Bassett, R.A.E. (1979).
The effect of mutant plastids upon meiosis among cultivars of *Pelargonium* ×
Hortorum Bailey. Annals of Botany 44, 385-386.

Adams, F.S. (1971)
Plant structure, anatomy and morphology. In: Geraniums. A manual on the
culture, diseases, insects, economics, taxonomy and breeding of geraniums,
2nd ed, Ed J.W. Mastalerz, Pennsylvania Flower Growers.

Albers, F. and van der Walt, J.J.A. (1984).
Untersuchungen zur Karyologie und Mikrosporogenese von *Pelargonium* sect.
Pelargonium (*Geraniaceae*). Plant Systematic Evolution 147, 177-188.

Almouslem, A.B. (1988).
Qualitative and quantitative genetical studies in *Pelargonium* × *Hortorum*
Bailey. Ph.D. Thesis, University of Swansea, Wales.

Badr, M. and Horn, W. (1971).
Genetische Untersuchungen an diploiden und tetraploiden *Pelargonium*
zonale-Hybriden. Zeitschrift fur Pflanzenzüchtung 66, 203-220.

Bergann, F. and Bergann, L. (1959).
Uber experimentell ausgelöste vegetative Spaltungen und Umlagerungen an
chimärischen Klone, zugleich als Beispiele erfolgreicher Staudenauslese. 1.
Pelargonium zonale Ait. 'Madame Salleron'. Züchter 29, 361-374.

Chow, T.W. and Harney, P.M. (1970).
Crossability between a diploid *Pelargonium* × *hortorum* Bailey cultivar and
some of its putative ancestral species. Euphytica 19, 338-348.

Clifford, D. (1970).
Pelargoniums, including the popular geranium, a monograph. 2nd. ed. Blandford
Press, London.

Cohan, S.M. (1969).
An investigation of factors related to male sterility expression in *Pelargonium* ×
hortorum Bailey. Ph.D. Thesis, The Pennsylvania State University, USA.

Craig, R. (1993).
Reproduction in Pelargoniums – significant advances in physiology,
genetics, and technology. In: Proceedings of the third international Geranium
Conference. 65-69. Ed. R. Craig. Ball Publishing, Batavia, Illinois, USA.

Daker, M.G. (1966).
'Kleiner Liebling' a haploid cultivar of *Pelargonium*. Nature 211, 549-550.

Daker, M.G. (1967).
Cytological studies on a haploid cultivar of *Pelargonium* and its colchicine-induced diploids. Chromosoma 21, 250-271.

Daker, M.G. (1969a).
Chromosome numbers of *Pelargonium* species and cultivars. Journal Royal Horticultural Society 94, 346-353.

Daker, M.G. (1969b).
Pelargonium 'Kleiner Liebling' – a most unusual cultivar. Journal Royal Horticultural Society 94, 353-354.

Dale, T. (1968).
A genetic study of male sterility systems in geranium, *Pelargonium* × *hortorum* Bailey. M.Sc. Thesis, University of New Hampshire, USA.

Dale, T. and Rogers, O.M. (1971).
Male sterility in *Pelargonium* × *hortorum* Bailey. HortScience 6, 173-174.

Gauger, W. (1937).
Ergebnisse einer zytologischen Untersuchungen der Familie *Geraniaceae* I. Planta 26, 529-531.

Glicenstein, L.J. and Craig, R. (1989).
Observing transmitting tissue and other structures in the pistil using a fluorescent stain. Stain Technology 64, 229-231.

Harney, P.M. and Chow, T.W. (1971).
Crossability between some *Pelargonium* species. Euphytica 20, 286-291.

Harney, P.M. and Kung, H.C.C. (1967).
Development of non-dehiscent anthers in partially male-sterile plants of *Pelargonium* × *hortorum* Bailey cv. 'Jacqueline'. Canadian Journal Genetics Cytology 9, 359-366.

Khera, P.K. and Tilney-Bassett, R.A.E. (1976b).
Fine structural observations of the cotyledons in germinating seeds of *Pelargonium* × *Hortorum* Bailey: with normal and mutant plastids. Protoplasma 88, 201-214.

Knicely, W.W. (1964).
Chromosome numbers and crossability studies in the genus *Pelargonium*. M.Sc. Thesis, The Pennsylvania State University, USA.

Kubba, A.J. (1980).
Genetical studies of fertilisation and embryo development in *Pelargonium x Hortorum* Bailey. Ph.D. Thesis. University College of Swansea.

Kubba, A.J. and Tilney-Bassett, R.A.E. (1980).
The occurrence and survival of twin embryos in *Pelargonium* × *Hortorum* Bailey. Annals of Botany 46, 113-117.

Kubba, A.J. and Tilney-Bassett, R.A.E. (1981a).
Genetical studies of fertilization in *Pelargonium* × *Hortorum* Bailey. Euphytica 30, 209-215.

Kubba, A.J. and Tilney-Bassett, R.A.E. (1981b).
Genetical control of positional preference for fertilization in *Pelargonium* × *Hortorum* Bailey. Annals of Botany 48, 221-226.

Kubba, A.J. and Tilney-Bassett, R.A.E. (1981c).
Genetical studies of embryo survival and embryo breakdown in *Pelargonium* × *Hortorum* Bailey. Euphytica 30, 881-887.

Meyer, V.G. (1966).
Flower abnormalities. Botanical Review 32, 165-218.

Philippi, G. (1961).
Untersuchungen über die Fertilitatsverhältnisse einiger Kulturformen von *Pelargonium zonale*. Zeitschrift für Pflanzenzuchtung 44, 380-402.

Tamai, T.S., Tokumasu, S. and Shinohara, K. (1958).
Studies on the breeding of *Pelargonium* species used for the essential oil production. I. Artificially induced tetraploid plant of *Pelargonium roseum*. Japanese Journal Breeding 7, 131-138.

Tamai, T.S. and Tokumasu, S. (1969).
Studies on the breeding of *Pelargonium* species used for the essential oil production. V. Variation of some characters among interspecific hybrid plants between *P. roseum* and *P. denticulatum*. Japanese Journal Breeding 19, 343-349.

Tamai, T.S., Tokumasu, S. and Yamada, K. (1963).
Studies on the breeding of *Pelargonium* species used for the essential oil production. II. Artificially induced tetraploid plant in *Pelargonium denticulatum*. Japanese Journal Breeding 13, 143-148.

Tilney-Bassett, R.A.E. (1963).
Genetics and plastid physiology in *Pelargonium*. Heredity 18, 485-504.

Tokumasu, S. (1974).
Expression of male sterility in *Pelargonium crispum* L'Her. ex Ait. Euphytica 23, 209-217.

Tsai, A.H., Harney, P.M. and Peterson, R.L. (1973).
Megasporogenesis and megagametogenesis in *Pelargonium x hortorum*.
Canadian Journal of Botany 51, 607-612.

Yano, F., Tokumasu, S. and Kato, M. (1975).
The behaviour of pollen tubes and the developmental process of ovules in *Pelargonium*. Euphytica 24, 251-259.

4
Growth of Embryo, Seedling and Plant

Fine structure of the embryo

Within the ovary each ovule consists of a short stalk, or funiculus, leading to a central body of parenchymatous cells, or nucellus. Around the nucellus are two thin sheets of cells, the integuments that cover most of the nucellar surface apart from a small hole, the micropyle. Within the nucellus the megaspore mother cell, or megasporocyte, enlarges prior to meiosis. After meiosis ends and the linear tetrad is formed, three of these cells abort, and the surviving megaspore becomes very large. The further development is now of the *Polygonum* type (Dyer 1974). The haploid nucleus of the giant megaspore undergoes three successive mitotic divisions to produce eight haploid nuclei. These migrate through the cytoplasm and produce the eight-cell stage of the megagametophyte. Two polar nuclei in the centre of the cell become the central cell or the diploid endosperm nucleus. Three migrate to the chalazal end and become the antipodal cells. Three cells migrate to the micropylar end to form the egg apparatus, which consists of two synergids between which lies the egg.

To follow the early course of embryo development, thin serial sections of the developing ovule need to be prepared. Sheehan (1969) found that formalin propionic acid was an excellent fixative for the young embryos. For dehydration she used tertiary butyl alcohol, and finally embedded in paraplast. The material was sectioned using a rotary microtome, cut 12 microns thick, and stained with Erhlich's acid haemotoxylin and eosin. Finally the sections were mounted in euparol and examined under the light microscope.

According to Philippi (1961), and my own observations, fertilization takes place normally between seven to 17 hours after pollination. Kubba (1980) has produced an illustrated description of the main events of embryo development as seen with the light microscope. Fertilization is achieved when one male gamete from the pollen tube fuses with the egg, and the other fuses with the diploid endosperm nucleus to form the triploid endosperm. The entry of the pollen tube destroys one synergid and the other degenerates after fertilization. By 24 hours after pollination the fertilized endosperm nucleus has already divided two or three times to give four or eight endosperm nuclei before the zygote divides. For a few days the endosperm nuclei divide synchronously to produce a non-cellular thin cytoplasmic layer around the embryo sac or the megagametophyte wall, and around the embryo itself. By the end of the first week the endosperm begins to become cellular and many layered around the suspensor, and to fill up the narrow embryo sac space in this region. During the next ten days the cellular and many layered structure of the endosperm spreads towards the chalazal end.

The first division of the zygote separates a larger basal cell from a smaller terminal cell. The terminal cell divides again, and again to produce a chain of four suspensor cells, with a four-cell embryo head. By the end of the third day the suspensor has elongated to an eight-cell chain terminated by the much smaller eight-cell embryo head. The long suspensor chain pushes the embryo out of the narrow neck region of the ovule and into the more spacious cavity of the embryo sac. By the end of the first week the embryo has the classical heart stage configuration in which the head has a small notch around which two tiny cotyledonary lobes have started to grow. Meanwhile the suspensor has divided rapidly to produce a thick tissue filled with very large parenchymatous cells, in contrast to the much smaller cells of the embryo proper. The young cotyledons continue to elongate through the torpedo stage, finally achieving recognizable structures by 12-14 days. The radicle also elongates.

When dissected out under the stereomicroscope the cotyledons are thin at first, and the green cells quite transparent. During the next few days they considerably thicken so that by 17-19 days the embryo completely fills the seed. The ovule has enlarged about tenfold from 1mm to about 1cm in length. At this stage the endosperm degenerates. Up till about 21 days the seed coat is transparent and all the embryo cells develop green chloroplasts. By this time the suspensor tissue appears as a small dark green zone at the tip of the radicle. The cotyledons and radicle when stretched out measure about 1cm, but the suspensor is not more than 1mm. Between the third and fourth week the seed coat becomes brown and opaque and chlorophyll disappears from the chloroplasts; at the same time water is lost and the seed shrinks and hardens. By the beginning of the fifth week the ripe fruit is ready to be dispersed.

The seed coat is often hard and impermeable, and the seed does not germinate quickly if the seed coat is not scarified (Craig and Walker 1959, Badr and Horn 1971). After scarification, in which the seed is rubbed with abrasive paper, the seeds germinate within one or two days; the optimum temperature is 20° – 25°C, in either light or darkness. The seeds of some cultivars germinate spontaneously and quickly without the need for scarification (Fries 1966, Craig 1968). There is in fact a continuous transition from a hard to a soft seed coat that leads to differences in the germination of untreated seeds. In a series of experiments with a number of cultivars Horn *et al.* (1973) treated seeds with sulphuric acid, gibberellic acid, hot water, stratification, and dry freezing; none of which improved germination. Moreover, sulphuric acid was harmful to seeds with a permeable coat. In addition they detected, by the analysis of variance, that there were genetic differences in the germ ability of the embryos. It is therefore advisable to test the seeds beforehand to find out whether they need scarification or not. Rogers (1985) reported that ethylene gas overcomes the scarification requirement. In some of my experiments I was able to avoid scarification by germinating the seed immediately it was ripe, and before it was fully dried out.

A tetrad of four cells arranged in a square, as opposed to a row, marks the end of pollen grain meiosis. Each of the four cells separates and gradually changes shape to form the individual pollen grain. The single haploid nucleus undergoes the first pollen grain mitosis, and produces the binucleate pollen grain. The division is not equal. One nucleus enters the large vegetative cell, and the other nucleus enters the small generative cell. In the majority of flowering plants the cytoplasm splits unequally. Most generative cells contain small amounts of endoplasmic reticulum, some ribosomes, a few mitochondria and no proplastids. The unequal division keeps the plastids out. In pelargonium, by contrast, Lombardo and Gerola (1968) showed that the plastids do not segregate irregularly, and the generative cell contains many proplastids.

The generative cell divides into two male gametes inside the pollen tube. These possess a plasma membrane but no cell wall. In addition, the two male gametes contain proplastids. Guo and Hu (1995) describe them as electron dense, mostly cup-shaped or dumbbell shaped, and devoid of starch grains. Plastids were detected in the sperm and egg cells by their fluorescence after staining with DAPI, a stain specific for plastid DNA (Sodmergen *et al.* 1992 and Kuroiwa and Kuroiwa 1992).

According to Guo and Hu (1995), using electron microscopy, the egg cell has a nucleus towards the chalazal end, and a full complement of plastids, mitochondria, endoplasmic reticulum, ribosomes and a large vacuole towards the micropylar end. They found that both plastids and mitochondria in the egg cell looked significantly different from those in the sperm cell. The egg plastids contain starch and are relatively electron dense.

The plastids of male and female origin could therefore be distinguished in the fertilized egg, the zygote, by their shape, size and electron density. Guo and Hu observed that 24h after pollination, when fertilization is complete, the cytoplasm of the zygote has intermingled and the plastids and mitochondria have been distributed throughout the cell at random. The zygote divides, two days after fertilization, into a two-celled embryo consisting of a smaller terminal cell and a larger basal cell. Vacuoles remain small in the terminal cell, whereas a much larger vacuole develops in the basal cell. Organelles from male and female gametes appear to be incorporated into both cells of the proembryo. Plastids and mitochondria appear unchanged from the zygote. If this description is correct for all embryos, the hypothesis that the failure of plastid mixing in the zygote accounts for the rapid sorting-out cannot be correct. But the genetic results cover such a wide range of behaviour that it would be premature to make such a conclusion. Similarly, within the endosperm, there are plastids and mitochondria of male and female origin, rough endoplasmic reticulum, Golgi bodies, lipid and possibly microbodies.

Khera (1975) and Khera and Tilney-Bassett (1976a,b) reported the further development of the pelargonium embryo from one week to ripening using green 'Flower of Spring', 'Dolly Varden', 'Foster's Seedling' and six variegated cultivars. The internal development of the cells is similar whether they are taken from the radicle or the cotyledons, but the development of the suspensor haustorium is quite distinctive. The many newly divided cells of the heart shaped embryo have thin walls with plasmodesmata through them and microtubules alongside them. A few small vacuoles are beginning to appear. The cytoplasm of the cotyledonary lobes is packed with loose groups of ribosomes. The endoplasmic reticulum occurs as short narrow tubular cisternae, and vesiculate profiles. Only a few ribosomes occur along the endoplasmic reticulum membranes. Active dictyosomes, and mitochondria are frequent. Microbodies and lipid droplets are occasionally seen. The chloroplasts are small compared to leaf chloroplasts with a mean area in section of $3.1\mu m^2$; there are usually 3-10 thylakoids per granum. Plastoglobuli occur with a frequency of 1-11 per plastid section. There are usually one or more starch grains of varying size.

The cells of the early suspensor haustorium have a diameter of about $20\mu m$. Their volume is tenfold that of the radicle and cotyledons. They have a highly lobed nucleus, and many plasmodesmata in their walls. There are no big vacuoles. The ribosomes occur in tight clusters, mostly around the endoplasmic reticulum and rarely free in the cytoplasm. The endoplasmic reticulum occurs as many short cisternae. Microbodies are frequent. Some lipid bodies occur. The many mitochondria have well developed cristae. The most striking difference is in the very numerous and well developed chloroplasts with a mean area in section of $4.2\mu m^2$; the thylakoids are stacked to form many grana per plastid. Up to 12 plastoglobuli per section are present in the stroma. Starch grains are small or absent.

After two weeks, when cell division is largely complete, the cells of the cotyledons and radicle have more numerous vacuoles, with small densely stained protein deposits inside them. The origin of some vacuoles appears to be initiated as differentiated zones of the cytoplasm around which the tonoplast is gradually built up from vesicles and small cisternae (Khera and Tilney-Bassett 1976c). The cytoplasmic ribosomes are mostly in groups largely attached to the endoplasmic reticulum. The endoplasmic reticulum has proliferated enormously with many long cisternae. The small lipid bodies are now numerous and scattered through the cytoplasm. The chloroplasts are mostly the same as at one week. The cells of the suspensor haustorium are up to 40µm diameter, two to four times as wide, which is up to 64 times the volume, as those of the cotyledon and radicle. A few of these have died. The mitochondria are either elongated or rounded, and their cristae are very long reaching into the centre of each mitochondrion. The chloroplasts have very large grana and sometimes the stacks are unusually high compared with those of cotyledon and radicle cells. Plastid ribosomes are clearly visible.

At three weeks the cotyledon and radicle cells have thickened considerably, and the embryo fills the seed. The protein bodies have partially filled the vacuoles. The lipid bodies in the cytoplasm are very numerous and restrict most of the cytoplasm to near the cell wall. The chloroplasts have changed little. Many cells of the suspensor haustorium have died. The vacuoles of the mature cells have increased in size. The mitochondria are minute, 0.5µm in diameter, half the diameter of those in the cotyledon and radicle cells; they have a very electron dense matrix. The chloroplasts are mostly elongated with as many as 40 thylakoids comprising the large grana, and they are more tightly packed than at two weeks. In some plastids abnormally large plastoglobuli are found.

At four weeks the embryo has completely transformed into the mature seed. The cell fine structure shows how extensively the cotyledon and radicle have become transformed into storage organs packed with lipid and protein, and some starch. The nucleus appears small. The thick cell walls contain plasmodesmata. No microbodies are visible. The cytoplasmic ribosomes are mostly scattered free, and the endoplasmic reticulum is greatly reduced. Several mitochondria display disfigured cristae. The chloroplasts have lost their pigment, and the grana have partially or completely gone; individual thylakoids are very swollen. Most of the cells of the suspensor haustorium appear dead.

Mutant cell tissues were also examined throughout the stages of development. There was little difference, except for the plastids, indicating that the changes in the plastids do not seriously affect the functioning of other organelles. The mutant plastids are unable to develop a proper thylakoid structure, and probably have an inability or very reduced ability to make plastid ribosomes. They do possess plastoglobuli and some starch. The mutant plastids of the suspensor haustorium tissue are very variable in shape. The membrane system is more developed. Irregular fenestrated thylakoids are present in the stroma, and there are long chains of minute vesicles attached to each other. Most plastids contain one to three spindle shaped grana of tightly packed thylakoids; only one fenestrated thylakoid extends out into the stroma from each side of the granum.

They appear to have a few ribosome-like particles in the suspensor haustorium cells.

Fine structure of the seedling

For our fine structural study of the process of germination in the cotyledons, we have used green 'Flower of Spring' and variegated 'Miss Burdette-Coutts' (Khera and Tilney-Bassett 1976b). On the first day of sprouting, as soon as the radicle has emerged from the seed coat, hydration and digestion have already begun. The big protein bodies have cavities in their matrix, and the lipid bodies no longer lined the cell walls but are spread through the cytoplasm. The cytoplasmic ribosomes appear in clusters associated with rare short profiles of endoplasmic reticulum. The membrane system of the plastids is represented by a few short thylakoids. The lumen of the thylakoids is still very narrow. One or two starch grains are present throughout germination, as well as a few or many plastoglobuli and plastid ribosomes. It is clear that it is the same population of plastids that lost their embryo thylakoid membrane system at maturity, and then regained them in the cotyledons of the germinating seed.

By the second day of sprouting the cotyledons have grown out of the testa and turn light green. Many protein bodies have coalesced to form a large central vacuole pushing the cytoplasm to the periphery. The few protein bodies remaining and the lipid bodies come to lie in this peripheral layer. The short cisternae, some vesicles, polysomes, dictyosomes, and microbodies all appear again. Several thylakoids become stacked to form short grana. Some plastids contain a large prolamellar body with several short thylakoids radiating out from it.

By the third day, the expanding cotyledons are dark green. The protein has almost disappeared from the central vacuole and from some of the smaller vacuoles. The lipid bodies remain plentiful. The endoplasmic reticulum system still occurs as sparsely distributed short cisternae and small vesicles. The dictyosomes are prominent and microbodies frequent. Mitochondria have well developed cristae. The young chloroplasts have long thylakoids and wide grana. The grana stacks are low and generally contain 3-6 thylakoids. Some plastids still have small prolamellar bodies. The fine structural changes of mutant cells are similar except for the plastids. They are more irregular in shape, and the internal membrane system is poorly developed. A few scattered vesicles, or a prolamellar body made up of very irregular tubules, are all there is. One or two starch grains are present, and up to 15 plastoglobuli per plastid section. The ribosomes are not apparent.

At the fourth day a few small protein deposits remain in the vacuole, and lipid bodies in the cytoplasm. The prolamellar bodies have almost disappeared. The grana system is more extensive than in embryo cells.

On the fifth day, the chloroplasts are well formed. The protein has gone, but some lipid remains. On one occasion we saw a mixed cell in a variegated seedling from a cross between the two parents. The normal and mutant plastids were quite distinct from each other. The mutant plastids completely lack the thylakoid system developed in the normal plastids.

We thus see that the whole sequence of sub-cellular changes can proceed almost as well with mutant plastids as with normal green chloroplasts. Nevertheless, we do observe that when the white embryo has a white mother there is a considerable drop in fertility. Presumably the variegated mother is rather inadequate in nourishing the developing embryo, a deficiency that can be overcome if the embryo partially nourishes itself by virtue of the green chloroplasts, but not if the embryo has colourless mutant plastids.

Plant height

The zonal pelargoniums seem to express a continuous variation from a few cms to over 2m in height. Cultivars exist to exploit all this range. The growth in height is much influenced by soil and temperature. In Greece and Spain we see beautiful specimens full of branches and lots of flowers, and many plants are over 2m high. In Britain, the short growing season, with cool summers and long winters, allows them to grow only about 1/2m high out of doors. After that they must be brought under glass and kept free of frost. There are, of course, clearly distinct types that are under genetic control. Nugent and Snyder (1967) reported a dwarf plant that on selfing segregated into three classes designated as tall, medium and dwarf. Their results provided an acceptable fit with the modified dihybrid ratio of 9 dwarf: 6 medium: 1 tall. They concluded that plant height was under the control of two dominant genes, A-B-, which gave the dwarf, the medium plants by one or other dominant gene, A-bb or aaB-, and tall by the double recessive, aabb. This may accurately convey the situation in some lines. It is not the genetic control found by Henault and Craig (1970).

They found that in a cross between a true breeding tall and a true breeding dwarf, or vice versa, they obtained reciprocal F1s that were all semi-dwarf. On selfing the F1s, they obtained segregation in the frequency of 37 tall, 57 semi-dwarf, and 25 dwarfs. The numbers are a reasonable fit with the 1: 2: 1 ratio expected from the segregation of a major gene with incomplete dominance. They also obtained 42 tall and 45-semi dwarfs, and 12-semi dwarfs and 17 dwarfs, in the two backcrosses between the F1 and the alternative parents. Both sets of data fit the 1: 1 ratio expected of such backcrosses. The two F1s from crosses between the dwarf and two tall parents were slightly on the dwarf side of the mid-point between the two parental means. This suggests that the dwarf is slightly more dominant than tall. Hence they symbolized the dwarf line as DwDw, the semi dwarf line as Dwdw, and the tall as dwdw.

The classification has been modified slightly as deciding the classes used for showing plants. The dwarf line is now referred to as miniature; this in a small plant grown in a 9cm pot that does not exceed 13cm high from soil surface to the tip of the foliage. The semi dwarf is now referred to as a dwarf; this is a larger plant grown in an 11cm pot that is greater than 13cm tall but does not exceed 20cm tall (Taylor 1988). Plants above 20cm fall into the tall category. These height measurements seem to correspond with those used by Henault and Craig, except that they measured the heights of the plants at 71 days from sowing, which makes them seem rather smaller. The mean heights of the parents were measured at 98 days from sowing, and this makes them correspondingly taller. In addition to these categories there are some micro miniatures, which are really very small. Also the tall plants are certainly modified by other genes with small effects, as many different growth forms exist.

Murgatroyd (1977) crossed 'Alde' with 'Snowstorm' and he got a mixture of dwarf and tall progeny. In the second generation he obtained a continuous variation from a micro-miniature 2cm high through to a tall 17cm high, with the mean 9.8cm. His results did not fit either those of Nugent and Snyder or Henault and Craig. He suggested that at least two genes were involved. His tall plants were really too short; he should have recorded them as dwarf according to the scheme outlined by Taylor, especially as they were scored after 140 days since germination. He also studied the branching habit. The plants either produced no side shoots, just one side shoot, or multiple shoots at the base of the stem, or multiple shoots further up the stem. He could not detect any correlation between tall and dwarf plant habit and shooting, or between plant height and the number of shoots. Nevertheless, he noticed that plants with multiple shoots were significantly shorter that those without side shoots. This could have interfered with his classification. In the short time of the student project no definite conclusion can be drawn, but his observations throw doubt as to whether plant height is simply under the control of a single gene. This is an area where much study is required to set out the various genetic, developmental and environmental factors.

References

Badr, M. and Horn, W. (1971).
Genetische Untersuchungen an diploiden und tetraploiden *Pelargonium Zonale*-Hybriden. Zeitschrift für Pflanzenzuchtung 66, 203-220.

Craig, R. (1968).
Past, present and future of seedling geraniums. Pennsylvania Flower Growers Bulletin 204, 1-2 and 7.

Craig, R. and Walker, D.E. (1959).
Geranium seed germination techniques. Geraniums Around the World VII/2, 4-7.

Dyer, A. (1974)
The visible events of mitotic cell division. In: Experimental Botany: An international series of monographs vol. 7. Ed. M.M. Yeoman. 49-110.

Fries, R.E. (1966).
Selection for high germination in *Pelargonium x hortorum*. Proc. XVII. International Horticultural Congress 1, 111.

Guo, F.L. and Hu, S.Y. (1995).
Cytological evidence of biparental inheritance of plastids and mitochondria in *Pelargonium*. Protoplasma 186, 201-207.

Henault, R.E. and Craig, R. (1970).
Inheritance of plant height in the Geranium. The Journal of Heredity 61, 75-78.

Horn, W., Bachthaler, E. and Badr, M. (1973).
Keimung und Blutezeit bei F1-Hybrid Sorten und Zuchstammen von *Pelargonium Zonale*-Hybriden. Gartenbauwissenschaft 20, 392-408.

Khera, P.K. (1975).
Plastid development in zonal pelargoniums. Ph.D. Thesis. University College of Swansea.

Khera, P.K. and Tilney-Bassett, R.A.E. (1976a).
Fine structural observations of embryo development in *Pelargonium x Hortorum* Bailey: with normal and mutant plastids. Protoplasma 88,7-23.

Khera, P.K. and Tilney-Bassett, R.A.E. (1976b).
Fine structural observations of the cotyledons in germinating seeds of *Pelargonium x Hortorum* Bailey: with normal and mutant plastids. Protoplasma 88, 201-214.

Khera, P.K. and Tilney-Bassett, R.A.E. (1976c).
The origin of vacuoles in young embryos of *Pelargonium x Hortorum* Bailey.
Planta (Berl.) 130, 333-338.

Kubba, A.J. (1980).
Genetical studies of fertilisation and embryo development in *Pelargonium x Hortorum* Bailey. Ph.D. Thesis. University College of Swansea.

Kuroiwa, H. and Kuroiwa, T. (1992).
Giant mitochondria in the mature egg cell of *Pelargonium zonale*. Protoplasma 168, 184-188.

Lombardo, G. and Gerola, F.M. (1968).
Cytoplasmic inheritance and ultrastructure of the male generative cell of higher plants. Planta 82, 105-110.

Murgatroyd, C.A. (1997).
A proposed genetic basis for plant height and branching in Pelargonia. B.Sc. Project, University of Wales Swansea.

Nugent, P.E. and Snyder, R.J. (1967).
The inheritance of floret doubleness, floret center colour, and plant habit in *Pelargonium hortorum* Bailey. Procedings American Society Horticultural Science 91, 680-690.

Philippi, G. (1961).
Untersuchungen über die Fertilitatsverhältnisse einiger Kulturformen von *Pelargonium zonale*. Zeitschrift für Pflanzenzuchtung 44, 380-402.

Rogers, O.M. (1985).
Ethylene overcomes scarification requirement in *Pelargonium*. HortScience 20, 187.

Sheehan, R. (1969).
Comparative techniques for the preparation of serial sections of young pelargonium embryos. B.Sc. Project. University College of Swansea.

Sodmergen., Suzuki, T., Kawano, S., Nakamura, S., and Kuroiwa, T. (1992).
Behaviour of organelle nuclei (nucleoids) in generative and vegetative cells during maturation of pollen in *Lilium longiflora* and *Pelargonium zonale*. Protoplasma 168, 73-82.

Taylor, J. (1988).
Geraniums and Pelargoniums. The complete guide to cultivation, propagation and exhibition. The Crowood Press, Ramsbury Marlborough, Wiltshire.

5
Hybrid Variegation

I should now like to introduce a method through which white-over-green or green-over-white chimeras can be produced. Whether or not any of the existing chimeras have been produced in this manner we do not know. We believe that most of these have not; instead we believe that they originated through a single plastid mutation, or nuclear mutation. The method depends upon the biparental inheritance of the plastids, in which the plastids enter from the pollen as well as from the egg. It also depends upon the evolution of plastids, so that speciation occurs as the nucleus changes; at the same time the plastids also evolve to keep in harmony with their nucleus. When two species, or two cultivars, are crossed it sometimes happens that the chloroplasts of one species develop normally, whereas those of the second species remain chlorophyll deficient, pale green, or yellow or white. The chloroplasts of the first species develop normally with the hybrid nucleus, whereas those of the second species do not. The normal development of the green chloroplasts requires a harmonious reaction between the young developing plastids and the hybrid nucleus, and when this harmony is lacking between one plastid and the nucleus the plastids fail to develop normally. This is when variegation occurs in a seedling following the crossing of two species. The plastids of one species develop normally into chloroplasts, but from the second species the chloroplasts fail to develop fully. The result of reciprocal crosses between two species A and B, or two cultivars, are as follows:

A x B = AB, Green + Variegated + White
B x A = AB, White + Variegated + Green

The A plastids are compatible with the hybrid nucleus and become green, while the B plastids are incompatible and become white. The frequencies of the three classes of seedling vary depending upon many conditions. These include the genotype of the female parent, the direction of the cross, the relative proportion of the plastids transmitted, and the speed of sorting-out of the plastids during embryo development.

Hybrid variegation is well known in the evening primrose where as many as five different plastid types were recognized by Stubbe (1964) in the subgenus *Euoenothera*. There is also evidence of its occurrence in a few other genera, including *Pelargonium denticulatum* and *P. filicifolium* (Kirk and Tilney-Bassett 1978). It has not been described in modern garden pelargoniums until relatively recently.

A restriction enzyme that is named after the bacterium from which it is extracted, like EcoR1 or BamH1, cuts the DNA at a specific nucleotide sequence. Digestion with one or more restriction enzymes generates a series of DNA fragments. These can be sized according to their electrophoretic mobility, and from this data a restriction site map is constructed. Using the restriction enzyme technique, Metzlaff, Börner and Hagemann (1981) treated the chloroplast DNA from the five species *Pelargonium fragrans, P. peltatum, P. radulans, P. roseum*, and *P. zonale* with the enzyme EcoR1. They all showed distinct differences. They also treated the chloroplast genomes of 16 cultivars of *P. zonale*. Here they found three plastid types. 'Madame Salleron' was plastome III, 'Trautlieb' and 'Mrs Parker' were plastome II, and the cultivars 'Stadt Bern', 'Kleiner Liebling', 'Wilhelm Langguth', 'Freak of Nature', 'Mrs Pollock', 'Flower of Spring', 'Gnom', 'Dresdener Rubin', 'Greifswald', 'Cloth of Gold', 'Happy Thought', 'Dolly Varden' and 'Alex Purpurball' were plastome I. A cross between a cultivar from plastome I, 'Flower of Spring', was crossed with a cultivar from plastome II, 'Trautlieb'. This hybrid produced some variegated seedlings, including chimeras. When they investigated the plastid DNA, using EcoR1, the white plastid type always contained plastome I, and the green type plastome II. This confirmed exactly the phenotypic characteristics of the W × G cross. No recombinant types, with a white plastome II or a green plastome I, were found.

The following year the three of them, plus the addition of Pohlheim (Metzlaff *et al.* 1982), obtained an example of hybrid variegation after a cross between the green *P. roseum* and the green *P. zonale* 'Stadt Bern'. Here they found, using the two restriction enzymes EcoR1 and BamH1, that the cleavage pattern of *P. roseum* was in the green tissue, and 'Stadt Bern' in the white tissue. Clearly this was a case of the bleaching of the normal development of the 'Stadt Bern' plastids.

> *Roseum* × Stadt Bern = 46 green + 11 variegated
> Stadt Bern × *Roseum* = 57 green + 32 variegated

The further demonstration of hybrid variegation occurred when Pohlheim (1986) obtained all three classes of progeny after reciprocal crosses between *P. zonale* and *P. inquinans*. The bleached progeny were yellowish-white; it was assumed, but not proven, that they contained the *inquinans* plastids.

> *P. zonale* × *P. inquinans* = 23 green + 2 variegated + 5 white
> *P. inquinans* × *P. zonale* = 2 green + 8 variegated + 3 white

Crosses were made between *P. hortorum* 'Mme Buchner' and four of its putative ancestral species *P. zonale, P. inquinans, P. scandens*, and *P. stenopetalum* (Chow and Harney 1970). Although they examined many aspects of fertility, they never reported any sign of hybrid variegation. Nyakaana found this strange, and so he (1989) repeated the crosses, and he added to them *P. kewense, P. salmonia,* and *P. acetosum.* Nyakaana obtained no seedlings at all when *P. acetosum* was used as the female parent with any of the six other species. Nor did he obtain any seedlings when *P. zonale* was crossed with *P. inquinans* or with *P. scandens.* All the 41other crosses had some success. Of these, twelve exhibited various degrees of incompatibility owing to their stunted and poor growth, or to the development of hybrid variegation, or complete hybrid bleaching. Three crosses *P. inquinans* × *P. stenopetalum, P. kewense* × *P. salmonia,* and *P. inquinans* × *P. zonale,* exhibited hybrid variegation. Two crosses *P. scandens* × *P. acetosum* and *P. kewense* × *P. acetosum* produced seedlings that were all stunted and bleached. The absence of hybrid variegation from the results of Chow and Harney is understandable in view of Nyakaana obtaining only three cases from 49 crosses. Unfortunately, not all the plants are true species, and amongst them all a certain amount of breeding has occurred; some of them are hybrids between species (Clifton 1990). We are not always dealing with the true species. Beyond any doubt is the variability of the plastid population.

The incompatible plastids that were not in harmony with the hybrid nucleus were not altered in any way; they had not received a plastid gene mutation, they were merely modified. Schötz (1962) was able to show that such a modified plastid could be returned to normal by crossing the hybrid plant back to its original parent (Kirk and Tilney-Bassett 1978). In other words, although the white plastids in a hybrid variegated plant looked like mutant ones they were not, they were only phenocopies. The change was reversible if they were returned to their correct nucleus.

I chose 'Pac Grosser Garten', bred by Wilhelm Elsner of Dresden, to investigate hybrid variegation because of its East German origin, making it unlikely to have had any English cultivars in its recent ancestry. Moreover, it looked somewhat odd; it was a darker green than the cultivars we were used to. There was a chance that is would have a distinct plastome. So Almouslem (1988) crossed it as female with the English cultivars. There were actually three cultivars: the green forms of 'Flower of Spring', 'Dolly Varden' and 'Foster's Seedling', together with two plants, which we called 'Darlington Orange Red' and 'Darlington Red', and two seedlings W1A and W2B. The normal male sterility of 'Pac Grosser Garten' meant that the reciprocal cross could not be made. When selfing did succeed only two seedlings were obtained and these were extremely small and slow growing. In nearly all cases, although both parents were green, there was a mixture of a majority green, an intermediate frequency of variegated, and a few white progeny. Only the cross with green 'Flower of Spring' produced a majority of variegated progeny (Table 5.1), but the estimate of green plastids was 64.3 per cent. Almouslem obtained the same result when he crossed 'Pac Grosser Garten' with green 'Dolly Varden', or 'Preston Park', and looked at the embryos. The majority were green, intermediate variegated, and the minority white. So once again hybrid variegation had been demonstrated (Table 5.1). Previous work with the English cultivars had given no indication of any plastome incompatibility among them. The incompatible plastids were white or yellow; curiously white or yellow types were sometimes present in the same cross, and even in the same seedling. This suggested some underlying variability or instability in the response of the defective plastids with the hybrid genome.

Parents Crossed	Numbers of Progeny			Green Plastids Transmitted*
Seeds	Green	Variegated	White	Per Cent Green
PGG x FOS	14	5	0	86.8
PGG x DV	16	42	10	73.7
PGG x DOR	42	8	5	83.6
PGG x DR	17	2	0	94.7
PGG x FS	10	25	0	64.3
PGG x W1A	34	6	0	92.5
PGG x W2B	27	12	2	80.5
Embryos				
PGG x PP	218	40	38	80.4
PGG x DV	181	79	78	65.2

*Per Cent Green Plastids Transmitted + [2G + 1V]/2Total

Table 5.1. Green, variegated and white progeny produced after crossing green parents, and the per cent green plastids transmitted.

Variegation affected the cotyledons, and entirely bleached parts of the leaves appeared in several hybrids. Usually the variegation sorted-out during development into green shoots, or if into yellow or white shoots they eventually died. A few stable variegated plants survived from the cross 'Pac Grosser Garten' × 'Dolly Varden' either as a white-over-green chimera, or as a weakly viable yellowing green form. The latter form indicates that the incompatible plastid type is capable of limited photosynthesis, which is not found in the plastid mutants assumed to result from plastid mutation. It is tempting to assume that the green plastids would have derived from the maternal parent, 'Pac Grosser Garten', except that in G × W plastid mutant crosses 'Pac Grosser Garten' behaved as a type II plant, in which the transmission of the plastids by the paternal parent is often as good or even better than by the maternal parent (Almouslem 1988; Tilney-Bassett and Almouslem 1989). This was never the case, hence it is not inconceivable that in the crosses the green plastids are derived from the male parent, equivalent to the W × G crosses in which the majority of offspring are usually green. To confirm this hypothesis the plastid DNA will have to be analysed, and this has not been done.

Another interesting cross that I made was that between 'Frills' as the pistillate parent and 'Preston Park' as the staminate parent. The cultivar 'Frills' is an unusual form. It is a miniature with small leaves and no zone. It has semi-double, coral pink flowers. 'Preston Park' has pale salmon flowers and a distinctive narrow peripheral zone (Amoatey and Tilney-Bassett 1993). The cross resulted in 10 seeds, which germinated into six green and four variegated progeny, with equal quantities of single and semi-double blooms. Nyakaana (1989) obtained the same set of results when he examined three-week-old embryos (Table 5.2). Clearly hybrid variegation had occurred. The hybrids were no longer miniature, but were characterised by the narrowness of the stem, a feature that they inherited from 'Frills'. I had not seen such a narrow stem on any previous zonal. Nyakaana (1989) took two variegated plants and obtained from them pure green, and stable white-over-green chimeral plants, and propagated them. The green and chimeral plants were therefore isogenic with each other as they had the same nucleus and differed only in their plastids. One half of the hybrid nucleus contained genes from 'Frills', while the other half contained genes from 'Preston Park'. He then crossed these plants back to the parental cultivars, and scored their embryos as green, variegated or white. One quarter of the backcross nucleus now contained genes from 'Frills', and three quarters contained genes from 'Preston Park', or vice versa. The results were quite illuminating. When the two hybrids with green plastids were crossed to 'Preston Park', nearly all the progeny were green, and green plastids accounted for 93.8 per cent. When the same two hybrids with white plastids were crossed to 'Preston Park', the majority of the progeny were again green, and green plastids accounted for 87.6 per cent. Evidently the backcrossing to 'Preston Park' restored the incompatible reaction between the nucleus and one of the plastids to a considerable extent. The original reaction between 'Frills' and 'Preston Park' produced over 50 per cent variegated plus white progeny embryos, and green plastids accounted for 65.8 per cent. The backcross to the 'Frills' parent did not restore the results at all. The proportion of variegated and white progeny was now in the majority, and the green plastids were down to 44.8 per cent with the green parent and 28.1 per cent with the white parent (Table 5.2). The cultivar 'Preston Park' shows a marked tendency to restore the damage done, while 'Frills' shows a strong tendency to enhance it.

Parents and Backcrosses	Numbers of Progeny			Green Plastids Transmitted*
Parents	Green	Variegated	White	Per Cent Green
FR x PP	31	34	8	65.8
Backcrosses				
(FR x PP) G x PP	126	7	5	93.8
(FR x PP) W x PP	128	12	13	87.6
(FR x PP) G x FR	33	12	42	44.8
(FR x PP) W x FR	8	2	32	28.1

* Per Cent Green Plastids Transmitted = [2G + 1V]/2Total

Table 5.2. Green, variegated and white embryos produced after crossing green 'Frills' with green 'Preston Park'. The hybrid with green or white plastids backcrossed to the two parents. Compare the estimates of the per cent green plastids transmitted.

Embryo mortality was very high when the hybrids were backcrossed to 'Frills', compared to when they were backcrossed to 'Preston Park' as the male parent. Moreover, the highest per cent mortality in each case was seen to occur amongst white embryos. These results suggest that there was substantial selection pressure exerted on a white embryo during development compared to green and variegated embryos. But owing to the small size of the four-way analysis of variance, the effects of the embryo category, maternal nuclear genotype, maternal plastid genotypes, and male nuclear genotypes were all non-significant. Nyakaana (1989) argued that it was probable that the incompatible plastid was introduced by 'Preston Park' entering from the male parent. This seems likely to me as well. Unfortunately, there is no substitute for knowledge of the DNA of the respective plastid genome.

In view of the mixed and unknown parentage of many variegated pelargoniums following biparental inheritance of normal and mutant plastids, and of the ability to form plastid chimeras by crossing green plastids, we cannot be sure that the two causes have always been kept apart, although we believe this to be the case. We shall await further developments with interest.

References

Almouslem, A.B. (1988).
Qualitative and quantitative genetical studies in *Pelargonium × Hortorum* Bailey. Ph.D. Thesis, University of Swansea, Wales.

Amoatey, H.M. and Tilney-Bassett, R.A.E. (1993).
Multiple alleles and the control of leaf zonation patterns in zonal pelargoniums. Journal of Horticultural Science 68, 45-52.

Chow, T.W. and Harney, P.M. (1970).
Crossability between a diploid *Pelargonium × hortorum* Bailey cultivar and some of its putative ancestral species. Euphytica 19, 338-348.

Clifton, R.T.F. (1990).
Geranium Family Species Check List. 4th ed. Part 4. *Pelargonium*. Compiled for the Geraniaceae Group of The British Pelargonium and Geranium Society.

Kirk, J.T.O. and Tilney-Bassett, R.A.E. (1978).
The Plastids: Their chemistry, structure, growth and inheritance, 2nd ed. Elsevier/North-Holland Biomedical Press, Amsterdam.

Metzlaff, M., Börner,T. and Hagemann, R. (1981).
Variations of chloroplast DNA in the genus *Pelargonium* and their biparental inheritance. Theoretical and Applied Genetics 60, 37-41.

Metzlaff, M., Pohlheim, F., Börner, T. and Hagemann, R. (1982).
Hybrid variegation in the genus *Pelargonium*. Current Genetics 5, 245-249.

Nyakanna, S. (1989).
Plastid inheritance and crossability studies in the zonal pelargoniums. MSc. Thesis. University College of Swansea.

Pohlheim, F. (1986).
Hybrid variegation in crosses between *Pelargonium zonale* (L.) l'Herit. ex Ait. and *Pelargonium inquinans* (L.) l'Herit. ex Ait. Plant Breeding 97, 93-96.

Schötz, F. 1962.
Zur Kontinuität der Plastiden. Planta 58, 411-434.

Stubbe, W. 1964.
The role of the plastome in evolution of the genus *Oenothera.* Genetica 35, 28-33.

Tilney-Bassett, R.A.E. and Almouslem, A.B. (1989).
Variation in plastid inheritance between pelargonium cultivars and their hybrids. Heredity 63, 145-153.

6
Plastid Chimeras

All the variegated plants that I have seen amongst pelargoniums are chimeras, with the exception of those that are caused by virus infection. They differ from each other because the leaves are variegated green or white, or the layers give rise to flowers of different colour, or the growth of one layer is stunted or inhibited compared to the other. All the variegated leaf chimeras that are caused by a nuclear gene difference must have arisen by mutation. Those that are caused by a plastid gene arose originally by mutation, but the widespread increase has mostly been through breeding, in which normal and mutant plastids come together in variegated seedlings owing to their biparental inheritance. The flower and stunting chimeras arise by mutation in nuclear genes, and so cannot arise through breeding. We shall look at examples of all of these. We shall begin by looking at examples of plastid chimeras, or probable examples of these, as breeding has not tested them all. These will lead into examples of trichimeras, where the plastid chimera has become a nuclear gene chimera as well. Finally, in the next chapter we shall consider chimeras solely with a nuclear gene differential.

Before I start on the examples, I should like to run through the way of testing all three layers (Tilney-Bassett 1963a). Among variegated leaf chimeras, whether of the white-over-green type of 'Flower of Spring', GWG, or the yellow-over-green type of 'Mrs Pollock', GYG, an examination of the epidermal pieces torn off from the underside of the leaf has proved especially useful. When the epidermis is normal the guard cell pair, lining the stomata, have an average of 38 green chloroplasts recognized with the high power of a compound microscope. The other epidermal cells have a few small, scattered chloroplasts too. By contrast, the epidermis of 'Mrs Parker' contains genetically mutant plastids, which are colourless with an average of 26 per guard cell pair (Börner and Forster, 1981). Also the elongated cells of the palisade mesophyll tissue, which are so clear in the green zone, are very much reduced in length in the white tissue. Hence, there is an excellent correlation between the colour of the plastids and their genotypes. Supportive evidence for a genetically green epidermis frequently occurs in the appearance of green flecks on the margin of white sub-epidermal tissue. These occur as the result of sporadic periclinal divisions in the epidermal cells giving rise to pockets of green mesophyll tissue. Conversely, white flecks in the margin of green leaves are indicative of a genetically white epidermis. I have recognized a white fleck on a green bud variation from 'Flower of Spring', GWG → WGG, as well as green flecks on the original sandwich chimera (Tilney-Bassett 1986).

It is a useful rule that the germ cells develop from sub-epidermal cells, and are therefore of L II origin. The seedlings usually point out the genotype of L II. On selfing white margined zonal pelargoniums Baur (1909) obtained a few wholly white seedlings, indicating that the germ layer corresponded with the outer white skin of the leaf. I also got a few white seedlings from the sandwich chimeras 'Flower of Spring', 'Dolly Varden' and 'Mrs J.C. Mapping', but the fertility was very low. It was later shown that a genetically green epidermis bound the white skin of many variegated pelargoniums, so these were sandwich chimeras, GWG.

Adventitious buds on leaf cuttings behave similarly to those on roots. In the zonal pelargoniums 'Freak of Nature', 'A Happy Thought', 'Mrs Pollock', 'Wilhelm Langguth' and 'Cloth of Gold' leaf cuttings produced adventitious shoots with the characteristics of the core component L III (Bergann and Bergann 1959). The green-over-white chimera 'Mrs C. Clark' gave a pure white shoot on a root proving the chimera structure was GGW (Tilney-Bassett 1963a,1986). In tissue culture terminal buds of the white-over-green 'Mrs J.C. Mapping' repeated the chimera structure, but adventitious buds arising from the callus developed into both green and white shoots (Tilney-Bassett 1986).

Two cases are described in great detail, but the cultivars are not identified (Stewart *et al.* 1974). In one case the white layer expands as well as the green. In the second case the white layer in the comparable position expands much less. Thus in the white-over-green chimera, GWG, the white margin is quite wide in the GW_1G chimera, but very narrow in the GW_2G chimera. Similarly, the white area in the GGW_1 chimera is quite large, the size of the green area in the GW_1G chimera. By contrast in the GGW_2 the white area is very small. The greater growth of the green tissue compensates for the lesser growth of the white tissue. The authors consider the effect of the mutant white area in all the six possible combinations of the chimera, GGW, GWW, WWG, WGG, GWG and WGW, as well as the two pure types, GGG and WWW. They show that the growth of the W_1 tissue is always comparable to that of the green. The leaf is about the same size in all chimeras. They illustrate the chimeras profusely both in overall appearance of the leaf, petiole, stem, stipule and the reproductive structures, and in their histology. They note that the first type of chimera can have four or even five layers running for many nodes before the stem changes colour. So the leaves may become white quickly, GWG → GWW, while the stem remains green, GWG → GWWG → GWWWG, for many nodes, changing only slowly. This kind of change does not happen in the second chimera. Because of the restricted growth of W_2, the white layer has generally much less effect on the green tissue in all parts of the plant. Thus the GGW_2 stem is lighter than the GW_2G stem, but much greener than the GGW_1 stem. The flower buds of the GW_1G chimera have broad white edged sepals derived from L II, and a narrower green centre from

L III. The flower buds of the GW_2G chimera have the tissue contributions almost reversed. They have a narrow white edge from W_2, and broad green centre from L III. In my experience the cultivars 'Flower of Spring' and 'Miss Burdett Coutts' are typical of the first chimera, as they both have wide white margins to the leaves, although 'Miss Burdett-Coutts' is somewhat broader, and 'Dolly Varden' is perhaps the second type. I say perhaps because although 'Dolly Varden' has a very narrow white margin, it is fertile and very stable, which is not typical of the unknown cultivar described.

Among many variegated-leaf pelargoniums the sandwich chimera, GWG, is the most obvious type. When they originate as variegated seedlings, all six types of chimera are equally common, but the white-margined type is likely to be strongly selected. This is the one that is most attractive. It could be either WWG or GWG. In fact the GWG is the only one that must be original. The WWG chimera may be original, but it may also be the result of an earlier change. Be that as it may, I have found several examples of the white-over-green chimera with a white epidermis, WWG. They are 'Caroline Schmidt', 'Chelsea Gem' and 'Lady Cullum'. Kümmler (1922) recognized two additional thick-skinned chimeras, WWG, 'Mrs Parker' and 'Mr Langguth'. Besides never producing green flecks on the white margins, the plastids in the guard cell pair were colourless. The sandwich chimeras, GWG, include 'Dolly Varden', 'Flower of Spring', 'Foster's Seedling', 'Mrs J.C. Mapping', 'Kathleen Harrop', 'Madame Salleron', 'Miss Burdett-Coutts' and 'Mrs Pollock' (Tilney-Bassett 1936a, 1963b). All have produced green marginal lobes or green flecks on the white margin of the leaves, particularly in the spring to early summer when their growth from cuttings is most rapid. There are many more cultivars like them. The sandwich chimeras are very stable, but over a period of time changes gradually arise. The one plant with which I am closely associated is 'Flower of Spring'. It undergoes reversal producing the thick-skinned green-over-white chimera, GWG → GGW, and from that to green, GGW → GGG, following the duplication and triplication of L I. It also produces the thin-skinned GWW chimera, in which green flecks are occasionally produced on the white shoots. It follows the duplication of L II, GWG → GWW, and thence to the pure white shoot, GWW → WWW. Finally, 'Flower of Spring' occasionally produces a green shoot with white flecks on the green leaves, owing to the perforation of L I by LII, and the shifting of the other layers, GWG → WGG (Tilney-Bassett 1986). The displacement of the inner layers by the duplication or triplication of L I, or L II, is more frequent than the perforation of an outer layer by an inner layer. The green bud variations are derived mostly from L I, except the adventitious green bud variation derived from the root L III.

Peter Grieve bred 'Mrs Pollock' in 1858, although Mary Campbell doubts whether the present day 'Mrs Pollock' is the same plant (1990). Nevertheless, we still use the same name. It is a yellow-over-green sandwich chimera, GYG, and occasionally produces green flecks on the yellow leaf margin. As the result of reversal it produces the thick-skinned green-over-yellow leaf, GYG → GGY, and the yellow shoot with green flecks, GYG → GYY, following the duplication of L I or L II respectively. It failed to produce any seed after selfing, but after crosses with 'Trautlieb' it produced a mixture of green, slightly more variegated, and a few yellow seedlings (Herrmann and Hagemann 1971). These results were in agreement with those of former workers (Noack 1924; Chittenden 1926; Roth 1927; Tilney-Bassett 1963b). When used as the male parent, there were mostly green seedlings. The non-Mendelian inheritance pattern was biparental. The yellow mutant was given the designation en: gil-1 (Herrmann and Hagemann 1971).

Under weak light, when the marginal yellow tissues became quite green and achieved maximum chlorophyll content, the plastids had regularly arranged grana, varying from very high to very flat and spread with fenestrated stroma thylakoids. With increasing light intensity, or increasing age, the grana become puffed up with vacuoles, which lead eventually to a complete vacuolisation of the plastids and a large accumulation of plastoglobuli. In yellow leaves the plastids were free of grana and then unpaired fenestrated thylakoids predominated (Knoth 1975). 'Mrs Pollock', even with maximum chlorophyll content of 45 per cent, was incapable of photosynthesis (Herrmann and Hagemann 1971). Further investigation showed the delayed light emission and an increase of in vivo fluorescence, which indicates that photosystem II is functioning, but not the light induced EPR signal normally associated with photosystem I. It was defective in photosystem I (Herrmann et al. 1974, 76), because a particular thylakoid protein connected with the chlorophyll protein complex, and associated with photosystem I, was lacking (Hagemann 1979).

Another white-over-green chimera is 'Mrs J.C. Mappin'. It undergoes reversal, GWG → GGW. When crossed with 'Crystal Palace Gem' about one third of the seedlings were variegated, two thirds green, and a very few white seedlings. As a male parent, less than 3 per cent of the seedlings were variegated. There is nothing unusual about this behaviour. It becomes unusual when one analyses the flower colour (Tilney-Bassett 1990). The chimera has a white flower, but it behaves as genetically red. When it undergoes reversal it still has a white flower, but now it behaves like a white flower. When it produces a white shoot, the flower colour is red and the behaviour is red. The reason for the changing behaviour is because 'Mrs J.C. Mappin' is a trichimera. At some time after the original cultivar was in cultivation, it underwent a nuclear mutation turning the chimera into a trichimera. It is a chimera for the leaves and for the flowers with the following layers:

L I Green, white flower
L II White, red flower
L III Green, red flower

The changes may be illustrated as follows:

$G_1W_2G_3 \rightarrow G_1G_1W_2$ White-over-green to green-over-white shoot
$W_1R_2R_3 \rightarrow W_1W_1R_2$ White flower, red genotype to white flower, white genotype

And the second change:

$G_1W_2G_3 \rightarrow W_2W_2W_2$ White-over-green to white shoot
$W_1R_2R_3 \rightarrow R_2R_2R_2$ White flower, red genotype to red flower, red genotype

It is worth remembering that the germ layer is normally formed from L II, but the flower colour is from L I. They are not always the same. Similarly, 'Foster's Seedling' is a sandwich chimera with a pink flower, but it behaves genetically as if it had a red flower. When it underwent a change from white-over-green to green-over-white GWG → GGW, the flower colour remained pink PRR → PPR, but it now *behaved as genetically pink and not red*.

GWG → GGW White-over-green to green-over-white
PRR → PPR Pink flower, red genotype to pink flower, pink genotype

Both kinds of flower colour change require one or two mutations, assuming the red flower was heterozygous. The genotype of flowers is discussed later.

'Mrs J.C.Mappin' Red → White R1r1,R2r2,ww → r1r1,r2r2,ww
The mutations are R1 → r1, and R2 → r2, at the same time the white locus needs to be homozygous ww.

'Foster's Seedling' Red → Pink R1R1,R2r2 → R1R1,r2r2
A simple mutation R2 → r2 is all that is required.

An atypical result occurred with 'Golden Brilliantissima', which is a white-over-green chimera with yellow lobes YWG. The few seedlings were all yellow and the expected white seedlings were absent (Chittenden 1926; 1927; Neilson-Jones 1934; Bergann 1962b). Either L I always replaced L II during the development of the germ cells, or perhaps the potentially white seedlings were too weak to germinate. L I is unstable in the epidermal tissue of the flower and frequently produces pockets of sub-epidermal tissue, where the yellow seedlings arose. The rule that the germ cells always arise in the sub-epidermal tissue is still correct, but the rule that the sub-epidermal layer is always derived from L II only remains correct so long as L I give rise only to the epidermis. This is usually so in pelargonium but as in this instance, exceptions do occur.

'Madame Salleron' is a useful plant for covering ground in the summer, where a display of decorative ornamental leaves is required, but there is little upward growth and no dead flowers to be removed. It is completely sterile and produces no flowers at all. On close inspection the internodes are very close together and do not elongate like other white-over-green chimeras. The plant has received a fair amount of attention. White bud variations without flecks, WWW, and with green flecks on the margins of the white leaves, GWW, and the reversal of white-over-green to green-over-white, GWG → GGW, as well as pure green shoots, GGG, have all been discussed (Bateson 1919, 1921; Küster 1919, 1927; Kümmler 1922; Renner 1936a, 1936b). Renner concluded that it was a GWG sandwich chimera, but he was unable to explain the cause of sterility.

Bergann and Bergann (1959) accounted for the origin of 'Madame Salleron' in three steps. In 1830 a strongly growing cultivar *P. × hortorum* 'Fothergillii (AAA) was grown in England. Clifton (1990) says Dr Fothergillii originally raised this cultivar as early as 1780. It was a 'Nosegay Geranium' with single scarlet flowers. A plastid mutation in L II then gave rise to a vigorous white margined sandwich chimera, which in 1855 was propagated as *P. × hortorum* 'Manglesii', or 'Mangles Variegated' (ABA). A third step took place in Melun, France in 1877 when a nuclear mutation to dwarf growth occurred in L III, causing loss of internode elongation, coupled with the loss of the ability to flower (ABC). Daker (1969a) found 2n = 17 chromosomes in 'Madame Salleron' roots, instead of the expected 2n = 18, leading him to suggest that the loss of flowering might be related to chromosome loss. This would also account for the other growth changes that occurred at the same time. Thus the trichimera consists of not two, as earlier workers had thought, but of three distinct layers with three genotypes as follows:

L I Green, with long internodes A
L II White, with long internodes B
L III Green, with short internodes C

Bergann and Bergann went on to produce all the combinations of genotype that could be derived from the chimeras, and observed and measured the differences. None of the combinations with the dwarfing genotype in one of the layers was fertile; this included CCC, BCC, BBC, ACC and AAC, whereas without the dwarfing layer AAA, BBB, ABB and AAB all flowered, including the white shoot with green flecks ABB. The presence of the dwarfing tissue prevented all flowering. The type ABC,

AAA, CCC, ABB, AAB, ACC and AAC all have green plastids in the guard cells, whereas the types BBB, BCC and BBC have white because these are the types with a genetically white epidermis. Bright green flecks occurred in the white margins of the ABB type, and white flecks on the green margins of the BCC type. All the observations are consistent with the original trichimera structure.

In a second paper Bergann and Bergann (1962b) described the origin of three new forms of chimera. The process involves one layer of the growing point on one side of the shoot sliding between the layers on the other side. This is coupled with the usual penetration and duplication of the layers. In this way a BBC shoot becomes changed into a BCB shoot, a green-over-white chimera with a white epidermis; in other words a WGW sandwich chimera. It is called 'Weißkern Salleron'. A second change is ABC to ABA, which is like 'Madame Salleron' without the growth inhibiting short internodes; it also flowers. It is, of course, 'Mangles Variegated'. The third change is ABC to BAC; it is green with white plastids in the guard cells, it is also of low growth, short internodes and sterile. These changes in chimera structure are not common, but they do occur. They can be followed at the time by the changes that are occurring in the shoot and leaves as one chimera leads into another.

Probably the most discussed of all the variegated pelargoniums is 'Freak of Nature'. It has leaves that vary from white to others that have large, green, billowing, marginal lobes leaving only a small white centre (Bateson 1916; Chittenden 1926, 1927; Noack 1930; Neilson-Jones 1934; Imai 1936; Ufer 1936; Renner 1936a, 1936b; Thielke 1948; Bergann 1962a; Tilney-Bassett, 1963a). Leaf cuttings gave rise to pure white shoots, WWW, but also bud variations occurred in which white shoots had occasional green flecks, GWW. Now the epidermis seemed quite normal and very stable. Pure green bud variations arose, GGG, and also the green-over-white chimera, GGW. But why was the green epidermis so unstable in the original chimera? Pohlheim (1973, 1977) saw, under the compound microscope, that the white cells in sections through the leaf were severely inhibited in growth in the chimera compared with the white cells in the white bud variation that produced occasional green flecks. The former highly inhibited white cells disappeared in the bud variations. He concluded that 'Freak of Nature' is a trichimera with three genetically distinct layers as follows:

L I Green, cell growth normal X
L II White, cell growth inhibited Y
L III White, cell growth normal Z

The extremely inhibited growth of the white cells in L II induced the frequent periclinal divisions of the green cells in L I. At each bud variation the inhibiting white layer was lost. When a white shoot was produced that had occasional green flecks the change was XYZ → XZZ, and when a green-over-white chimera was produced the change was XYZ → XXZ. The bud variations of 'Freak of Nature' are very like those of the sandwich chimera 'Flower of Spring', GWG. It was, therefore, no great surprise when I found a 'Flower of Spring' like shoot growing on 'Freak of Nature' (reported in Bergann and Bergann 1962). The most likely explanation is the re-arrangement of the lateral shoot apex as seen in 'Madame Salleron'. This might involve loss of the inhibitory layer on both sides of the shoot apex, followed by a duplication of the normal white layer on one side, the triplication of the normal green layer on the other side, and finally the sliding of the white layer between the two green layers. A very rare event, but it can happen.

Rudolph Hagemann, and members of his group, has investigated the cause of the plastid mutation in white-over-green chimeras 'Mrs Parker', 'Flower of Spring', 'Freak of Nature', 'Madame Salleron', 'Greifswald' and 'Gnom' (Börner *et al.* 1972, 1973, 1974). They found that the mutants all belong to the same group; they have almost no plastid ribosomes. When the total ribosomal RNA was separated by gel electrophoresis, the polyacrylamide gels combined strong bands for the 25S and 18S cytoplasmic ribosomes, with absent, or strongly reduced, bands for the 23S and 16S RNA plastid ribosomes. It follows that if the plastid ribosomes are absent, the plastid protein will not be synthesised. Accordingly, they found only very small quantities of the large subunit of ribulose-1,5-diphosphate carboxylase, a normally abundant protein that has a large subunit synthesized by the plastid ribosomes. The white mutants do contain plastid DNA that is replicated (Knoth *et al.* 1974). Hence the DNA polymerase performing this task must be coded by nuclear DNA, and synthesised on cytoplasmic ribosomes, from where it is transported into the plastids. Another important component is the double membrane envelope around the plastids, that is present in all the mutant plastids, and is therefore encoded by cytoplasmic ribosomes. In dark grown leaves prolamellar bodies are found, and in young leaves grown under dim light not more than 1.5 per cent of chlorophyll and 10 per cent of carotenoids are found, so these too are produced under the control of enzymes produced by cytoplasmic ribosomes. Similarly, the starch grains found in mutant plastids must be synthesised on cytoplasmic ribosomes.

The white-over-green chimera 'Kleiner Liebling', GWG, is also interesting for its flowers. It has small flowers, which are pale pink with a white edge to the petals, and it is quite sterile. Root cuttings have deep pink flowers, which are completely fertile. The leaves and stems are thicker and the flowers are larger (Bateson 1926; Chittenden 1927; Cassels and Minas 1983). It is evidently a thin-skinned periclinal flower chimera WPP.

L I   Green, off-white flower
L II   White, pink flower
L III   Green, pink flower

Daker (1966, 1967) discovered that the chimera was haploid 2n = 9. This finding is at odds with Chittenden's report that root cuttings are fully fertile. I think that Chittenden's plant had L I and L II haploid, and L III diploid, while Daker's plant had all three layers haploid. As it was a haploid, it made a good test system for studying the effect of X-irradiation as any change would be manifest at once instead of waiting for recessive mutations to segregate in the second generation, as happens with diploids. With increasing dose up to 1250r, there was a proportional increase in damage, and many mutations (Pohlheim *et al.* 1972). One mutant had highly distorted leaves, and an extremely reduced L II layer, reminiscent of 'Freak of Nature' (Pohlheim 1973).

"Weißer Liebling' is a variant form of 'Kleiner Liebling' with wholly white petals. Adventitious shoots from the roots flower red. The epidermis has remained haploid, but the inner core tissue is diploid. It is therefore a flower chimera, WRR, as well as a 9.18.18 cytochimera (Pohlheim and Rössel 1989). Red spots occur on the petals owing to perforation of the white L I by the red L II. These red zones are greater in size that the white zones they replace. Moreover, the diploid red epidermal cells are larger in size than the white epidermal cells.

L I   9 chromosomes, white petals
L II   18 chromosomes, red petals
L III   18 chromosomes, red petals

"Rose Liebling' is another variant from 'Kleiner Liebling'. It has petals with white margins and a rose-coloured central zone, less intense than in the original 'Kleine Liebling'. Adventitious shoots from the roots flower red. The epidermis has become diploid while the inner core has remained haploid. There are pure white flowered shoots, which no longer form red flowers on adventitious shoots from the roots. It is therefore a flower chimera, WRR, as well as a cytochimera with 18.9.9 chromosomes.

L I   18 chromosomes, off-white petals
L II   9 chromosomes, red petals
L III   9 chromosomes, red petals

The diploid cells of the white tissue of the petals, including the diploid mesophyll tissue derived from L I, are larger than those of the haploid parent, and the tissue is wider. Where red spots are formed, owing to the red L II perforating L I, the haploid red cells are smaller than the diploid white cells. So the underlying, but colourless, red L II layer causes the rose coloured zone in the centre of the petals. This is an example of partner induction, which is absent in the comparable example of 'Weißer Liebling'.

References

Bateson, W. (1916).
Root cuttings, chimaeras and 'sports'. Journal of Genetics 6, 75-80.

Bateson, W. (1919).
Studies in variegation. I. Journal of Genetics 8, 93-99.

Bateson, W. (1921).
Root-cuttings and chimaeras. II. Journal of Genetics 11, 91-97.

Bateson, W. (1926).
Segregation. Journal of Genetics 16, 201-236.

Baur, E. (1909).
Das Wesen und die Erblichkeitsverhältnisse der 'Varietates albomarginatae hort' von *Pelargonium zonale*. Z. Vererbungsl. 1, 330-351.

Bergann, F. (1962a).
Uber die Beteiligung des 'dermatogens' an der Mesophyllbildung. Paradigmatische Schichtenverlagerungen an den Blättern albovariegater Periklinalchimären. Wiss. Z. Pad. Hochsch. Potsdam 7, 75-86.

Bergann, F. (1962b).
Uber histogenetisch bedingte Anomalien bei der generativen Aufspaltung periklinal Chimären. Wiss. Z. Pad. Hochsch. Potsdam 7, 87-94.

Bergann, F. and Bergann, L. (1959).
Uber experimentell ausgelöste vegetative Spaltungen und Umlagerungen an chimärischen Klone, zugleich als Beispiele erfolgreicher Staudenauslese. 1. *Pelargonium zonale* Ait. 'Madame Salleron'. Züchter 29, 361-374.

Bergann, F. and Bergann, L. (1962).
Uber Umschichtungen (Translokationen) an den Sproßscheiteln periklinal Chimären. Züchter 32, 110-119.

Börner, T. and Förster, H. (1981).
Zum Einfluß des Plastoms auf Plastidenzahl und Zellform bei der Sorte 'Mrs Parker' von *Pelargonium zonale* hort. Wiss. Z. Univ. Halle 30, 79-83.

Börner, T., Herrmann, F. and Hagemann, R. (1973).
Structure and function of the genetic information in plastids. VIII. Plastid ribosome deficient mutants of *Pelargonium zonale* Ait. FEBS Letters 37, 117-119.

Börner, T., Knoth, R., Herrmann, F. und Hagemann, R. (1972).
Struktur und Funktion der genetischen Information in den Plastiden. V. Das Fehlen von ribosomaler RNS in den Plastiden der Plastommutante 'Mrs Parker' von *Pelargonium zonale* Ait. Theoretical and Applied Genetics 42, 3-11.

Börner, T., Knoth, R., Herrmann, F.H. und Hagemann, R. 1974.
Struktur und Funktion der genetischen Information in den Plastiden. X. Das
Fehlen von Fraktion-1-Protein in den weißen Plastiden einiger Sorten von
Pelargonium zonale Ait. Biochem. Physiol. Pflanzen 165, 429-432.

Campbell, M.E. and others (1990).
Fancy-leaved Pelargoniums Peter Grieve and after. (Ed. E.J. Willson).
The British Pelargonium and Geranium Society.

Cassells, A.C. and Minas, G. (1983).
Beneficially-infected and chimeral pelargonium: Implications for
micropropagation by meristem and explant culture. Acta Horticulturae 131, 287-
297.

Chittenden, R.J. (1926).
Studies in variegation. II. *Hydrangea* and *Pelargonium*. Journal of Genetics 16,
43-61.

Chittenden, R.J. (1927).
Vegetative segregation. Bibliogr. genet., 3, 355-442.

Clifton, R.T.F. (1990).
Geranium Family Species Check List. 4th ed. Part 4. *Pelargonium*. Compiled
for the Geraniaceae Group of The British Pelargonium and Geranium Society.

Daker, M.G. (1966).
'Kleiner Liebling' a haploid cultivar of *Pelargonium*. Nature 211, 549-550.

Daker, M.G. (1967).
Cytological studies on a haploid cultivar of *Pelargonium* and its colchicine
induced diploids. Chromosoma 21, 250-271.

Daker, M.G. (1969a).
Chromosome numbers of *Pelargonium* species and cultivars. Journal Royal
Horticulture Society 94, 346-353.

Hagemann, R. (1979).
Genetics and molecular biology of plastids of higher plants. Stadler Symposium
11, 91-116.

Herrmann, F. and Hagemann, R. (1971).
Struktur und Funktion der genetischen Information in den Plastiden. III.
Genetik, Chlorophylle und Photosyntheseverhalten der Plastommutante 'Mrs
Pollock' und der Genmutante 'Cloth of Gold' von *Pelargonium zonale*. Biochem.
Physiol. Pflanz. 162, 390-409.

Herrmann, F.H., Matorin, D., Timofeev, K., Börner, T., Rubin, A.B. and Hagemann, R. (1974).
Structure and function of the genetic information in plastids. IX. Studies of primary reactions of photosynthesis in plastome mutants of *Antirrhinum majus* and *Pelargonium zonale* having impaired photosynthesis. Biochem. Physiol. Pflanzen 165, 393-400.

Herrmann, F.H., Schumann, T., Börner und Knoth, R. (1976).
Struktur and Funktion der genetischen Information in den Plastiden. XII. Die plastidalen Lamellarproteine der photosynthesedefekten Plastommutante en: gil-1 (Mrs Pollock) und der Genmutante 'Cloth of Gold' von *Pelargonium zonale* Ait. Photosynthetica 10, 164-171.

Imai, Y. (1936).
Geno- and plasmotypes of variegated pelargoniums. Journal of Genetics 33, 169-195.

Knoth, R. (1975).
Struktur and Funktion der genetischen Information in den Plastiden. XIV. Die Auswirkungen der Plastommutationen en:alba-1 *Antirrhinum majus* und en: gilva-1 von *Pelargonium zonale* auf die Feinstruktur der Plastiden. Biol. Zbl. 94, 681-694.

Knoth, R., Herrmann, F.H., Böttger, M. und Börner, T. (1974).
Struktur and Funktion der genetischen Information in den Plastiden. XI. DNA in normalen und mutierten Plastiden der Sorte 'Mrs Pollock' von *Pelargonium zonale*. Biochem. Physiol. Pflanzen 166, 29-148.

Kümmler, A. (1922).
Uber die Funktion der Spaltöffnungen weißbunten Blätter. Jb. Wiss. Bot., 61, 610-669.

Küster, E. (1919).
Uber weissrandige Blätter und andere Formen der Buntblättrigkeit. Biol. Zbl., 39, 212-251.

Küster, E. (1927).
Anatomie des panaschierten Blattes. In: Handbuch der Pfllanzenanatomie. II. Abteilung, 2. Teil: Pteridophyten und Anthophytes, Bd VIII (Ed. K. Linsbauer) 1-68. Gebrüder Borntraeger, Berlin.

Neilson-Jones, W. (1934).
Plant chimeras and graft hybrids. Methuen, London.

Noack, K.L. (1924).
Vererbungsversuche mit buntblättrigen Pelargonien. Verh. Phys. –med. Ges. Würzb. N.F. 49, 45-93.

Noack, K.L. (1930).
Untersuchungen an *Pelargonium* 'Freak of Nature'. Z. Bot., 23, 309-327.

Pohlheim, F. (1973).
Untersuchungen zur periklinalchimärischen Konstitution von *Pelargonium zonale* 'Freak of Nature'. Flora 162, 284-294.

Pohlheim, F. (1977).
Umlagerungen an der Trichimäre *Pelargonium zonale* 'Freak of Nature' – ein Beitrag zur Herstellung von Plastommutanten. Pädagogische Hochschule 'Karl Liebnecht' Potsdam. Wiss. Z. 21, 115-127.

Pohlheim, F., Pohlheim, E. and Günther, G. (1972).
Die haploide *Pelargonium zonale* 'Kleine Liebling' als Testsystem fur Mutagene. Pädagogische Hochschule 'Karl Liebnecht' Potsdam. Wiss. Z. 16, 65-70.

Pohlheim, F. and Rössel, K. (1989).
Partnerinduktion bei chimärischen Blatt- und Blütenfarbmustern von *Pelargonium.* Tag. –Ber., Akad. Landwirtsch. –Wiss. DDR, Berlin 281, 107-115.

Renner, O. (1936a).
Zur Kenntnis der nichtmendelnden Buntheit der Laubblätter. Flora 130, 218-290.

Renner, O. (1936b).
Zur Entwicklungsgeschicte randpanaschierter und reingrüne Blätter von *Sambucus, Veronica, Pelargonium, Spiraea, Chlorophytum.* Flora 130, 454-466.

Roth, L. (1927).
Untersuchungen über die periclinal bunten Rassen von *Pelargonium zonale.* Zschr. induct. Abstamm. Vererb. Lehre. 45, 125-159.

Stewart, R.N., Semeniuk, P. and Dermen, H. (1974).
Competition and accommodation between apical layers and their derivatives in the ontogeny of chimeral shoots of *Pelargonium × hortorum.* American Journal of Botany 61, 54-67.

Thielke, C. (1948).
Beiträge zur Entwicklungsgeschichte und zur Physiologie panaschierter Blätter. Planta 36, 2-33.

Tilney-Bassett, R.A.E. (1963a).
The structure of periclinal chimeras. Heredity 18, 265-285.

Tilney-Bassett, R.A.E. (1963b).
Genetics and plastid physiology in *Pelargonium.* Heredity 18, 485-504.

Tilney-Bassett, R.A.E. (1986).
Plant Chimeras. Edward Arnold, London.

Tilney-Bassett, R.A.E. (1990).
'Mrs J.C. Mappin'. In Pelargonium News, 12-14. The official journal of The British Pelargonium and Geranium Society.

Ufer, M. (1936).
Erblichkeitsuntersuchungen an 'Freak of Nature'. Ein Beitrag zur Frage der nichtmendelnden Vererbung chlorophyll-defekter Formen von *Pelargonium*. Z. Vererbungsl., 71, 281-298.

7
Nuclear Chimeras

In this chapter I shall look at examples of chimeras that are nuclear controlled. They either involve characters that are not known to be under plastid control but which have not been tested, or characters that are known to be under nuclear control. Roots do not have layered growing points, and do not form periclinal chimeras. Their genotype corresponds to that of the inner corpus tissue, L III. Consequently, when adventitious buds from the roots derive shoots, it is the inner corpus tissue that develops. When the adventitious shoot differs in some respect from the parental plant, it is a clear indication of the chimera structure of the parent. Bateson (1916, 1921) made good use of the property when he investigated fancy pelargoniums. The regal pelargonium 'Escot' had white flowers with a large purplish red blotch on each of the petals, which tended to roll back. When propagated by root cuttings the flowers were larger, the petals also were pinkish, and the blotches were much redder on the petals, which did not roll back. Bateson interpreted 'Escot' as a periclinal chimera in which the petals had a white skin of somewhat restricted growth over a pink core. Similarly, 'Mrs Gordon' had white and pink flowers with lightly represented guide marks on the petals, whereas plants grown from the core had fully pink petals and deep crimson guide marks, which corresponded with 'Cardiff'. The cultivar 'Pearl' was a semi-double having small, purple petals in the area of the guide marks, whereas flowers from root cuttings were heavily marked with red like 'Mme Thibaut' or 'Emmanuel Lias'. The root cutting evidence was corroborated in 'Pearl' by the occasional red patch where the underlying tissue broke through. The plants are clearly flower chimeras.

'Salmon Fringed', or 'Skelly's Pride' as it is sometimes called, has crumpled, glossy leaves, laciniated petals and sterile flowers, whereas root cuttings have hermaphrodite flowers with normal petals and flat, matt leaves (Chittenden 1927). Cassels and Minas (1983) have shown that the condition is not caused by a graft transmissible, infectious agent, but is a chimera. It tends to be true to type when propagated by bud tip culture, but it reverts to the root cutting type when propagated by petiole explant culture. This was compared with the propagation of ivy-leaved and zonal pelargonium cultivars infected with virus. The presence of pelargonium net vein agent, or pelargonium petal streak agent, was proven in *P. peltatum* 'Crocodile' and *P. × hortorum* 'Mexicana' by graft transmission, and by the loss of their symptoms after micro-propagation by bud tip culture, whereas the viruses were maintained during explant culture.

'Double New Life' has peculiar double flowers that were devoid of anthers, while its root cuttings produced normal hermaphrodite flowers.

The cultivar 'Single New Life' is presumably a mutation derived from it. It is characterised by red petals that are extensively striped with white. It is fertile; when crossed it behaves as a red flower heterozygous for salmon, R1r1, R2R2, according to the classification of red flowers (Almouslem *et al.* 1991; Tilney-Bassett *et al.* 1995). It is clearly a thin-skinned chimera with the striped flower type occupying L I and the red flower genotype L II and L III, SRR. In the double-flowered form the flower consists of a mixture of scarlet petals and white petaloid structures with no stamens present, but it is fertile as a female (Chittenden 1927).

'Mr Wren' has red flowers with a white border to the petals. This seems to be caused by a pattern gene as normally the genotype of L I determines the epidermis. It is unlikely to be caused by partner induction between a red L II and I as this implies that L I is wholly white and the partner induction is incomplete. One might, therefore, expect to obtain some truly white flowers owing to the rare duplication of L I, WRR → WWR; I have never observed this. It is a thin-skinned chimera, R^wGG, as 'Mr Wren' behaves as if it has a heterozygous red flower, R1r1, R2R2, in crossing experiments. There is no longer any indication of the white border to the red flowered progeny in either the F1 or the following Mendelian 3:1 and 1:1 ratios. It also broke down into its chimeral components after explant culture.

The golden phenotype in zonal pelargoniums was first analysed in 'Verona' by Baur (1907, 1909). When 'Verona' was selfed, the offspring segregated in a ratio of 1 green: 2 golden together with a few white seedlings. He concluded that the golden genotype was heterozygous; the Mendelian ratio was really 1:2:1 but the white seedlings were largely inviable. He gave no data, but only the proportions. He designated the heterozygous golden genotype as +/-, but Hagemann (1964) and Herrmann and Hagemann (1971) called the phenotype aurea, and the more suitable gene designation Aur^+/Aur.

Baur's hypothesis is testable by selfing heterozygous golden plants, or golden-over-green chimeras, when the progeny should segregate in a ratio of 1 green: 2 golden: 1 white. As the white were largely inviable it is sensible to test for 1 green: 2 golden. This I did (Tilney-Bassett 1963b) for the two cultivars 'Crystal Palace Gem' and 'Golden Harem', which are thick-skinned chimeras, and for two pure golden plants ' Golden Crampel' and 'Robert Fish'. Sterility was the fate of 'Robert Fish', but the other three cultivars gave 68 green and 131 golden seedlings plus 5 white, which corresponds with a green: golden ratio of 1: 2 [$\chi^2 = 0.063$] and so confirmed the expectation. A second test is to make a backcross between the heterozygous golden plant and the pure green, when a ratio of 1 green: 1 golden is expected. 'Crystal Palace Gem' was the chimera used as the golden plant, and the variegated plants 'Dolly Varden' and 'Mrs J.C. Mapping' as the other parents. The result was pure green, or green with variegation, pure golden, or golden with variegation, and a few white seedlings. In this experiment we are not concerned with variegation, so the white seedlings are ignored and the variegated scored with the green or golden respectively. The resulting segregation of 203 green and 231 golden has a reasonable fit with the 1: 1 ratio [x^2 = 2.073], and confirms the expectation. There is no doubt that 'Crystal Palace Gem' is a golden-over-green thick-skinned chimera, in which the golden skin that occupies the germ layer is the result of mutation in a nuclear gene.

The German workers Noack (1924) and Roth (1927), and the Japanese worker Imai (1936), have made similar experiments, which Almouslem (1988) combined with those of Tilney-Bassett (1963b) to give a joint segregation of 475 green: 1004 golden, corresponding with the 1: 2 ratio [x^2 = 0.986] from the selfed heterozygote. Similarly, Almouslem added the data of Herrmann and Hagemann (1971), which used the chimera 'Cloth of Gold', to that of Noack, Roth and Imai, in a cross with green. This gave a ratio of 1 green: 1 golden. He also added the data of Noack (1925) to that of Tilney-Bassett in the backcross utilising the variegated parents, which again gave a ratio of 1 green: 1 golden. The total segregation of 929 green and 858 golden [x^2 = 3.241] was a fair agreement with the 1: 1 ratio expected.

Almouslem solved the problem of the missing white embryos by looking at what was happening in the developing embryos. He selfed 'Verona' and obtained green, golden and white seedlings with a large deficit of white [x^2 = 17.136]. When he examined fully formed embryos prior to germination, he still found a significant but smaller deficit [x^2 = 8.717]. When he scored the additional sickly or dead white embryos the deficit was negligible [x^2 = 3.768]. The goodness of fit with the 1: 2:1 ratio was now fine (Table 7.1).

Stage	Green	Golden	White	Total	χ^2	P
Germinating Seedlings	47	109	21	177	17.136	< 0.001
Full embryos (all alive)	73	155	48	276	8.717	0.05 - 0.01
All embryos (± alive)	79	159	60	298	3.765	0.1 - 0.05

Table 7.1 Segregation into green, golden, and white progeny after selfing the golden-leaved pelargonium 'Verona'; scored at three stages of development

The broad yellow skin of the leaves of the mutant 'Cloth of Gold' has a lesser chlorophyll content than the green leaves (Herrmann and Hagemann 1971). In particular, the chlorophyll b content is very low, but they are photosynthetically active. As the leaves age, they become increasingly green and this is reflected in the normalization of the chlorophyll a/b ratio, and the building and maintenance of some grana stacks upon the continuous stromal membranes (Knoth *et al.* 1976).

Almouslem used 'Verona' extensively with many green and variegated cultivars, but he always obtained a segregation ratio of 1 green: 1 golden after backcrosses. In the course of this work he scored the results of his backcrosses for evidence of linkage. Unfortunately he found no evidence of linkage between the aurea gene, and the genes for red spotted trichome, pink white eye, male sterility, red/pink flower colour and type I versus type II plastid segregation. The petals of 'Verona' were found to have small red spots on the upper epidermis; they tend to concentrate on the lower half of the lower three petals. The spots occur with the position of a trichome arising from the upper epidermis. Each trichome consists of a bright red, dense central cell, which is surrounded by reddish epidermal cells. In other plants trichomes exist but without red spots. Hence, it is the existence of red spots, rather than the existence of a trichome, that is unique to 'Verona'. Selfing 'Verona' gave 57 spotted: 20 spotless in agreement with a 3:1 ratio [χ^2 = 0.039], indicating that the spotted gene was dominant; we designated it as red spotted versus spotless trichomes Rst/rst (Almouslem and Tilney-Bassett 1989). Backcrossing 'Verona' with a variety of cultivars gave 72 green spotted: 77 green spotless: 78 golden spotted: 69 golden spotless in good agreement with a 1: 1: 1: 1 ratio [χ^2 = 0.728], showing independent assortment of the two genes. This was supported by selfing 'Verona', which gave 12 green spotted: 4 green spotless: 29 golden spotted: 9 golden spotless in agreement with a 3: 1: 6: 2 ratio [χ^2 = 0.370], which again supported independent assortment of the two genes. The expected segregation of 3 spotted: 1 spotless is superimposed on the 1 green: 2 golden segregation.

A very unusual chimera is 'A Happy Thought' with a thick green skin over a pale green core. Unlike most green over white chimeras, the central pale zone is not masked by the overlying green skin, but is bleached and consequently the core shows through clearly. Pohlheim and Rössel (1989) described this phenomenon as partner-induction. They found that the bleaching of the green cells by the neighbouring pale cells stretched in both a horizontal and a vertical direction, so that the neighbouring cells showed a gradual change from pale green to green. This accounted for the fuzziness at the margin of the two zones. Bud variations occur rarely, and they may be either green shoots from the skin, or pale green shoots from the core. In strong light the pale shoots bleach to yellow or to almost white.

Selfing experiments suggested to Chittenden (1926) that the green skin might be heterozygous. He obtained 26 green and 37 pale green and found these results confusing. He came to no definite conclusion (Chittenden 1927). Roth (1927), by contrast, found only 6 pale and 47 green seedlings on selfing, but when he crossed the chimera with green plants the seedlings were all green. Finally, Imai (1936) obtained only 2 pale and

105 green seedlings on selfing. With such varied and unsatisfactory results I decided to self 'A Happy Thought' myself (1962). In three consecutive years I obtained 125 green and 48 pale green seedlings (x^2 = 0.696), in good agreement with a Mendelian ratio of 3:1. A pale green bud variation from the core enabled me to backcross to the chimera, which gave 12 green and 18 pale green (x^2 = 1.200), in agreement with the 1:1 ratio expected. The pale green seedlings tended to die off, but became greener with the low light in wintertime. In over 200 days, 75% died off in the first generation. In the second generation this was reduced to 50%. The pale green bred true. Evidently, the pale green core is homozygous recessive, and the green skin is heterozygous. We may designate the gene as P/p.

The chimera has crimson flowers. There is another almost identical chimera with pink flowers that I know as 'Pink Happy Thought'. On selfing 'A Happy Thought', I recently obtained 15 crimson and 5 pink progeny, so pink is easily obtained. Hence, as 'A Happy Thought' is heterozygous for flower colour as well as for the Pp gene, it would only require a single mutation in the flower colour gene to produce the change. There is no need to assume the mutation arose a second time and came, by chance, to occupy the inner tissue.

References

Almouslem, A.B. (1988).
Qualitative and quantitative genetical studies in *Pelargonium* × *Hortorum*
Bailey. Ph.D. Thesis, University of Swansea, Wales.

Almouslem, A.B., Nasser, N.S. and Tilney-Bassett, R.A.E. (1991).
Complementary genes for red flower colour in zonal pelargoniums. Journal of
Horticultural Science 66, 651-659.

Almouslem, A.B. and Tilney-Bassett, R.A.E. (1989).
Inheritance of red-spotted petals and golden leaves in zonal pelargonium.
HortScience 24, 501-502.

Bateson, W. (1916).
Root cuttings, chimaeras and 'sports'. Journal of Genetics 6, 75-80.

Bateson, W. (1921).
Root-cuttings and chimaeras. II. Journal of Genetics 11, 91-97.

Baur, E. (1907).
Untersuchungen über die Erblichkeitsverhältnisse einer nur in Bastardform
lebenfähigen Sippe von *Antirrhinum majus*. Ber. Dtsch. Bot. Ges. 25, 442-454.

Baur, E. (1909).
Das Wesen und die Erblichkeitsverhältnisse der 'Varietates albomarginatae
hort' von *Pelargonium zonale*. Z. Vererbungsl. 1, 330-351.

Cassells, A.C. and Minas, G. (1983).
Beneficially-infected and chimeral pelargonium: Implications for
micropropagation by meristem and explant culture. Acta Horticulturae 131, 287-
297.

Chittenden, R.J. (1926).
Studies in variegation. II. *Hydrangea* and *Pelargonium*. Journal of Genetics 16,
43-61.

Chittenden, R.J. (1927).
Vegetative segregation. Bibliogr. genet., 3, 355-442.

Hagemann, R. (1964).
Plasmatische Vererbung. VEB Gustav Fischer, Verlag, Jena.

Herrmann, F. and Hagemann, R. (1971).
Struktur und Funktion der genetischen Information in den Plastiden. III.
Genetik, Chlorophylle und Photosyntheseverhalten der Plastommutante 'Mrs
Pollock' und der Genmutante 'Cloth of Gold' von *Pelargonium zonale*. Biochem.
Physiol. Pflanz. 162, 390-409.

Imai, Y. (1936).
Geno- and plasmotypes of variegated pelargoniums. Journal of Genetics 33, 169-195.

Knoth, R., Herrmann, F.H. and Börner, T. (1976).
Struktur und Funktion der genetischen Information in den Plastiden XV. Beziehungen zwischen Chlorophyllgehalt, Photosyntheseverhalten und Plastidenfeinstruktur in Kerngen-bedingten Aureamutanten von *Antirrhinum majus* (Mutante 'Aurea') und *Pelargonium zonale* (Sorte 'Cloth of Gold'). Biochem. Physiol. Pflanzen 170, 433-442.

Noack, K.L. (1924).
Vererbungsversuche mit buntblättrigen Pelargonien. Verh. Phys. –med. Ges. Würzb. N.F. 49, 45-93.

Noack, K.L. (1925).
Weitere Untersuchungen über das Wesen der Buntblättrigkeit bei Pelargonien. Verh. Phys. –med. Ges. Würzb. N.F. 50, 47-97.

Pohlheim, F. and Rössel, K. (1989).
Partnerinduktion bei chimärischen Blatt- und Blütenfarbmustern von *Pelargonium*.
Tag. –Ber., Akad. Landwirtsch. –Wiss. DDR, Berlin 281, 107-115.

Roth, L. (1927).
Untersuchungen über die periclinal bunten Rassen von *Pelargonium zonale*. Zschr. induct. Abstamm. Vererb. Lehre. 45, 125-159.

Tilney-Bassett, R.A.E. (1962).
Cytoplasmic inheritance and virus diseases. D.Phil.Thesis, University of Oxford.

Tilney-Bassett, R.A.E. (1963b).
Genetics and plastid physiology in *Pelargonium*. Heredity 18, 485-504.

Tilney-Bassett, R.A.E., Munshi, A.A., Almouslem, A.B. and Nasser, N.S. (1995).
The inheritance of red, salmon, rose-pink and soft-pink flower colours in zonal pelargoniums. Journal of Horticultural Science 70, 499-508.

8

Breeding Variegated Plants

Historical introduction

By crossing existing variegated plants with green ones, and then selecting out the new variegated plants from the numerous green and white ones obtained at the same time, we can easily obtain new variegated plants. By carefully selecting the best parents, and by selecting the best progeny, the quality of variegated plants is gradually improved as Peter Grieve so convincingly demonstrated. For most breeders this is sufficient. If questions are to be asked then much more is required. The method remains the same, but the plants that are used for the crosses become much more important. If two different plants are used as the female parent, are the results the same? Can the parents be grouped into categories? Do the dissimilar plastids have any effect on the results? Are male parents always the same? These questions, and more, can be answered by scoring the numbers of green, variegated and white progeny after G × W crosses, or the reciprocal W × G crosses. The design of the experiments must be carefully worked out, and this is what has enabled me to find out as much as I have as revealed in the progress below. Let us begin at the beginning.

The origin of the first variegated-leaf pelargoniums is well over two and a half centuries ago. Peter Grieve mentions the stripe-leaved geranium discussed by Sir Thomas More, Bart. in the 'Flower Garden Displayed', second edition 1734, which he obtained from the Paris gardens in France. He describes the leaves as edged with cream colour. The flower, which appears at almost every season of the year, is a peach blossom colour. Cuttings propagate it freely. In Miller's 'Gardeners' Dictionary' mention is made of a pelargonium with fine variegated leaves, and in Loudon's "Hortus Britanicus" it is probably the same plant as is recorded as marginatum. It is named *Pelargonium zonale* by Willd, and known to some gardeners as *P. variegatum*. It dates before 1785 from Cavanalli's *Geranium marginatum* (Clifton 1990).

A more recent variegated-leaved cultivar is 'Lee's Variegated', from which Mr Kinghorn raised 'Flower of the Day' in 1848. This was followed by 'Attraction', considered as the first Silver Tricolor, 1850, closely followed by 'Countess of Warwick'. Several other cross-breeders appeared to have entered the field and their efforts resulted in 'Queen's Favourite' and 'Burning Bush', raised by Mr Elephantine and Mr Hally, respectively. At about this time, 1853 – 1854, Peter Grieve fertilized blooms of 'Flower of the Day' with pollen taken from 'Tom Thumb', from which he raised 'Culford Beauty' and 'Rainbow', which proved to be most vigorous. Even this cultivar, however, was superseded by the more beautiful 'Italia Unita', which remained unsurpassed among the silver edged cultivars.

The timing of the origin of the golden, or yellow edged form is again uncertain. Grieve believed an old plant of this type was in existence as early as 1822 or 1823. It was probably the same plant as 'Golden Chain', which Grieve was in no doubt was from *Pelargonium inquinans*. In 1855 Grieve used it as the pollen parent in crosses with 'Cottage Maid'. Two distinct cultivars arose, both of which were improvements on 'Golden Chain'. These were 'Golden Tom Thumb' and 'Golden Cerise Unique'. During the following summer the improved cultivar 'Gold Pheasant' was achieved by crossing 'Emperor of the French' with pollen from 'Golden Tom Thumb'. Grieve next crossed 'Emperor of the French' with pollen from 'Gold Pheasant' to produce two further cultivars 'Sunset' and 'Mrs Pollock', in 1858. He then used 'Emperor of the French', and some similar zoned seedlings, as the seed bearing parents with pollen taken from 'Sunset' and 'Mrs Pollock'. The net result was the production of the beautiful cultivars 'Lucy Grieve', 'Mrs Benyon' and 'Lady Cullum'. By the time Grieve wrote his book, about ten years later, these beautiful plants would appear to have induced many cross breeders to produce numerous cultivars of these golden edged, variegated pelargoniums. Nevertheless, he comments, many of these new cultivars were rather weak and unlikely to last, especially not as bedding plants.

A few of these cultivars are still available today; at least the name is. Mary Campbell (1990) points out that the description given in the catalogues today does not agree with the description for the cultivar when raised, and has not done so for some time past. For many cultivars I am inclined to agree. We have seen how many variegated-leaf chimeras later became trichimeras, either flower or stunting chimeras. Moreover, for any plant to keep true it would have to be propagated vegetatively solely by cuttings often for over a century. During this long period a similar daughter plant could so easily be substituted.

The Nosegay cultivars are chiefly distinguished by their narrow petals and by their long trusses of bloom. The earliest cultivar of the section is possibly 'Fothergillii' raised in 1780 (Clifton 1990) of unknown parentage. It is probably a garden hybrid or sport from *P. zonale*. It is equally possible the Nosegay cultivars represent the earliest condition under which the species was introduced, and then the broader petal sorts have developed from them. Grieve took the cultivar 'Mangles Variegated', which had been around for many years, and crossed it with the Nosegay cultivar 'Mrs Vernon', to produce the cultivar 'Stella Variegated'.

Peter Grieve is acknowledged as an outstanding plant breeder. He produced many famous *Pelargonium* cultivars; a few of their names are still well known today. He crossed them with the green form both as male and female parent. He recognized the silver and the golden margined types. Over half a century was to elapse before Baur (1909) drew our attention to *Pelargonium* as an object of scientific study; as we shall see some very important principles were drawn. Baur found that on selfing, white margined cultivars give white offspring, green cultivars give green offspring and reciprocal crosses between the two give various proportions of green, variegated and white offspring. The F1 seedlings are neither of one uniform type, nor of two or more types segregating in a Mendelian ratio; instead their proportions vary with the direction of the cross. Baur concluded that the inheritance of the plastid character was not Mendelian; this prompted him to put forward his theory of the sorting-out of plastids, as follows:

"The fertilised egg, which originated through the union of a green with a white sex cell, contains two kinds of plastid, green and white. At cell division, by which the growing egg cell develops into the embryo, the plastids are distributed quite randomly into the daughter cells. Should a daughter cell have only white plastids, then this will have only white cell descendants, and a white area will develop; should a daughter cell contain only green plastids, then a constant green cell complex will be formed. Cells with both kinds of plastid will be able to segregate further. Indeed, I do not imply that segregation need occur at a single division. If segregation should have already occurred after one of the first divisions, such that the cells, which develop further into the cotyledons and apical growing-points, have only green plastids, then a pure green hybrid will develop; in the reverse case a pure white hybrid is developed. It is now a simple matter, which I do not need to explain at length, to establish, that after a larger number of divisions the cells with both types of plastid must decrease in percentage in direct contrast to the cells with only one kind of plastid."

Recently Hagemann (2000) has reviewed Baur's conclusions, and commented on the work of Otto Renner in validating and extending them especially with the evening primrose.

Several papers followed Baur; the results were heterogeneous and non-reciprocal (Noack 1924, 1925; Chittenden 1926; Roth 1927; Imai 1936). Sometimes there were more variegated than green offspring, but usually the green offspring were in the majority even when the green chloroplasts entered with the pollen. The pure white seedlings were very few, and often this class was absent, even when the white parent was the female. This meant that the male germ cell often made a greater contribution to the progeny, and often the white female failed to contribute anything to the progeny (Darlington 1958). Nevertheless, for the following reasons, the published information did not take us much further forward. The green parents in the crosses were usually unnamed; presumably owing to the false assumption that they are of less importance that the chimeral parent. Many crosses were too small, and the many isolated, non-reciprocal crosses were of little value. Most workers gave no selfing or fertility data and Imai, the exception, made the mistake of giving only the aggregate fertility data even though the results of his crosses were heterogeneous. Imai's fertility data did not separate bad seed from the bad germination of good seed.

Early innovations

To overcome these inadequacies I introduced a number of important innovations (Tilney-Bassett 1963b). I selected plants that had a reasonably good fertility. In particular, I chose 'Flower of Spring', because this is a white-over-green sandwich chimera, GWG, which makes a good source for mutant plastids. For the green plastids, I selected and propagated the green shoot from 'Flower of Spring'. I therefore had two plants with identical nuclei, but with different plastids. This enabled me to make the important isogenic crosses, G × G, G × W, W × G and W × W, in which all were nuclear selfs, but with four plastid combinations.

FS G × G FS	and similarly	DV G × G DV
FS G × W FS		DV G × W DV
FS W × G FS		DV W × G DV
FS W × W FS		DV W × W DV

Using 'Flower of Spring' and 'Dolly Varden', and crosses between them, I could now obtain data on all 16 nuclear and plastid selfs and crosses (Tilney-Bassett 1970a). A comparison of the segregation frequencies for the eight mixed plastid crosses showed no significant change between total embryos and healthy three-week-old embryos. Between three-week-old embryos and germination, there was a highly significant selection against white embryos for the DV G × W FS and the DV G × W DV plastid crosses. Nevertheless, the effect of this selection was fairly mild as the white embryos were the least frequent class from the outset. The analysis of variance statistics allowed me to distinguish the effects of the cultivars from the effects of the plastids. The cultivar parentage had no significant effect on mean fertilisation, or mean survival of three-week-old embryos. Similarly, the plastid parentage had no significant effect on mean fertilisation, but it had an effect on mean survival of three-week-old embryos, because of the particular low viability of white embryos produced by W × W selfs or crosses. Hence, the combination, in all G × W and W × G crosses, of no difference in mean fertilisation, no difference in embryo survival between fertilisation and three weeks later, and no change in the proportion of green, variegated and white embryos, demonstrated that there is no visible selection against white embryos in early embryo development. The absence of early selection against white embryos supports the observation of a predominantly paternal inheritance of plastids in all W × G plastid crosses. Between the G × W plastid crosses, the difference in the behaviour of 'Dolly Varden' and 'Flower of Spring' is confirmed (Table 8.1).

Crosses	Nos. of Embryos			Green Plastids	Nos. of Seedlings			Green Plastids
Green Plastids Female Parent	G	V	W	%	G	V	W	%
FS G x W FS	365	40	358	50.5	104	14	73	58.1
FS G x W DV	236	115	224	51.0	47	26	78	39.7
DV G x W FS	412	110	59	80.4	380	75	7	90.4
DV G x W DV	259	123	81	69.2	153	71	11	80.2
Green Plastids Male Parent								
FS G x W FS	283	94	19	83.3	115	27	2	89.2
FS G x W DV	337	74	11	88.6	129	44	2	92.0
DV G x W FS	394	199	71	74.4	129	89	39	67.5
DV G x W DV	237	155	35	73.6	84	63	14	71.7

Table 8.1. Segregation of embryos and seedlings, and the proportion of green plastids transmitted, after plastid crosses within and between 'Flower of Spring' and 'Dolly Varden'. Adapted from Tilney-Bassett (1970a).

I next compared the proportion of green, variegated and white segregations for the eight mixed plastid crosses in two successive years, but I could find no significant difference between them. Nor could I find evidence of the proportions being significantly disturbed by variations in environmental conditions (Tilney-Bassett 1970b). It thus appeared that plastid segregation during embryo development is well buffered against the fluctuating environment (Table 8.2). The wide difference between green 'Flower of Spring' and green 'Dolly Varden', as the female parent, was attributed to an underlying genetic control.

Crosses	Conditions	Nos. of Embryos			Green Plastids	Range of Green Plastids
Green Plastids Female Parent		G	V	W	%	%
FS G x W FS	3	787	131	709	52.4	51.0 - 53.2
DV G x W DV	4	581	355	115	72.2	68.3 - 74.2
FS W x G FS	2	534	173	23	85.0	83.5 - 86.4
DV W x G DV	5	1111	809	137	73.7	71.7 - 74.6

Table 8.2. The total segregation of embryos, and the proportion of green plastids transmitted, after plastid crosses within 'Flower of Spring' and 'Dolly Varden'. The conditions were that the crosses were made in the greenhouse, in a dark room, at 15°C and 25°C, and upside down. Adapted from Tilney-Bassett (1970b).

I proceeded now to examine the effects of crossing green 'Flower of Spring' and green 'Dolly Varden' with the white-over-green, sandwich chimeras of 'Foster's Seedling', 'Flower of Spring', 'Mrs J.C. Mapping', 'Dolly Varden', 'Lass O' Gowrie' and 'Miss Burdette-Coutts' (Tilney-Bassett 1970c). The analysis of variance of fertility data showed that the W × G crosses were generally less fertile than the reciprocal G × W crosses, but this was not correlated with selection against any particular class of embryo. The analysis proved that the segregation pattern was essentially the same with a constant female, but change the female and the pattern was radically altered. Thus the G × W crosses were essentially of the 'Flower of Spring' type, or the 'Dolly Varden' type, and the six different males made little difference to the results (Table 8.3). They are referred to as the type II and type I patterns (Fig. 8.1 and 8.2). The W × G crosses, with the constant green males, could be arranged in a sequence in which white plastids were increasingly successful, and white and variegated embryos increasingly frequent. A similar sequence was demonstrated with three different green females 'Flower of Spring', 'Dolly Varden' and 'Crystal Palace Gem' and two constant white males (Tilney-Bassett 1970c). In this sequence 'Crystal Palace Gem' had very few variegated offspring and no white ones when crossed with either the white-over-green 'Dolly Varden' or 'Mrs J.C. Mapping'. It was concluded that the major control of plastid inheritance was determined by the female nuclear and plastid genotypes, with the male having only a minor, modifying influence even when the male plastids were more successfully transmitted than the female ones.

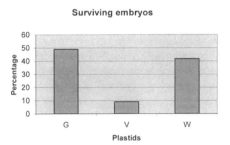

Fig. 8.1. The type II segregation pattern after green 'Flower of Spring' was crossed with six different white males (see Table 8.3).

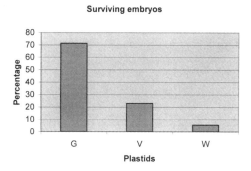

Fig. 8.2. The type I segregation pattern after green 'Dolly Varden' was crossed with six different white males (see Table 8.3).

Baur (1909) had envisaged that the two kinds of plastids sorted-out from variegated zygotes in a random manner. I found the very low frequency of less than ten per cent variegated embryos, after G × W crosses with 'Flower of Spring' as the female parent (Fig. 8.1), so incompatible that I rejected his hypothesis. But it may be right when one has a frequency of more than 80 per cent variegated embryos after the W × G crosses between 'Miss Burdette-Coutts' and 'Dolly Varden'. Sorting-out is clearly more complicated that Baur envisaged.

Crosses	Green Plastids 'Flower of Spring'				Green Plastids 'Dolly Varden'			
	Nos. of Embryos			Green Plastids	Nos. of Seedlings			Green Plastids
Mutant Plastids Male Parent	G	V	W	%	G	V	W	%
FoS	136	5	107	56.3	193	45	16	89.1
FS	156	12	136	54.6	195	57	23	83.8
JCM	211	9	174	55.0	333	60	4	93.6
DV	100	47	83	54.5	148	85	24	77.2
LG	139	37	136	50.1	149	78	13	80.3
MBC	157	60	131	55.0	206	70	15	87.6
Mutant Plastids Female Parent								
FoS	104	38	3	89.1	113	15	0	98.3
FS	180	71	10	85.2	203	48	3	95.5
JCM	128	74	23	77.3	150	66	5	88.1
DV	104	63	18	71.6	85	71	8	78.3
LG	74	187	58	51.3	68	180	20	62.6
MBC	12	180	52	34.6	1	251	44	42.0

Table 8.3. The segregation of good embryos, and the proportion of green plastids transmitted, after green 'Flower of Spring' and green 'Dolly Varden' were crossed with six different mutant cultivars 'Foster's Seedling' - FoS, 'Flower of Spring' - FS, - 'Mrs J.C.Mapping' - JCM, 'Dolly Varden' - DV, 'Lass O'Gowrie' - LG, and 'Miss Burdette-Coutts' - MBC. Adapted from Tilney-Bassett (1970c).

One gene model

So far I had shown that there was a high degree of variability between some cultivars, while others were very similar. This meant that I could take two cultivars, 'Dolly Varden' and 'Flower of Spring', and begin to treat them as genetically different, and not the result of selection or environmental effects (Tilney-Bassett 1973). I therefore made isogenic plastid crosses and collected the seed. When germinated, these gave a mixture of green, variegated and white seedlings, of which I kept and grew on only the variegated. These quickly sorted out to give some with a pure green shoot. I therefore had a number of plants from the isogenic crosses. Nevertheless, I could not tell their genotypes until I crossed them with the white plastids of 'Dolly Varden' or 'Flower of Spring' and scored the segregating embryos. The results were dramatic, 17 plants from selfed 'Dolly Varden' were true breeding and gave the 'Dolly Varden' pattern. That is green was the most frequent class, variegated intermediate frequency, and white the least frequent class, G > V > W. By contrast 35 plants from selfed 'Flower of Spring' segregated into two patterns, either type I or type II; in type II green and white embryos were both frequent and variegated the minority class G > V < W. Clearly 'Dolly Varden' was homozygous and 'Flower of Spring' was heterozygous (Table 8.4a). I will indicate the homozygosity of pattern I by the gene symbol Pr1Pr1, and the heterozygosity of pattern II by the genes symbols Pr1Pr2. The symbol Pr was chosen because it was thought to have an effect on plastid replication.
I next made four plastid crosses between the two cultivars; in all four the

Crosses	Segregation Pattern		Range of Green Plastids Transmitted	
	Type II	Type I	Type II	Type I
a. (FS W x G FS/2-31)G x W FS	11	14	75.4 – 42.1	100 – 90.2
a. (DV G x W DV/1-10)G x W DV	0	10	-	97.6 – 73.5
a. (DV W x G DV/1-7)G x W DV	0	7	-	98.3 – 62.1
b. (FS G x W DV/1-13)G x W FS	1	12	52.2	99.9 – 84.3
b. (DV W x G FS/1-38)G x W FS	15	20	73.1 – 45.2	99.9 – 77.5
b. (DV G x W FS/1-15)G x W DV	3	9	59.9 – 53.7	99.9 – 77.3
b. (FS W x G DV/1-12)G x W DV	0	12	-	99.7 – 84.0
c. (DV W x G FS/28)A-AD G x W FS	13	12	71.4 – 48.3	100 – 99.1
c. (DV W x G FS/37)A-O G x W FS	5	8	70.1 – 56.3	100 – 99.2

a. Green shoots of selfs backcrossed to 'Flower of Spring' or 'Dolly Varden'.
b. Green shoots of F1 hybrids backcrossed to 'Flower of Spring' or 'Dolly Varden'.
c. Green F2 hybrids backcrossed to 'Flower of Spring'.

Table 8.4. Segregation of plants into type II or type I pattern, supported by the percentage of green plastids transmitted. Adapted from Tilney-Bassett (1973, 1974b).

nuclear cross was equivalent. Seeds were collected and germinated, and the variegated seedlings retained. Again mostly they stabilised, and the plants with a green shoot were selected. They were now pollinated with the white plastids of 'Dolly Varden' or 'Flower of Spring'. The embryo segregation was scored as the type I or type II pattern, and the parental plants labelled accordingly (Table 8.4b). Comparing the two show that either segregation pattern can be produced when the green female plastids are derived from either 'Dolly Varden' or 'Flower of Spring', indicating that there is no difference between their green plastids in this respect. The heterozygosity, which was associated with 'Flower of Spring', had been transferred to the hybrid nucleus to give an overall segregation of 19 plants having the type II pattern and 53 plants having the type I pattern. I next took two green plants, that had proved to be heterozygous, and selfed them (Tilney-Bassett 1974b). All the F2 seedlings were green. When they flowered they were crossed with white 'Flower of Spring', and the developing embryos scored to determine their genotype. As expected, they segregated into 18 type II and 20 type I plants (Table 8.4c). Many of the type I plants had no variegated embryos, and none had white embryos. The type II plants mostly had few or no variegated embryos and a high frequency of green and white embryos. The two segregation patterns were quite distinct from each other.

The fertility analysis showed that heterozygous plants are just as fertile as homozygous ones, and that embryos of segregating families are no less viable than embryos of true-breeding families. It is therefore improbable that there is a strong selection against heterozygous plants between fertilization and germination, or during their growth to flowering. There is no reason to think that the ratio of homozygous to heterozygous plants grown up into green F2 plants is any different from the ratio of homozygous to heterozygous zygotes immediately after fertilization. Zygotic selection is therefore not the mechanism to account for the observed 1 homozygous: 1 heterozygous F2 ratio following the inbreeding of the heterozygous plants. Whereas a 1: 2: 1 or 3: 1 Mendelian monohybrid ratio was expected. A similar set of crosses was made by Abdel-Wahab (1979). He made four isogenic plastid crosses between 'Miss Burdette-Coutts' and 'Flower of Spring', and obtained a large number of sibs with green flowering shoots. These he backcrossed to white 'Flower of Spring', as source of mutant white plastids, and determined their genotype. They segregated into 19 type II and 38 type I offspring. A second set of two isogenic plastid crosses between 'Lass O'Gowrie' and 'Flower of Spring' gave green seedlings, or green shoots of variegated seedlings, which when backcrossed to white 'Flower of Spring' segregated into 19 type II and 15 type I plants. These results were quite like the previous crosses between 'Dolly Varden' and 'Flower of Spring', and so did not take us any further forward.

The failure to obtain the Pr2Pr2 homozygote led me to think that on the female side the Pr2 allele was a gametophytic lethal (Tilney-Bassett and Abdel-Wahab 1982). Alternatively, or additionally, it was suggested that an incompatibility mechanism was involved in which the Pr1 was a self-compatible allele, Pr2 a self-incompatible allele, and Pr1 – Pr2 cross compatible alleles. Successful fertilisation was then determined by sporophytic control on the male side and gametophytic control on the female side.

Two genes model

By 1985 I had accumulated a large collection of cultivars. Some were new, others were hybrids of the original cultivars; many flower colours were present. There were reds, orange-reds, salmons, pinks and whites as well as a number of zonal leaf sorts. Almouslem (1988) was examining the inheritance of flower colours as well as the type I and type II segregation pattern. He crossed the red flower of type I 'Darlington Red' with the white flower of a hybrid between green 'Mrs J.C. Mapping' and green 'Flower of Spring', it was known as W2. In one cross he obtained 22 progeny, and the reciprocal cross he obtained 30 progeny. All were type II. This was a completely new result. It was clearly the result of complementation between two dominant genes of which each parent contained only one. We called the genotype of 'Darlington Red' pr1pr1,Pr2Pr2 and that of W2 Pr1Pr1,pr2pr2, or more simply aa,BB and AA,bb.

aa,BB × AA,bb gave 52 type II plants Aa,Bb.

As the result of further crosses one more type I plant was recognized. When he crossed the type I 'Darlington Orange Red' with type I W1, a seedling from 'Mrs J.C. Mapping' selfed, he obtained 57 progeny of which 28 were type I and 29 type II. W1 and W2 were the same genotype. This 1:1 ratio amongst the offspring is indicative of heterozygosity, so he identified 'Darlington Orange Red' as having the type I heterozygous genotype pr1pr1,Pr2pr2 or aa,Bb.

aa,Bb × AA,bb gave 29 type II plants Aa,Bb and 28 type I plants Aa,bb.

Altogether he made many crosses and found several examples of all three genotypes. In particular, 'Dolly Varden' had the same type I genotype as 'Darlington Red'.

The complementary gene model replaced the attempts to explain the results on the basis of one gene. The matrixes for the phenotypic ratios for all possible genotypes were set out in 1989 (Tilney-Bassett and Almouslem 1989). This new model proposed that there were two independently assorting nuclear genes, each with a pair of alternative alleles. These are called Pr1/pr1 and Pr2/pr2, but for simplicity may be referred to as A/a and B/b. We further propose that the genes interact in a complementary manner; in other words the two recessives behave as isoepistatic and are epistatic to the dominant genes: (a=b) > B,A. Hence, a maternal parent, containing one or two copies of both dominant alleles, produces the type II segregation pattern after being pollinated by a variegated male (Fig. 8.1), whereas a maternal parent, lacking both copies of one or other or both dominant genes, produces the type I segregation pattern (Fig. 8.2).

There now followed a wealth of crosses to further confirm the complementation pattern. Almouslem (Tilney-Bassett *et al.* 1992) derived several more type II plants; they included 'Foster's Seedling' and a male sterile isolate 'MS1H' which, together with those previously mentioned, he crossed with each other in many ways to produce a generally good agreement with the 9 type II: 7 type I ratio; they were all double heterozygotes Aa,Bb (Table 8.5a. and k, n). He selfed the type Is of the same genotype – AA,bb or aa,BB or aa,Bb – and found them true-breeding (b-d). When he made crosses between them, they were all type II AA,bb × aa,BB (g); all type I aa,BB × aa,Bb(e); or segregated in about the same frequency of each type AA,bb × aa,BB (f). Almouslem also crossed some type IIs with some type Is and obtained ratios of 1 type II: 1 type I AA,bb × Aa,Bb or aa,BB × Aa,Bb(h, i, l, m); or 3 type II: 5 type I aa,Bb × Aa,Bb (j); or selfing type II AA,Bb or Aa,BB gave 3 type II: 1 type I (o). In calculating the chi-square values I removed five values that were particularly high. The cultivars behaved normally in other crosses so I attributed the biased result to chance. Of course with 81 crosses made one expects at least four to be outside the 5 per cent probability level (P = 0.05 = 1: 20), but not as much as these five were.

Amoatey (Amoatey and Tilney-Bassett 1994) made a few similar crosses with the same result. Because 'Darlington Orange Red' was a single heterozygote the hybrid between it and W1 or W2 was actually a mixture of type II and type I, which Amoatey selfed (Table 8.6a, b), or backcrossed to W1 and W2 (c. d), or to 'Darlington Orange Red' (f). They produced the same 1: 1 and 3: 5 ratios as Almouslem had found. Additionally Amoatey found a forth type I Aabb. When this was backcrossed to 'Darlington Orange Red' it produced the new ratio of 1 type II: 3 type I (Table 8.6e).

Crosses	Crosses Made	Type II	Type I	Total	Ratio Tested	χ^2	P
a. AaBb	16^2	351	333	684	9 : 7	0.271	0.9-0.5
b. AAbb	3	0	101	101	-	-	-
c. aaBB	4	0	52	52	-	-	-
d. aaBb	1	0	20	20	-	-	-
e. aaBB × aaBb	5	0	45	45	-	-	-
f. AAbb × aaBb	2	36	37	73	1 : 1	0.014	1-0.9
g. AAbb × aaBB	4	188	0	188	-	-	-
h. AAbb × AaBb	4	56	35	91	1 : 1	4.846	0.05-0.01
i. aaBB × AaBb	14^1	199	225	424	1 : 1	1.594	0.5-0.1
j. aaBb × AaBb	7^1	66	117	183	3 : 5	0.161	0.9-0.5
k. AaBb	5	50	53	103	9 : 7	2.486	0.5-0.1
l. AaBb × aaBB	5	46	44	90	1 : 1	0.044	0.9-0.5
m. AaBb × AAbb	4^1	48	35	83	1 : 1	2.036	0.5-0.1
n. AaBb	7	106	98	204	9 : 7	1.525	0.5-0.1
o. AABb or AaBB	2	61	20	81	3 : 1	0.004	1-0.9

1 or 2. One or two rows of data pulled out as a very high χ^2 value was recorded.

a. Selfing or inter-crossing type IIs. 'Foster's Seedling', 'Flower of Spring', 'Mrs J.C. Mapping', 'Pac Grosser Garten', 'Verona' and MS1H.

b. Selfing or inter-crossing type Is. W1 and W2.

c. Selfing or inter-crossing type Is. 'Darlington Red', 'Dolly Varden' and 'Lass O' Gowrie'.

d. Selfing type I. 'Darlington Orange Red'.

e. Crossing type Is. 'Darlington Orange Red', 'Darlington Red', 'Dolly Varden', 'Lass O'Gowrie' and 'Miss Burdette-Coutts'.

f. Crossing type Is. 'Darlington Orange Red', W1 and W2.

g. Crossing type Is. 'Darlington Red', 'Dolly Varden', CC4, W1 and W2.

h. Crossing type Is with type IIs. CC2, W1 and W2, 'Mrs J.C. Mapping', 'Pac Grosser Garten'.

i. Crossing type Is with type IIs. 'Darlington Red', 'Dolly Varden', 'Lass O'Gowrie', 'Foster's Seedling', 'Flower of Spring', 'Mrs J.C. Mapping', 'Pac Grosser Garten' and 'Verona'.

j. Crossing type Is with type IIs. 'Darlington Orange Red', 'Miss Burdette-Coutts', 'Foster's Seedling', 'Flower of Spring', 'Pac Grosser Garten', and 'Verona'.

k. Selfing type II. H4, H5, H6, H24 and H 27.

l. Crossing type Is with type IIs. 'Darlington Red', H4, H5, H6, H24, and H27.

m. Crossing type Is with type IIs. W2, H4, H5, H6, H24, H27.

n. Selfing type II F2 and F3 hybrids. 'Dolly Varden', 'Lass O'Gowrie', 'Miss Burdette-Coutts' and 'Flower of Spring'.

o. Selfing type IIs. 'Eggshell' and hybrid between 'Preston Park' and 'Snowstorm'.

Table 8.5. Selfs and crosses revealing no segregation or segregation into monohybrid and dihybrid ratios of type II and type I patterns. Adapted from Tilney-Bassett et al. (1992).

In total there were 29 type IIs among 895 altogether, i.e. 3.24 per cent type IIs (Table 8.6a, c). Most of these were likely to be the result of misclassification through underscoring the type I class. To allow for this probable misclassification we have presented an adjusted segregation; the result is that all the ratios improve slightly. The probability values were a reasonable fit with these conclusions. The results were highly supportive of the complementary gene model, but we had only looked at one type II, and a possible second, out of four, compared with four out of five for the type I genotypes. We decided we should look at more of the type II genotypes.

Crosses	Progeny Tested	Type II	Type I	Total	Ratio Tested	χ^2	P
a. **Aabb × Aabb**	8	6	319	325	-	-	-
b. **AaBb × AaBb**	4	102	96	198	9: 7	1.804	0.5-0.1
c. **Aabb × AAbb**	8	23	547	570	-	-	-
d. **AaBb × AAbb**	5	201	156	357	1: 1	5.672	0.05-0.01
Adjusted	5	197	160	357	1: 1	3.835	0.1-0.05
e. **Aabb × aaBb**	7	142	358	500	1: 3	3.083	0.1-0.05
Adjusted	7	130	370	500	1: 3	0.267	0.9-0.5
f. **AaBb × aaBb**	5	91	142	233	3: 5	0.241	0.9-0.5
Adjusted	5	86	147	233	3: 5	0.035	0.9-0.5

a. Type I self.
b. Type II self.
c. Type I backcrossed to W1/W2.
d. Type II backcrossed to W1/W2.
e. Type I backcrossed to 'Darlington Orange Red'.
f. Type II backcrossed to 'Darlington Orange Red'.

Table 8.6. Selfs and crosses revealing no segregation or segregation into monohybrid and dihybrid ratios of type II and type I patterns. All the original crosses are hybrids between 'Darlington Orange Red' and W1 or W2. The 20 hybrids are partly type II and partly type I. Adapted from Amoatey and Tilney-Bassett (1994).

There were some results, which clearly looked promising; these were the selfed 'Eggshell', and the crosses SS × PP/7 and 8 (Tilney-Bassett *et al.* 1992). The two plants and their descendants had been kept from the cross between 'Snowstorm', with white flowers, and 'Preston Park', with salmon flowers and a narrow peripheral zone to the leaves. When the descendants of these plants were crossed with the white plastids from 'Flower of Spring' they segregated as follows: From 'Eggshell' we obtained 12 plants type II and 3 plants type I. From SS × PP/8 we obtained 22 plants type II and 3 plants type I. These both looked like 3: 1 ratios. From SS × PP/7 we obtained 30 plants type II and 15 plants type I. This looked like a 9: 7 ratio (Tilney-Bassett *et al.* 1992). A few plants failed to flower. The two 3: 1 ratios suggested that a single heterozygote was involved, whereas the 9: 7 ratio suggested that a double heterozygote was involved. These suggestions could all be resolved by crossing the same descendants with pollen from 'Dolly Varden' and 'W1', allowing the resulting plants to grow and flower, and then pollinating these with 'Flower of Spring' as source of mutant plastids. A scrutiny of the model indicates that all type II genotypes can be distinguished from each other by crossing with the two true-breeding type Is, 'Dolly Varden' and 'W1' or 'W2', with the genotypes aa,BB and AA,bb respectively (Fig. 8.3).

Phenotypes		II	II	II	II	I	I	I	I	I
Genotypes		AA BB	Aa BB	AA Bb	Aa Bb	aa BB	AA bb	aa Bb	Aa bb	aa bb
II	AA BB	II	II	II	II	II	II	II	II	II
II	Aa BB	II	3II: 1I	II	3II: 1I	1II: 1I	II	1II: 1I	3II: 1I	1II: 1I
II	AA Bb	II	II	3II: 1I	3II: 1I	II	1II: 1I	3II: 1I	1II: 1I	1II: 1I
II	Aa Bb	II	3II: 1I	3II: 1I	9II: 7I	1II: 1I	1II: 1I	3II: 5I	3II: 5I	1II: 3I
I	aa BB	II	1II: 1I	II	1II: 1I	I	II	I	1II: 1I	I
I	AA bb	II	II	1II: 1I	1II: 1I	II	I	1II: 1I	I	I
I	aa Bb	II	1II: 1I	3II: 1I	3II: 5I	I	1II: 1I	I	1II: 3I	I
I	Aa bb	II	3II: 1I	1II: 1I	3II: 5I	1II: 1I	I	1II: 3I	I	I
I	aa bb	II	1II: 1I	1II: 1I	1II: 3I	I	I	I	I	I

Fig. 8.3. The two genes each with two alleles form 9 genotypes. These are crossed in 9 x 9 possible ways. The 81 crosses consist of 9 selfs, in the diagonal from left to right (25% shading), and two reciprocal crosses of 36 each. The type II x II crosses have light shading, and the type I x I crosses have medium shading; the type II x type I crosses have no shading. The ratios in the table are those formed as the result of complementary gene action. 'Dolly Varden' is aa,BB and W1 or W2 is AA,bb. Adapted from Amoatey and Tilney-Bassett (1994).

Wasi'an proceeded to test them further (2000). He selected mainly type II plants, but included a few whose pattern of segregation with 'Flower of Spring' made them borderline. He crossed 12 descendants of SS × PP/7 with the tester 'Dolly Varden', from which he raised 212 families that were scored as type II or type I after pollinating with 'Flower of Spring'. He crossed 9 descendants of SS × PP/7 with the tester 'W1', from which he raised 146 families that were scored as type II or type I after pollinating with 'Flower of Spring'. Why did he raise so many families from rather few descendants? He raised 358 families from 21 descendants, an average of 17 families from each descendant. He needed to raise a number of families from each descendant because he had to distinguish a descendant that was all type II, or all type I from a descendant that was segregating in a ratio of 1 type II: 1 type 1. Only by having five families of a descendant could he be 95% certain that he had not hit on a run of only one type when there ought to have been two. So with an average of 17 families per descendant his results are extremely safe. Similarly with SS × PP/8 he raised

6 descendants and 105 families with 'Dolly Varden', and 7 descendants and 160 families with 'W1', an average of 20 families per descendant. Finally with 'Eggshell' he raised 5 descendants and 99 families with 'Dolly Varden', and 4 descendants and 52 families with 'W1', an average of 18 families per descendant. All the families were scored after pollinating with 'Flower of Spring'. In total, for these 774 families, Wasi'an scored 53,949 embryos, an average of 69.7 embryos per family.

In retrospect Wasi'an would have obtained a better result overall if he had tested rather more type II descendants, but fewer families and fewer embryos per family. Moreover, he should have kept 'Dolly Varden' and 'W1' in balance, as a surplus of one over the other is of little value. Unfortunately, 'W1' turned out to be less satisfactory than 'Dolly Varden'. It did not flower for as long or as well as 'Dolly Varden'. With so much crossing to do, this became a limiting factor.

Of the 12 descendants of SS × PP/7, Wasi'an crossed nine with both 'Dolly Varden' and 'W1'. Five of these proved to be double heterozygous type II plants Aa,Bb; one was a single heterozygous plant Aa,BB; and three were type I plants aa,BB (Table 8.7). The three that he crossed with 'Dolly Varden' alone were either double or single heterozygotes Aa,Bb or Aa,BB. The five descendants of SS × PP/8 crossed with both testers were single heterozygotes AA,Bb (Table 8.7). Two descendants were crossed with 'W1' only; they were the single heterozygote AA,Bb, or improbably the double heterozygote Aa,Bb. One descendant crossed with 'Dolly Varden' only was a single heterozygote AA,Bb; or the double homozygous dominant AA,BB. Finally, the four 'Eggshell' descendants that were crossed with 'Dolly Varden' and 'W1' yielded the three expected genotypes. Two were the single heterozygote Aa,BB; one was the homozygous dominant AA,BB, and one was a type I homozygote aa,BB (Table 8.7). Two descendants were crossed with 'Dolly Varden' only; they were the single heterozygote Aa,BB; or improbably the double heterozygote Aa,Bb.

Parents and Descendants	Descendants x 'Dolly Varden' pollinated by 'Flower of Spring'		Descendants x 'W1' pollinated by 'Flower of Spring'		Genotypes
	Type II	Type I	Type II	Type I	
SS x PP/7					
22	7	4	10	0	Aa,BB
15	14	14	9	6	Aa,Bb
24	13	6	5	9	Aa,Bb
28	10	5	6	8	Aa,Bb
29	12	16	8	4	Aa,Bb
41	14	9	7	8	Aa,Bb
12	0	13	24	0	aa,BB
23	0	26	14	0	aa,BB
33	0	9	28	0	aa,BB
SS x PP/8					
2	22	0	10	21	AA,Bb
10	6	0	8	14	AA,Bb
12	29	0	6	7	AA,Bb
13	21	0	11	12	AA,Bb
16	20	0	9	8	AA,Bb
Eggshell					
11	19	0	28	0	AA,BB
1	14	16	13	0	Aa,BB
4	6	5	20	0	Aa,BB
13	0	23	11	0	aa,BB

Table 8.7. The descendants of three plants are crossed with the testers 'Dolly Varden' and 'W1', and the resulting plants are pollinated with 'Flower of Spring'. Crosses with only one tester are not included. The exact genotype is shown in the right hand column. Adapted from Wasi' an (2000)

It is not practical to illustrate the numerous crosses; instead I have taken two examples E 11 and E 1 from the 'Eggshell' series. In each case I have allocated twenty rows to each. The E 11 is the wholly true-breeding type II. I have shown the result of crossing ten of the descendants with 'Dolly Varden' and subsequently pollinating with variegated 'Flower of Spring', and then the result of crossing ten of the descendants with W1 and again pollinating with 'Flower of Spring' (Table 8.8). All of the segregation is clearly type II AA,BB. The very high percentage of white embryos from many of the plants is particularly interesting, but we have not investigated it further. In the second example I have taken E 1 after crossing with 'Dolly Varden' and pollinating with 'Flower of Spring'. Now there are clearly two types; half the embryos are type II and half the embryos are type I (Table 8.9). This is definitely a single heterozygote Aa,BB, segregating. Wasi'an has 45 tables of a similar nature.

Family Number	Number of Embryos			Green Plastids
	G	V	W	%
'Eggshell': E11 x G DV pollinated by 'Flower of Spring'				
3	45	0	33	57.7
4	22	0	14	61.1
6	47	0	38	55.3
7	19	0	14	57.6
8	52	0	39	57.1
9	47	0	39	54.7
10	48	0	35	57.8
12	47	1	20	69.9
14	51	1	37	58.0
15	50	0	32	61.0
'Eggshell': E11 x G W1 pollinated by 'Flower of Spring'				
1	3	1	88	3.7
2	54	6	32	60.8
3	6	0	80	7.0
4	10	1	69	12.9
5	67	1	61	52.3
6	20	1	74	21.9
7	10	2	27	28.6
8	16	0	108	12.9
9	5	0	77	6.1
10	0	2	87	0.7

Table 8.8. The first ten results from E 11 crossed with 'Dolly Varden' and 'W1', and pollinated by 'Flower of Spring'. The results with 'Dolly Varden' are typical of type II. The results with 'W1' are mostly strongly biased in favour of the mutant parent, but they retain the type II pattern. This was the only plant that gave the type II segregation with both 'Dolly Varden' and 'W1'.

Family Number	Number of Embryos			Green Plastids
	G	V	W	%
'Eggshell': E1 x G DV pollinated by 'Flower of Spring'				
Type II				
4	40	0	21	65.6
6	50	0	38	56.8
8	44	1	39	53.3
12	47	0	36	56.6
14	47	1	36	56.2
15	46	1	29	61.3
16	38	0	16	70.4
18	50	0	23	68.5
19	35	0	43	44.9
22	38	3	41	47.7
Type I				
2	78	0	3	96.3
3	73	0	0	100
7	68	4	0	97.9
9	72	0	0	100
13	65	0	3	95.6
17	59	3	6	89.0
27	80	1	0	99.6
29	86	1	4	95.4
30	99	0	0	100
32	91	0	0	100

Table 8.9. The first twenty results from E1 crossed with 'Dolly Varden' and pollinated with 'Flower of Spring'. They divided almost equally into type II and type I segregation patterns.

So the two single heterozygotes were not the same. 'Eggshell' was Aa,BB and SS × PP/8 was AA,Bb. Moreover, one of them had produced the double homozygous dominant AA,BB, among its offspring. We had obtained the complete segregation from 'Eggshell':

Aa,BB gave rise to 1 AA,BB: 2 Aa,BB: 1 aa,BB

But unfortunately not the complete segregation from SS × PP/8, although AA,BB remained a possibility:

AA,Bb gave rise to (1 AA,BB): 2 AA,Bb: (1 Aa,bb)

The double heterozygote could, in theory, have given nine possible genotypes, but we had selected only type II plants, so we might have expected four, plus a few type I plants. We obtained only two:
Aa,Bb gave rise to Aa,BB, the double heterozygote Aa,Bb and the type I aa,BB. But the sample size was very small to expect them all. Altogether we have now detected eight of the nine genotypes; we have not yet detected the double homozygous recessive aa,bb. We have also seen that the complementary gene model worked exceedingly well for the major gene switch between type II and type I, but as we shall see, there is evidence for many modifying genes to influence the system.

References

Abdel-Wahab, O.A.L. (1979).
Genetical studies of zonal pelargoniums. Ph.D. Thesis, University College of Swansea.

Almouslem, A.B. (1988).
Qualitative and quantitative genetical studies in *Pelargonium* × *Hortorum* Bailey. Ph.D. Thesis, University of Swansea, Wales.

Amoatey, H.M. and Tilney-Bassett, R.A.E. (1994).
A test of the complementary gene model for the control of biparental plastid inheritance in zonal pelargoniums. Heredity 72, 69-77.

Baur, E. (1909).
Das Wesen und die Erblichkeitsverhältnisse der 'Varietates albomarginatae hort' von *Pelargonium zonale*. Z. Vererbungsl. 1, 330-351.

Campbell, M.E. and others (1990).
Fancy-leaved pelargoniums Peter Grieve and after. (Ed. E.J. Willson). The British Pelargonium and Geranium Society.

Chittenden, R.J. (1926).
Studies in variegation. II. *Hydrangea* and *Pelargonium*. Journal of Genetics 16, 43-61.

Clifton, R.T.F. (1990).
Geranium Family Species Check List. 4th ed. Part 4. *Pelargonium*. Compiled for the Geraniaceae Group of The British Pelargonium and Geranium Society.

Darlington, C.D. (1958).
Evolution of genetic systems, 2nd ed. Oliver and Boyd, Edinburgh and London.

Grieve, P. (1868).
A history of variegated zonal pelargoniums; with practical hints for their production, propagation, and cultivation. Printed for the author, London.

Hagemann, R. (2000).
Erwin Baur or Carl Correns: Who really created the theory of plastid inheritance? The Journal of Heredity 91, 435-440.

Imai, Y. (1936).
Geno- and plasmotypes of variegated pelargoniums. Journal of Genetics 33, 169-195.

Noack, K.L. (1924).
Vererbungsversuche mit buntblättrigen Pelargonien. Verh. Phys. –med. Ges. Würzb. N.F. 49, 45-93.

Noack, K.L. (1925).
Weitere Untersuchungen über das Wesen der Buntblättrigkeit bei Pelargonien. Verh. Phys. –med. Ges. Würzb. N.F. 50, 47-97.

Roth, L. (1927).
Untersuchungen über die periclinal bunten Rassen von *Pelargonium zonale*.
Zschr. induct. Abstamm. Vererb. Lehre. 45, 125-159.

Tilney-Bassett, R.A.E. (1963b).
Genetics and plastid physiology in *Pelargonium*. Heredity 18, 485-504.

Tilney-Bassett, R.A.E. (1970a).
Genetics and plastid physiology in *Pelargonium*. III. Heredity 25, 89-103.

Tilney-Bassett, R.A.E. (1970b).
Effect of environment on plastid segregation in young embryos of *Pelargonium* × *Hortorum* Bailey. Annals of Botany 34, 811-816.

Tilney-Bassett, R.A.E. (1970c).
The control of plastid inheritance in *Pelargonium*. Genetical Research, Cambridge 16, 49-61.

Tilney-Bassett, R.A.E. (1973).
The control of plastid inheritance in *Pelargonium* II. Heredity 30, 1-13.

Tilney-Bassett, R.A.E. (1974b).
The control of plastid inheritance in *Pelargonium* III. Heredity 33, 353-360.

Tilney-Bassett, R.A.E. and Abdel-Wahab, O.A.L. (1982).
Irregular segregation at the Pr locus controlling plastid inheritance in *Pelargonium*: Gametophytic lethal or incompatibility system. Theoretical and Applied Genetics 62, 185-191.

Tilney-Bassett, R.A.E. and Almouslem, A.B. (1989).
Variation in plastid inheritance between pelargonium cultivars and their hybrids. Heredity 63, 145-153.

Tilney-Bassett, R.A.E., Almouslem, A.B. and Amoatey, H.M. (1992).
Complementary genes control biparental plastid inheritance in *Pelargonium*. Theoretical and Applied Genetics 85, 317-324.

Wasi'an. (2000).
Studies of plastid inheritance in zonal pelargoniums.
Ph.D. Thesis, University of Wales Swansea.

9

Factors Modifying the Breeding Results

Variation in the plastids

The two-gene model, that we have just described, groups together into two alternate patterns a large number of individual results. For example, the type I segregation pattern groups together those plants that regularly produce green, variegated and white progeny after G × W crosses with others that produce entirely green progeny. The plants that produce the variegated as the smallest class amongst the type II segregation are surely different from those plants that never produce any variegated progeny. We have investigated these differences, which help to reveal the plants that are able to produce a high proportion of variegated progeny. Some of the experiments stress the importance of choosing the best plastid, others the best nucleus. At least we should gain a few ideas as to what to avoid, and what is the more favourable response.

Hagemann and Scholze (1974) observed differences in the multiplication rates of unlike plastids. They crossed the green plastids of 'Trautlieb' with the yellow plastids of 'Mrs Pollock', and with the white plastids of 'Mrs Parker' and 'Flower of Spring'. After both G × W and W × G crosses the segregation was green > variegated > white. 'Trautlieb' is evidently a typical type I plant, not unlike 'Dolly Varden'. With 'Trautlieb' as female parent, there was no significant difference in the frequency of green seedlings when crossed with white 'Flower of Spring' (78.7%) and white 'Mrs Parker' (75.7%) as male parent. The frequency of green seedlings was significantly lower with the yellow plastids of 'Mrs Pollock' (60.8%). In the reciprocal W × G crosses all three mutants were distinguishable. The frequency of green seedlings associated with 'Trautlieb' was least for 'Mrs Pollock' (44.0%), in the middle for 'Mrs Parker' (53.8%), and most for 'Flower of Spring' (66.5%). This may be attributed to their three different nuclei. But Hagemann and Scholze suggested that the yellow plastids of 'Mrs Pollock', in the zygotes and embryos, although still inferior to the green, were more successful than the white plastids of 'Mrs Parker', and still more successful than the white plastids of 'Flower of Spring'. Hence, 'Mrs Pollock' produced the highest frequency of variegated seedlings after W × G crosses, and the highest frequency, although somewhat less, after G × W crosses.

They scored the cotyledons as wholly green (0), wholly white (1), or at 0.05 intervals into twenty categories. 'Flower of Spring' and to a lesser extent 'Mrs Parker', showed a steep decline from many seedlings with predominantly green cotyledons to a relatively few with predominantly white cotyledons. 'Mrs Pollock' showed a more gradual decline, with a much higher proportion of seedlings towards the yellow end of the scale. A trend in keeping with the relative success of the plastids as measured by the proportion of green seedlings.

They next measured the extent of variegation in the first six leaves against the variegation in the cotyledons. In general the correlation was good. The yellow plastids of 'Mrs Pollock' had about the same multiplication rate as the green plastids and cells. The white plastids of 'Mrs Parker' were slightly slower, and those of 'Flower of Spring' slightly faster. It was not shown that these differences were significant. It seems that in mixed cells and tissues the mutant plastids keep up with the green plastids, although this is less true when the variegated seedlings have a high proportion of mutant tissue. Without sufficient green cells to nourish them, the mutant tissues simply die through their inability to photosynthesise.

During the change from the first three leaves (1 - 3) to the second three leaves (4 - 6) the proportion of green cells shows an increase. Hence these green cells were able to multiply faster than the yellow or white ones. But they did not differ by much as they were able to form 69 white-over-green or 66 green-over-white periclinal chimeras. At least when they have sorted out into distinct layers, the white layer is able to keep pace with the green layer.

Besides the greater multiplication rate of the yellow plastids of 'Mrs Pollock' compared with the white plastids of the other two cultivars, we also found a difference between the plastids associated with our type I plants and those associated by chance with our type II plants. The plastids of two type II plants, 'Foster's Seedling' and 'Flower of Spring', remain colourless in summer but become quite green in winter. Abdel-Wahab (1979) measured the winter greening in the margins of variegated 'Flower of Spring' as reaching about 57% of the normal chlorophyll content, with no significant change in the chlorophyll a/b ratio. The plastids of two type I plants, 'Lass O' Gowrie' and 'Miss Burdette-Coutts', remain colourless in both seasons (Khera 1975). They are different from each other. The cultivar 'Mrs J.C. Mapping' is like 'Flower of Spring' and 'Dolly Varden' is like 'Lass O' Gowrie'. In addition, the plastids from the type II plants are stable, but the plastids from the type I plants are unstable and undergo restitution. They form pinpricks of green against the otherwise white leaf margins, or white embryos. When these two plastids were compared in crosses, the stable white plastids did not compete as well as the unstable white plastids. The unstable plastid was superior to the stable plastid (Abdel-Wahab 1979; Abdel-Wahab and Tilney-Bassett 1981). This supported our observation that the crosses with 'Dolly Varden' invariably had a higher percentage of variegated progeny than those with 'Flower of Spring'.

A very interesting experiment was that between six variegated cultivars and the six green clones derived from them. The six variegated cultivars were 'Foster's Seedling', 'Flower of Spring', 'Mrs J.C. Mapping', 'Dolly Varden', 'Lass O' Gowrie' and 'Miss Burdette-Coutts'. These were reciprocally crossed, as G × W and W × G crosses, to make 72 crosses. Each of these was scored for the segregation of green, variegated and white embryos. I then converted this raw data into percentages and estimated the percentages of green plastids contributed by each cross (Tilney-Bassett 1976). Part of this experiment I shall consider further in the next section, but a part I shall consider now as it concerns differences between the stable and unstable plastids. I have extracted from the 72 crosses four groups, two are G × W and two are W × G crosses. In each case I have summed, and averaged, six crosses as green or white females and six crosses as green or white males to provide a constant. I have then crossed the constant, the average of six cultivars, with each of the six individual cultivars and their six green clones to provide the variable. With these four groups of crosses, I have obtained the average frequency of variegated embryos when the variable parent is one of the two types (Table 9.1). We see from the table that when the green cultivar is the variable female parent in G × W crosses the results are almost identical (type II 20.6% and type I 22.8% variegated embryos). This is again true when the green cultivar is the variable male in W × G crosses (type II 45.4% and type I 46.1% variegated embryos). Contrast these two groups of crosses with the results of the variegated parent as the variable male in G × W crosses (type II 12.0% and type I 31.5% variegated embryos). Again when the variegated parent is the variable female in W × G crosses (type II 27.7% and type I 63.7% variegated embryos). These are highly significant differences. There are more variegated embryos associated with the type I genotype than with the type II genotype, but only when the two genotypes are associated with white plastids. This response clearly shows that whereas there are no differences in the green plastids, the two kinds of mutant plastids make their own distinct contribution.

G x W Crosses	Percentage Embryos			Embryos Scored	% Green Plastids
	G	V (Variable parent female)	W		
FoS x 6 W♂'s	39.6	28.1	32.3	1156	52.5
FS x 6 W♂'s	47.2	9.8	43.0	2751	52.6
JCM x 6 W♂'s	41.6	23.9	33.5	1330	54.0
Average Type II		20.6			
DV x 6 W♂'s	70.5	24.5	5.0	2318	84.4
LG x 6 W♂'s	71.9	26.9	1.2	1089	92.0
MBC x 6 W♂'s	82.9	17.1	0	1046	96.4
Average Type I		22.8		9690	
W x G Crosses		Variable parent male			
6 W♀s x Fos	43.8	50.2	6.0	1267	72.6
6 W♀s x FS	49.2	40.8	10.0	2123	69.9
6 W♀s x JCM	45.3	45.1	9.6	1034	71.9
Average Type II		45.4			
6 W♀s x DV	53.2	43.1	3.7	1848	77.4
6 W♀s x LG	44.3	47.2	8.5	1017	68.1
6 W♀s x MBC	46.3	48.0	5.7	1085	74.1
Average Type I		46.1		8374	
G x W Crosses		Variable parent male			
6 G♀s x Fos	66.3	9.9	23.8	1227	73.7
6 G♀s x FS	66.4	13.2	20.4	2277	75.0
6 G♀s x JCM	65.1	12.8	22.1	1587	73.7
Average Type II		12.0			
6 G♀s x DV	45.3	35.2	19.5	1916	65.8
6 G♀s x LG	58.6	27.1	14.3	1312	73.6
6 G♀s x MBC	52.0	32.1	15.9	1371	70.2
Average Type I		31.5		9690	
W x G Crosses		Variable parent female			
FoS x 6 G♂'s	76.4	21.3	2.3	1064	92.0
FS x 6 G♂'s	73.5	23.5	3.0	1468	90.2
JCM x 6 G♂'s	57.4	38.4	4.2	1164	82.1
Average Type II		27.7			
DV x 6 G♂'s	51.2	42.3	6.5	2145	72.4
LG x 6 G♂'s	20.3	71.4	8.3	1275	59.9
MBC x 6 G♂'s	3.4	77.3	19.3	1258	37.3
Average Type I		63.7		8374	

Table 9.1. A comparison of the green, variegated and white embryos produced after reciprocal crosses between six different variegated cultivars and their green clones. Notice the much greater disparity of variegated embryos between type I and type II when the variegated cultivar is the variable parent.

Among the mutant males, there was no significant heterogeneity within the three cultivars of either type. This suggests that the mutant plastids, which behaved differently between types, behaved alike within types. The male effect was examined further by comparing the mean percentage of variegated embryos after crossing 93 type I and 36 type II parents with 'Dolly Varden' and 'Flower of Spring' mutants (Table 9.2). With the female parents type I or type II, the percentage variegated progeny was much higher with 'Dolly Varden' (Is 25.5%, IIs 23.4%) than with 'Flower of Spring' (Is 6.2%, IIs 3.6%). Hence, although there were big differences in the ratio of G: W plastids, and in the G: V: W segregation patterns, determined largely by the Pr1/Pr2 genotype of the female parent, the proportion of variegated progeny was similar for the same male plastid, but capable of considerable change for a different male plastid. The similarity between the frequencies of variegated embryos, after type I and type II G × W crosses, suggests that the frequencies are independent of the Pr1/Pr2 genotype. The significantly lower frequencies with the 'Flower of Spring' plastid mutant, compared with the 'Dolly Varden' plastid mutant, suggests that the plastids of 'Flower of Spring' have less opportunity to mix in the zygote and early embryo with the wild-type plastids than those of 'Dolly Varden', and consequently produce fewer variegated progeny.

Pollen Source	93 Type I Plants	36 Type II Plants
Variegated Dolly Varden	25.5%	23.1%
Variegated Flower of Spring	6.2%	3.6%

Table 9.2. The average percentage of variegated embryos contributed by 'Dolly Varden' and 'Flower of Spring' to type I and type II plants.

Variation in the nucleus

I split the 72 crosses into 36 G × W and 36 W × G crosses. For each cross I converted the numbers into percentages of green, variegated and white embryos, and estimated the percentage green plastid contribution. I took the values of the green plastids and the variegated embryos, transferred these values into angles, and laid them out as a 6 × 6 analysis of variance (Table 9.3). The model for the anovar (analysis of variance)

Is Ho = $Y_{ij} = \mu + \male_i + \female_j + e_{ij}$ in which each observed value is dependent upon a mean, plus an effect of the male cultivar, plus an effect of the female cultivar, and a residual error term. As there is no replication, the interaction mean square is used as an estimate of the residual error. Tests for independence, homogeneity of variances, and for the normality of the data, show that the conditions required to permit the use of anovar on the transformed data are adequately met (Sokal and Rohlf 1969). The main effects of the analysis are set out in table 9.4. They point out that the variance shown by the difference in female cultivars is highly significant in both G × W and W × G crosses, and both for the analysis of green plastids and for variegated embryos. There are also significant effects of the male. The test for non-additivity shows that multiplicative effects are generally very small; the exception, just significant at the 5% level, after G × W crosses, appears anomalous.

White Males	G × W crosses: Green female cultivars						Row Totals
	FoS	FS	JCM	DV	LG	MBC	
FoS	43.74	47.75	47.15	71.76	80.20	83.71	374.31
	15.34	8.91	20.53	24.88	21.22	15.45	106.33
FS	52.83	45.63	50.94	65.42	74.55	86.47	375.84
	23.97	13.18	19.09	28.25	27.20	10.30	121.99
JCM	43.74	46.32	47.81	75.23	77.21	83.58	373.89
	22.38	8.72	25.10	22.79	26.71	15.23	120.93
DV	44.26	45.86	42.65	56.66	71.28	70.45	331.16
	39.70	26.57	33.52	34.70	41.67	41.15	217.31
LG	50.94	45.29	51.30	64.82	72.15	80.28	364.78
	39.11	19.91	37.82	35.61	29.33	23.42	185.20
MBC	43.11	48.22	44.08	70.09	68.36	77.62	351.48
	45.17	24.58	35.85	30.26	38.76	30.92	205.54
Column	278.62	279.07	283.93	403.98	443.75	482.11	2171.46
Totals	185.67	101.87	171.91	176.49	184.89	136.47	957.30

Table 9.3a. Layout for anovar showing the angular transformed data for estimates of the green plastid contribution (Upper values), and for the percentages of variegated embryos (Lower values). Adapted from Tilney-Bassett (1976).

White Females	W × G crosses: White female cultivars						Row Totals
	FoS	FS	JCM	DV	LG	MBC	
FoS	72.85	73.89	62.80	59.02	47.01	42.48	358.05
	29.53	32.90	38.47	39.47	68.03	65.20	273.60
FS	71.66	67.78	62.97	59.87	47.12	36.81	346.21
	25.91	30.00	37.41	35.49	51.24	56.29	236.34
JCM	71.95	73.46	64.90	56.63	51.59	36.93	355.46
	29.13	24.43	38.76	42.65	60.20	56.35	251.52
DV	82.29	75.46	70.31	60.07	53.76	41.32	383.21
	18.72	25.10	33.02	39.41	57.99	69.82[b]	244.06
LG	72.34	68.11	64.97	56.26	46.43	32.01	340.12
	32.77	30.72	41.73	42.25	54.39	57.99	259.85
MBC	72.90	73.15	64.38	58.31	58.89[a]	36.06	363.69
	27.56	30.13	40.28	44.03	55.80	65.57	263.37
Column	443.99	431.85	390.33	350.16	304.80	225.61	2146.74
Totals	163.62	173.28	229.67	243.30	347.65	371.22	1528.74

Table 9.3b. Layout for anovar showing the angular transformed data for estimates of the green plastid contribution (Upper values), and for the percentages of variegated embryos (Lower values). The values marked "a" and "b" are outliers; their calculated errors are over three standard deviations above the mean. An estimated value for "a" is 48.73 and an estimated value for "b" is 55.98. Adapted from Tilney-Bassett (1976).

After G × W crosses the mean frequency of the output of green plastids was 53.1% for type II, and 92.3% for type I plants. After W × G crosses the mean frequency of the output of green plastids was 88.7% for type II and 56.8% for type I plants. This huge difference between type II and type I accounts for 92.8% of the variance of G × W crosses, and 72.0% of the variance of W × G crosses. The two males for the G × W crosses, and the two males for the W × G crosses, fell within the range of 72.2% to 78.6% and had hardly any significance. These percentage values are created by obtaining the average of the transformed values of table 9.3, and then back transforming to obtain the percentage value from them. They correspond closely, but not exactly, to the untransformed values used in table 9.1. The contrast between the frequencies of variegated embryos is also interesting.

Source of Variance	Analysis of green plastids			Analysis of variegated embryos		
	d.f.	M.S.	P	d.f.	M.S.	P
G × W Crosses						
Green females	5	1426.543	<<0.1%	5	187.459	<<0.1%
White males	5	51.797	1%-0.1%	5	394.795	<<0.1%
Non-additivity	1	70.073	5%-1%	1	1.737	n.s.
Interactions	24	12.538	-	24	19.989	-
Total	35	-	-	35	-	-
W × G Crosses						
White females	5	1143.729	<<0.1%	5	1263.260	<<0.1%
Green Males	5	37.760	0.5%-0.1%	5	30.642	n.s.
Non-additivity	1	0.438	n.s.	1	1.186	n.s.
Interactions	24	7.964	-	24	18.401	-
Total	35	-	-	35	-	-

Table 9.4. The main effects of the anovar for the angular transformed data of the green plastid contribution, and the percentages of variegated embryos. Adapted from Tilney-Bassett 1976. The statistical abbreviations mean: d.f. = Degrees of freedom, n.s. = Not significant, M.S. = Mean Square, P = Probability that the mean square value is due to chance. Adapted from Tilney-Basett (1976).

In G × W crosses the type II males created far fewer variegated progeny, 11.0%, compared with the type I males, 30.9%. In W × G crosses the type II females created far fewer variegated progeny, 27.2%, compared with the type I females, 64.5%. The white males account for 94.2%, and the white females for 68.8% of the total variance. The difference between the type II and type I crosses was huge, but what of the individual cultivars.

The main effects were examined by breaking them down into orthogonal contrasts. For one degree of freedom I was interested in comparing the type II and type I plants. The type II plants were green and white-over-green 'Foster's Seedling', 'Flower of Spring' and 'Mrs J.C. Mapping'.

The type I plants were green and white-over-green 'Dolly Varden', 'Lass O' Gowrie' and 'Miss Burdette-Coutts'. Within the first of these groups inspection of the green plastid output suggested that 'Foster's Seedling' and 'Flower of Spring' were closer to each other than either is to 'Mrs J.C. Mapping', so the second contrast was between 'Foster's Seedling' and 'Flower of Spring', and the third contrast between these two together and 'Mrs J.C. Mapping'. Similarly, the difference between the type I 'Lass O' Gowrie' and 'Miss Burdette-Coutts' is the fourth contrast, and these two together against 'Dolly Varden' is the fifth contrast.

I shall consider only the highly significant differences of less than 0.1% probability (Table 9.5). The cultivar 'Foster's Seedling' gave significantly more variegated embryos, 26.5%, than 'Flower of Spring', 8.6%, after G × W crosses, otherwise they are quite similar. The mean frequency of W × G crosses is 91.4% green plastids for the two together against 82.8% green plastids for 'Mrs J.C. Mapping'. Similarly among variegated embryos 'Mrs J.C. Mapping' has a value of 38.4% compared with the two together of 22.2%. Clearly 'Mrs J.C. Mapping' is significantly different from 'Foster's Seedling' and 'Flower of Spring' as a white female.

Source of Variance	Analysis of green plastids			Analysis of variegated Embryos		
	d.f.	M.S.	P	d.f.	M.S.	P
G × W Crosses						
Type I ♀s against type II ♀s	1	6621.077	<<0.1%	1	40.960	n.s.
FoS ♀ against FS ♀s	1	0.017	n.s.	1	585.203	<0.1%
FoS + FS ♀s against JCM ♀	1	2.873	n.s.	1	87.984	5%-1%
LG ♀against MBC ♀	1	122.624	0.5%-0.1%	1	195.375	0.5%-0.1%
LG + MBC ♀s against DV ♀	1	386.122	<0.1%	1	27.773	n.s.
Total (Green females)	5	**7132.713**	-	5	**937.295**	-
Type I ♂s against type II ♂s	1	163.073	0.5%-0.1%	1	1860.484	<<0.1%
FoS ♂against FS ♂	1	0.195	n.s.	1	20.436	n.s.
FoS + FS ♂s against JCM ♂	1	0.156	n.s.	1	5.093	n.s.
LG ♂ against MBC ♂	1	14.741	n.s.	1	34.476	n.s.
LG + MBCI ♂s against DV ♂	1	80.820	5%-1%	1	53.485	n.s.
Total (White males)	5	**258.985**	-	5	**1973.974**	-
Error mean square	1	12.538	-	1	19.989	-
W × G Crosses						
Type I ♀s against type II ♀s	1	4130.204	<<0.1%	1	4347.204	<<0.1%
FoS ♀against FS ♀	1	12.282	n.s.	1	7.776	n.s.
FoS + FS ♀s against JCM ♀	1	251.645	<0.1%	1	416.432	<0.1%
LG ♀ against MBC ♀	1	522.588	<<0.1%	1	46.295	n.s.
LG + MBC ♀s against DV ♀	1	801.928	<<0.1%	1	1498.593	<<0.1%
Total (White females)	5	**5718.647**	-	5	**6316.300**	-
Type I ♂s against type II ♂s	1	20.703	n.s.	1	0.941	n.s.
FoS ♂against FS ♂s	1	11.682	n.s.	1	115.692	5%-1%
FoS + FS ♂s against JCM ♂	1	1.232	n.s.	1	1.323	n.s.
LG ♂against MBC ♂	1	46.295	5%-1%	1	1.033	n.s.
LG + MBC ♂s against DV ♂	1	108.889	0.5%-0.1%	1	34.222	n.s.
Total (Green males)	5	**188.801**	-	5	**153.211**	-
Error mean square	1	7.964	-	1	18.401	-

Table 9.5. The main effects of the analysis (table 9.4) are sub-divided into orthogonal contrasts. Adapted from Tilney-Bassett (1976).

'Lass O' Gowrie' is different from 'Miss Burdette-Coutts' in W × G crosses at the 0.1% level of significance. It contributes 60.0% green plastids compared with 'Miss Burdette-Coutts' with 37.2% green plastids. In G × W crosses 'Dolly Varden' with 85.1% green plastids is significantly different from 'Lass O' Gowrie' and 'Miss Burdette-Coutts' together with a mean of 95.1% green plastids. After W × G crosses 'Dolly Varden' is significantly different from the two in the frequency of variegated embryos. A mean of 42.3% variegated embryos were produced by 'Dolly Varden' compared to a mean of 74.8% for the 'Lass O' Gowrie' and 'Miss Burdette-Coutts'.
There is no doubt that the three type I plants are all significantly different from each other at the 0.1% probability level. There is a chance of less than one in a thousand of being wrong. We must conclude that in addition to the huge difference between type II and type I plants, there is also a difference between individual cultivars.

Among the type II plants, 'Mrs J.C. Mapping' is more maternal, or rather less paternal, than the other two because the green plastid output is relatively depressed after W × G crosses. Among the type I plants, after G × W crosses, the segregation pattern for 'Dolly Varden' is predominantly maternal, but switches to predominantly paternal after W × G crosses. With 'Lass O' Gowrie' the transmission pattern is visibly shifted towards the maternal influence. Finally, 'Miss Burdette-Coutts' is such a strong female that it is the only cultivar in which there are no white embryos after all six G × W crosses (Table 9.1). The maternal influence is so strong that it is the only cultivar with more white than green embryos after W × G crosses. The six cultivars may be arranged in order of decreasing maternal strength as follows:

'Miss Burdette-Coutts' > 'Lass O' Gowrie' > 'Dolly Varden' > 'Mrs J.C. Mapping' > 'Flower of Spring' = 'Foster's Seedling'.

Further evidence that the type I green families were not all alike came from a number of G × W crosses with 'Dolly Varden' as the pollen parent (Tilney-Bassett 1974a). Margaret Moses found that 'George Burgwin', 'Thomas Earle', 'Drummer Boy', 'Roedale Glory' and 'Vera Dillon' all gave green and variegated embryos, but no white. The transmission of green plastids was estimated at 84% to over 99%. The cultivars 'Murray Horne', 'Phyllis', 'Miriam Basey', 'Copper Kettle', 'Mrs Quilter' and 'Banbury Cross' gave a mixture of green, variegated and white embryos. The transmission of green plastids was estimated at 82% down to 60%. These undoubtedly form a heterogeneous group.

A few of the green shoots derived from variegated first generation selfs backcrossed to 'Flower of Spring' gave neither variegated nor white embryos. They rejected all the mutant plastids (Tilney-Bassett 1973). A similar result occurred after 'Joan Fontaine' was crossed with 'Flower of Spring' (Tilney-Bassett 1974a). Many of the F2 green plants derived from selfing the green F1 between 'Dolly Varden' and 'Flower of Spring' gave only green embryos. They showed only maternal inheritance of the plastids when crossed with the white plastids of 'Flower of Spring' (Tilney-Bassett 1974b). Evidently the genotype of some plants was so strongly maternal that the mutant plastids of 'Flower of Spring' could not compete with them at all in G × W crosses.

Variation within Type II and Type I families

The variation between 214 families with similar maternal nucleus and plastids is very wide both for type II and type I G × W and W × G crosses (Tilney-Bassett 1984). With the type I G × W crosses, the variance is more flat and drawn out when 'Dolly Varden' is the male parent. When 'Flower of Spring' is the male the variance is much more skewed towards the 100% maternal transmission.

By including the published results of earlier workers, I have assembled data on over 70 W × G crosses (Tilney-Bassett 1988). They reveal an extraordinary range of variation from one family with 100% of zygotes with some maternal plastids to the other extreme with one family that had 0.5% zygotes with some maternal plastids. There was such a continuous range of variation that the mode of 40-50% was not very strong. Where data were available on both, the W × G crosses showed no correlation with the reciprocal G × W crosses (Table 9.6); the type II and type I individuals were scattered across the range (Table 9.7); they are not only, of course, the isogenic crosses where a correlation was found.

Chimera	Percentage Maternal Plastids	
	G × W	W × G
Scarlet Gem	100	16.3
Mädchen aus der Fremde	99.1	25.0
Fujinozuki	98.3	21.4
Snowflake	95.2	25.0
Mrs. Lennox	91.1	10.4
Mrs. J.C. Mapping	90.1	12.5
Manazuru	89.2	29.4
Yachizonishiki	88.1	2.9
Perugino	86.3	29.7
Flower of Spring	82.6	11.1
Hinomanu	82.4	44.4
Sekainozu	81.8	25.0
Dolly Varden	53.8	15.6
Miss Burdette-Coutts	51.5	34.3

Table 9.6. The absence of correlation between G × W and W × G crosses is based upon seedling results from early experiments. The correlation coefficient r = 0.04 for type Is; there were no type IIs. Adapted from Tilney-Bassett (1994).

Chimera	Percentage Maternal Plastids	
	G × W	W × G
Type I		
CH 16	99.9	10.1
Miss Burdette-Coutts	99.6	64.1
CH 15	99.4	28.6
CH 19	96.2	16.6
CH 6	93.5	25.1
Frank Headley	93.2	3.9
Lass O'Gowrie	92.9	46.3
CH 5	88.2	13.6
Dolly Varden	82.7	25.2
Type II		
CH 12	64.2	20.6
Hills of Snow	64.0	4.6
Foster's Seedling	63.5	9.9
Mrs. J.C.Mapping	60.3	20.7
CH 14	59.8	43.1
CH 2	55.9	36.0
Flower of Spring	51.1	14.3

Table 9.7. The absence of correlation between G × W and W × G crosses is based upon seedling results from my own experiments. The correlation coefficient r = 0.22 for type Is and r = 0.28 for type IIs. Adapted from Tilney-Bassett (1994).

The structure of the type II and type I populations was expanded in 1988 and finally updated in 1989 (Tilney-Bassett 1988; Tilney-Bassett and Almouslem 1989). A few hybrids between cultivars were selfed and 88 nuclear crosses were made. Altogether 11 cultivars were crossed in various ways. They were type II 'Flower of Spring', 'Foster's Seedling', 'Hills of Snow', 'Mrs J.C. Mapping', 'Pac Grosser Garten' and 'Verona'. The type I plants were 'Alde', 'Dolly Varden', 'Fleurette', 'Lass O' Gowrie' and 'Miss Burdette-Coutts'. The programme created 2601 green progeny, called families, each of which was tested for the type II or type I phenotype by crossing with variegated 'Flower of Spring' as pollen parent, and scoring the resulting embryos.

The families tested gave 1303 as type II, and 1298 as type I. The segregating populations were converted into percentages, and the estimates of the average proportion of maternal, biparental and paternal zygotes for the population of embryos borne to each family scored. For each family three values were measured – the maternal plastid percentage (maternal and biparental zygotes), the biparental percentage (biparental zygotes), and the paternal plastid percentage (biparental and paternal zygotes). The families within type II and within type I were next classified into groups with either 100% maternal plastid percentages, or with successively lower values descending in four per cent intervals, and the frequencies of each group scored. The paternal plastid percentages were grouped and their frequencies scored in similar fashion; the biparental percentages were grouped in two per cent intervals.

The type I families fell into a very skewed distribution with over 70% of them with at least some maternal plastids in every zygote. Thereafter, the frequency of families with a maternal plastid percentage less that 100% fell off steeply, and no family fell below 80%. The average family had a value of 98.7%. Almost 50% of families had zero per cent of paternal plastids. Thereafter, the frequencies of increasing paternal contribution fell off sharply at first and then more gently (Fig. 9.1). Less than 5% of families had a paternal plastid percentage above 25%, and no family reached 50%. The average family had a value of 4.7%. The ratio of maternal: paternal percentage of 98.7: 4.7 for the average family is equivalent to a maternal bias of about 21: 1.

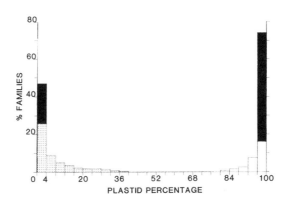

Fig. 9.1. The frequencies of 1298 type I families (G>V>W) set out with respect to the percentage of zygotes (embryos) with paternal (stippled) and with maternal (open) plastids. There are no white families with only paternal plastids, but there are many green families with 100% maternal plastids (black). The distribution shows a high preponderance of maternal and a correspondingly low proportion of paternal plastids. Adapted from Tilney-Bassett and Almouslem (1989).

The frequencies of maternal and paternal plastid percentages among type II families were normally distributed with large variances. The maternal plastid percentages fell into a range from 24% to 96% with a mode at 60-64%, and a family average of 63.2% (Fig. 9.2). The paternal plastid percentage fell into a range from 4% to 80%, with a mode at 40-44%, and a family average of 38.1%. Hence, about 85% of families expressed a maternal bias and 15% a paternal one. The ratio of maternal: paternal percentages of 63.2: 38.1 for the average family is equivalent to a maternal bias of about 5: 3.

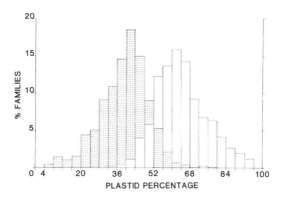

Fig. 9.2. The frequency of 1303 type II families (G>V>W) set out with respect to the percentages of zygotes (embryos) with paternal (stippled) and with maternal (open) plastids. The distributions show a large variance of both types of plastid with the mean of the maternal plastid significantly higher than the mean of the paternal plastid. Adapted from Tilney-Bassett and Almouslem (1989).

Families with variegated progeny totalled 843 (64.7%) among type IIs and 605 (46.6%) among type Is. Among families with variegated embryos, the most frequent groups were those with less that 4% of biparental zygotes. Thereafter, the frequencies of families with increasing percentages of biparental zygotes fell sharply at first and then more gently (Fig. 9.3). Only 10 families had more than 20% of biparental zygotes, which were largely from type I; no family reached as high as 40% biparental zygotes. These are the families most likely to produce variegated progeny that sort-out into green-over-white or white-over-green periclinal chimeras.

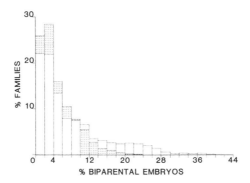

Fig. 9.3. The frequencies of 1448 families with biparental zygotes (embryos) including both type II (stippled) and type I (open) families. The distributions show that the most frequent families are those with less than 4 per cent biparental zygotes. Thereafter, the families with increasing percentages of biparental zygotes fall sharply at first and then more gently. Adapted from Tilney-Bassett and Almouslem (1989).

Within the overall data there existed a subset that enabled us to determine the linear regression of offspring on parents for the type II cultivars. The data show that the variation between cultivars was highly significant at the 0.1% level, which is indicative of significant genetic differences. It was estimated that 45.3% of variance was between and 57.3% within them. The F-ratio returned a regression significant at the 1% level. The regression coefficient was 0.62, which is an estimate of the heritability, but the 95% confidence limits varied from 0.164 to 1.076, which is a very broad band. Nevertheless it demonstrates a significant heritable component.

The selection of plastids

Plastid inheritance is biparental with maternal and paternal plastids randomly distributed in the zygote. At the first mitotic division into a larger basal cell and a smaller terminal cell both maternal and paternal plastids are again present in both cells (Guo and Hu 1995). This appears to be situation after normal fertilisation, but it tells us little about the fate of cells where there is a mixture of normal and mutant plastids. Except that it supports the general assumption that the zygote is a mixed cell receiving organelles and their genes from both parental gametes.

A very interesting and informative study is that between the six cultivars in every direction so that we have 36 G × W and 36 W × G crosses. These may also be divided into 18 type I and 18 type II crosses in each direction. If we look at the maternal plastids, these are derived from the green plastids after G × W crosses, and from the white plastids after W × G crosses. In the type I plants, after G × W crosses, the absence of one or both dominant genes from the Pr1/Pr2 genotype favours the replication of the maternal green plastids (81 – 99% maternal). This strong maternal influence is weakened in the W × G crosses, but with 'Miss Burdette-Coutts', the strongest female, they actually do better than the green plastids (55 – 72% maternal). In the type II plants, after G × W crosses, the presence of both dominant genes from the Pr1/Pr2 nuclear genotype favours the replication of neither parent. As a result, when the female contains normal plastids, these do little better than the mutant entering with the pollen parent (45 – 63% maternal). Occasionally the paternal parent is extremely favoured. Wasi'an obtained three plants from his numerous crosses that gave almost wholly white progeny (under 4% maternal) from type II plants. In the reciprocal W × G crosses, when the maternal parent has the double disadvantage of being both female and mutant the maternal transmission is very poor (2 – 21% maternal). Differences between cultivars may be seen because 'Dolly Varden' and 'Lass O' Gowrie' are weaker females than 'Miss Burdette-Coutts', and this is a reflection of their different genotypes. Similarly, 'Mrs J.C. Mappin' is a stronger female than 'Flower of Spring' or 'Foster's Seedling', but not so strong as the type I plants. We can now account for the crossing results in terms of whether nuclear and plastid genotypes are acting in the same direction, both selecting for maternal or paternal plastids, or in opposition. For example, in the cross MBC G × W FS the strong female plus the green plastids both select for the maternal plastids (over 99% maternal), whereas in the reciprocal cross FS W × G MBC the weak female parent and white plastids both select against the maternal plastid (8% maternal). Examples of nuclear and plastid genotypes being in opposition are the crosses MBC W × G FS – strong female, white plastid (64% maternal), and FS G × W MBC – weak female, green plastids (56% maternal) (Table 9.8).

Isogenic Crosses	Genotype of Maternal Parent		Maternal Plastids
	Nucleus	Plastids	Percentage
MBC G × W FS	I	Green	99.6
MBC W × G FS	I	White	64.1
FS G × W MBC	II	Green	55.6
FS W × G MBC	II	White	8.4

Table 9.8. All four are isogenic crosses. They differ as to whether the maternal nucleus is type I or type II. They also differ as to whether the maternal parent carries green or white plastids. The result from top to bottom is strong female and green plastids to weak female and white plastids.

Besides this effect of modifying genes is the presence of unlike plastids. The faster multiplying plastids of the mutant 'Dolly Varden' invariably produce more variegated embryos than the slower multiplying plastids of the mutant 'Flower of Spring'. Two other cultivars that carry the mutant plastids are 'Mrs J.C. Mapping' and 'Foster's Seedling'. They are like 'Flower of Spring'. The two mutants 'Lass O' Gowrie' and 'Miss Burdette-Coutts' have plastids like those of 'Dolly Varden'.

These are the consequences of selection. Less certain is the mechanism. The analysis of many patterns of segregation (Tilney-Bassett and Birky 1981) show that the type I are L-shaped, and the type II U-shaped and without modes or peaks, except at the end of the distribution. The peak of the input distribution may be about 50% with a slight bias in favour of one parent or the other. The problem is to explain why in type I plants we have complete, or almost complete, fixation of the maternal plastid in G × W crosses to give a typical 30: 1 ratio. While in type II plants this fixation alternates between maternal and paternal plastid to give an approximate 1: 1 ratio. When biparental zygotes are achieved, and with some genotypes they do not occur after G × W crosses with type II plants, their frequencies tend to be linear apart from an increase at the beginning of the distribution.

The distributions suggest that there is some repeated stochastic event or events occurring in zygotes and early embryos that change the initial frequencies. Such events could contribute to pure uniparental inheritance by fixing either the wild type plastid or the mutant plastid in some embryos. It would also eliminate the original Gaussian distribution of the plastids. This assumes that the population of plastids that came together in the zygote is a random mixture made up of the natural variance in numbers of male and female plastids.

What this stochastic event is we are not able to say. There are several possibilities that could account for the non-survival of mutant plastids in the type I genotypic background. The mutant plastid might fail to replicate and so within the course of a few cell divisions become diluted out. Alternatively, the mutant plastids might degenerate – not waiting for dilution, or they might be physically destroyed – not waiting for degeneration. Or, of course, their removal might be through a combination of these activities. In the case of type II plants, either the normal or the mutant might be selected for this treatment. It is almost a matter of chance, except in those few cases where the mutant almost alone is selected, and the normal receives the knock out treatment (Tilney-Bassett 1994).

There are crosses that produce high frequencies of biparental progeny with extremely high variance of green and white plastid frequencies for which we must accept a high degree of mixing of at least several plastids. It is difficult to imagine that conditions within the zygote are so variable as to virtually exclude all mixing in some cases and for it be so thorough in others especially when comparing isogenic crosses as, for example, MBC G × W FS (3% biparental) and MBC W × G FS (69% biparental), and these are not the most extreme cases. Nevertheless, the shapes of the green and white plastid frequency distributions, in which there is no mode corresponding to the mean and in which the end classes among the biparentals (0 – 20% and 80 – 100%) show a rise in frequency, is inconsistent with a thorough mixing of the plastids of the two parents. Rather it suggests that after fertilisation the two groups of plastids, from male and female parent, become mixed gradually and rarely completely by a migration of plastids between the two groups. Hence, irrespective of what changes may influence the frequency of biparentals within the zygote population, each sample of plastids that enters the terminal cell at zygote division, if it contains both kinds of plastid, invariably retain the bias towards one or other parent.

The selection of green or white plastids for replication in the zygote and in the initial mixed cell of biparental zygotes is by chance. This chance has a certain probability attached to it determined by the nuclear controlled cytoplasmic environment and by the plastid genotype and initial frequencies, but there is still a stochastic choice. When the probability of selecting a plastid is weighted in favour of one genotype, usually the green plastid, or in favour of one parent, usually the maternal one, this introduces the element of selection. The segregation and replication of plastids appears to have a strong random element, which results in random drift of plastids within single cells. This coupled with selection, leads to a fixation of plastids in some plants giving uniparental, maternal or paternal, inheritance and extremely high variance of green and white plastid frequencies among others.

References

Abdel-Wahab, O.A.L. (1979).
Genetical studies of zonal pelargoniums. Ph.D. Thesis, University College of Swansea.

Abdel-Wahab, O.A.L. and Tilney-Bassett, R.A.E. (1981).
The role of plastid competition in the control of plastid inheritance in the zonal pelargonium. Plasmid 6, 7-16.

Guo, F.L. and Hu, S.Y. (1995).
Cytological evidence of biparental inheritance of plastids and mitochondria in *Pelargonium*. Protoplasma 186, 201-207.

Hagemann, R. and Scholze, M. (1974).
Struktur und Function der genetischen Information in den Plastiden. VII. Vererbung und Entmischung genetisch unterschiedlicher Plastidensorten bei *Pelargonium zonale* Ait. Biologisches Zentralblatt 93, 625-648.

Khera, P.K. (1975).
Plastid development in zonal pelargoniums. Ph.D. Thesis. University College of Swansea.

Sokal, R.R. and Rohlf, F.J. (1969).
Biometry. W.H. Freeman and Company, San Francisco.

Tilney-Bassett, R.A.E. (1973).
The control of plastid inheritance in *Pelargonium* II. Heredity 30, 1-13.

Tilney-Bassett, R.A.E. (1974a).
A search for the rare type II (G > V < W) plastid segregation pattern among cultivars of *Pelargonium × Hortorum* Bailey. Annals of Botany 38, 1089-1092.

Tilney-Bassett, R.A.E. (1974b).
The control of plastid inheritance in *Pelargonium*. III. Heredity 33, 353-360.

Tilney-Bassett, R.A.E. (1976).
The control of plastid inheritance in *Pelargonium*. IV. Heredity 37, 95-107.

Tilney-Bassett, R.A.E. (1988).
Inheritance of plastids in *Pelargonium*. In: The division and segregation of organelles. Society for Experimental Biology Seminar Series 35, (Boffey, S.A. and Lloyd, D. eds), 115-129. Cambridge University Press, Cambridge.

Tilney-Bassett, R.A.E. (1994).
Nuclear controls of choroplast inheritance in higher plants. Journal of Heredity 85, 347-354.

Tilney-Bassett, R.A.E. and Almouslem, A.B. (1989).
Variation in plastid inheritance between pelargonium cultivars and their hybrids.
Heredity 63, 145-153.

Tilney-Bassett, R.A.E. and Birky, C.W. Jr. (1981).
The mechanism of the mixed inheritance of chloroplast genes in *Pelargonium*:
Evidence from gene frequency distributions among the progeny of crosses.
Theoretical and Applied Genetics 60, 43-53.

Wasi'an. (2000).
Studies of plastid inheritance in zonal pelargoniums.
Ph.D. Thesis, University of Wales Swansea.

10
Leaf Zonation and Flower Doubling

Leaf zonation

The zonal pelargonium is also known as the horseshoe geranium owing to the characteristic shape of the zone of dark-red pigmentation on the upper side of the leaf; the open end faces the petiole. The expression of the zone is variable and the colour intensity alters with seasonal and local environmental conditions. The variation is compounded by differences between the cultivars in depth of colour, some of which are strong and in others medium or faint. There are some cultivars in which there is a green zone; the outline of the zone is visible but there is no red colouration. It is not always clear when a faint red colouration becomes a green zone. Others show no sign of a zone; they are zoneless. Yet another character is found in cultivars in which the red pigments are diffused throughout the leaves and petioles or peduncles instead of being localised. Finally, some cultivars are completely devoid of red pigment in their leaves although they may be present on the stem.

The wide variation in the zoning, and changes in the intensity of colour, makes the different types merge into each other. How can we be sure that a green zone, which is faintly red, should indeed be classified as a green zone? Or if the green zone is poorly marked, how can we be sure that it is not a zoneless type? In a nursery collection, in which several hundred cultivars are on display, one is uncertain what some of them are. We only see the cultivar and a number of cuttings of identical genotype; we accept that we cannot be sure. We must begin by looking at cultivars with more obvious phenotypes, self them and cross them. We shall then see the different types of zonation segregate clearly from each other, and so we can be sure of the correct classification of the types we examine.

Imai (1936) found that dark purpled leaved plants on selfing segregated into 3 purple: 1 green leaved plant. When the purple stocks, or black as he called them, were backcrossed to green, the progeny segregated into 1 purple: 1 green leaved plants. Horn (1994) found that 233 progeny from 'Tip Top Dwarf Scarlet' were green, and 30 progeny from 'Sprinter' were dark. Crosses between green and dark produced 25 progeny that were dark. When selfed the dark F1 gave 168 dark and 59 green [$\chi^2 = 0.119$, df. = 1, P = 0.9-0.5]; and when the F1 was backcrossed to the recessive green parent there were 323 dark and 363 green progeny [$\chi^2 = 2.332$, df. = 1, P = 0.5-0.1]. He named the gene G/g for dark versus green leaf. In addition to the gene G, he considered that the environment, ontogenesis and possibly a modifying gene had an effect on the dark leaf.

Craig (1963) found that zoneless plants were dominant over plants with zones, and red-zoned plants were dominant over green-zoned plants. He concluded that zonation is controlled by two alleles of the zonation gene Z/z. When the recessive allele is present alone, the zone is present zz, and when the dominant allele is present ZZ or Zz, zonation is absent. Another gene V/v, which also affects flower and stigma colour, determined whether the zone is green vv or red VV and Vv. The gene Z/z is epistatic to the V/v gene so that the anthocyanin does not appear in the absence of a zone, except under unfavourable conditions, so that the interaction between the genes is of recessive epistasis. The dihybrid ratio from the zoneless F1, itself derived from a cross between zoneless and green zoned, is 12 zoneless: 3 red-zoned: 1 green-zoned.

Almouslem (1988) expanded the red-zone into four types according to the position of the zone. The zone was at the leaf edge (REZ), or it was at the leaf centre (RCZ), or it was a narrow width (RNZ), or a wide width (RWZ) of the leaf blade. He used Craig's categories of a green zone (GZ) or zoneless (ZL). He selfed all the zoned and zoneless parents, and inter crossed them in many ways. The plant with the leaf edge zone proved to be completely sterile and had to be abandoned. He found dominance relationships between the leaf zonation patterns as follows. The wide zone was dominant to the narrow zone, which was dominant over zoneless, which was dominant over the green zone. The wide zone was dominant over the centre zone. The narrow zone was dominant over zoneless, which was dominant over the green zone, and lastly the zoneless type was dominant over the green zone. In most cases clear 3: 1 ratios and 1: 1 backcross ratios were obtained, but the fit was rather poor in some crosses between the various types and the green zone. There was also a fair amount of contamination or misclassification, as the types were not always well expressed. Unfortunately, he mostly used nameless plants; the exception was 'Darlington Orange Red', which proved to be heterozygous for the wide zone and the centre zone. He did not cross the centre zone with the other types. He introduced the terminology for the wide zone Zo^w, for the narrow zone Zo^n, for the centre zone Zo^c, and for the green-zone Zo^g, and zoneless Zo^l. But he was not too sure whether they were all alleles of the same gene. The green-zone might not have been, we must remember the segregation was not very convincing. The result of these experiments was really rather curious owing to the apparent discrepancy between Almouslem and Craig with regard to zoneless. Craig found that zoneless was dominant to the zonal types, whereas Almouslem found that zoneless was recessive, the exact opposite conclusion.

Amoatey (1991) took up the challenge, and he chose the following plants for his study. 'Preston Park' has a thin dark red zone that is very peripheral, almost at the edge of the leaf. 'Dolly Varden' has the typical wide zone inside the peripheral zone towards the middle of the leaf. A narrow zone towards the middle of the leaf is represented by *P. stenopetalum*. A hybrid of ours 'WDS3' had a basal zone, previously described as centre, 'Verona' is zoneless, and *P. inquinans* is zoneless. The basal zone is the only solid zone in that there is no green tissue inside it; the petiole joins the leaf at the zone. We have thus divided the zone according to its appearance and position in the leaf as peripheral Zo^p, middle wide Zo^w, middle narrow Zo^n, basal Zo^b, and zoneless Zo^l. Besides these zonation patterns I have seen in a nursery a pattern in which the red zone is on the extreme margin of the leaf. It is therefore marginal to our peripheral zone, and on the edge of the leaf lobes. The cultivars belong to *P. x hortorum*, but *P. inquinans* is recognized as a separate species, while *P. stenopetalum* is thought to be a cultivar, possibly a hybrid between *P. zonale* and *P. scandens*, but not a distinct species (Clifton 1990), although Miller (1996) lists it as a separate species. They were all fertile. The green-zoned type was not included. The marginal zone is the same phenotype as Plavcova (1988) described as a true-breeding mutant occurring within his collection in Tschechoslowakia. After crossing with a middle wide zoned type, the F1 progeny all had middle wide zones. These then segregated in the F2 into 84 with wide zones and 29 with narrow marginal zones, in agreement with the wide zone leaf being dominant over the recessive narrow marginal zoned leaf. The backcross between the F1 and the recessive type resulted in 264 wide and 232 narrow marginal zoned leaf confirming that the F1 was truly heterozygous for one gene. We shall call it Zo^m; the homozygous marginal is $Zo^m Zo^m$, and the heterozygote with the wide allele is $Zo^w Zo^m$. The shape of the leaf with the marginal zone is more deeply lobed and more obviously crenate than the wide zoned leaf. The leaf shape of 'Preston Park' is very similar. The two features seem to segregate together, which suggests that they are pleiotropic effects of the same allele, when homozygous, or that the two characters are fairly tightly linked.

The six crosses (12 reciprocals) between the four zonal parents produced F1 progeny that were narrow or wide in the middle of the leaf blade, depending upon the allele contained within the hybrid. The three crosses that included the narrow allele produced the narrow F1 zones. These are the peripheral by narrow $Zo^p Zo^n$, the narrow by wide $Zo^n Zo^w$, and the narrow by basal $Zo^n Zo^b$. Three crosses produce the F1 wide zones: peripheral by wide $Zo^p Zo^w$, peripheral by basal $Zo^p Zo^b$, and wide by basal $Zo^w Zo^b$. The narrow by wide cross $Zo^n Zo^w$ was only slightly narrower than the wide crosses. The position of the F1 zone was towards the periphery or towards the base depending upon the alleles within. In two cases, $Zo^p Zo^w$ and $Zo^p Zo^n$, the F1 was so close to the wide or narrow parent as to be inseparable, and a segregation ratio of 3: 1 was obtained in the F2. Plavcova also reported no intermediate and obtained a 3: 1 segregation. The F1 for the other four crosses was distinguishable from both parents, and a segregation ratio of 1: 2: 1 was obtained in the F2 (Fig.10.1). All the backcrosses between the hybrids and either parent segregated in a 1: 1

ratio, except for the two hybrids that were indistinguishable from the wide or narrow parent, and they segregated in a 1: 1 ratio for the one cross between the hybrid and the recessive parent.

Zone Type	Marginal $Zo^d Zo^d$	Peripheral $Zo^p Zo^d$	Wide $Zo\,Zo$	Narrow $Zo^n Zo^n$	Basal $Zo^b Zo^b$	Zoneless $Zo'\,Zo'$
Marginal $Zo^d Zo^d$	Marginal	-	F1 Wide F2 3:1	-	-	-
Peripheral $Zo^p Zo^d$		Peripheral	F1 Wide F2 3:1	F1 Narrow F2 3:1	F1 Wide F2 1:2:1	F1 Zoned F2 1:2:1
Wide $Zo\,Zo$			Wide	F1 Narrow F2 1:2:1	F1 Wide F2 1:2:1	F1 Zoned F2 1:2:1
Narrow $Zo^n Zo^n$				Narrow	F1 Narrow F2 1:2:1	F1 Zoned F2 1:2:1
Basal $Zo^b Zo^b$					Basal	F1 Zoned F2 1:2:1
Zoneless $Zo'\,Zo'$						Zoneless

Fig.10.1. Selfs and crosses between the six alleles for zoning. The F2 segregate into 1 zoned like the parent, 2 zoned like the F1, and 1 zoned like the second parent or zoneless. The 3: 1 ratios appear when the heterozygote is too like the dominant parent.

On selfing, the zoneless plants bred true. In all our crosses between zoned and zoneless parents, irrespective of the type of zone, the F1 were zoned and the F2s segregated in a ratio of 1 zoned like the parent: 2 zoned like the F1: 1 zoneless (Amoatey and Tilney-Bassett 1993). Backcrosses between the F1 and the zoned parent segregated in a ratio of 1 zoned like the parent: 1 zoned like the F1. Backcrosses between the F1 and the zoneless parent segregated in a ratio of 1 zoned like the F1: 1 zoneless. We have no doubt that the ratios are truly indicative of the monohybrid segregation of a single gene Zo/zo, in which zonation is dominant to its absence, and the F1s are heterozygous for a pair of alternative alleles. We confirm the conclusion of Almouslem that zoned is dominant to zoneless.

The three F2 that showed segregation in a 3: 1 ratio had a hybrid that was approximately the same as the two parents. The spread was too close to the wide and to the narrow parent to separate them clearly in the F2. It is probable that dominant and recessive alleles should not be awarded in these cases, although it is clear that Almouslem did not distinguish the heterozygote. These results show that in every cross we are observing the behaviour of a single gene with alternative alleles. As there are five distinct segregation patterns, each phenotype must be determined by a separate allele of the same gene. Had there been at least two genes controlling the patterns, these would have been brought together within the matrix of crosses, and the ensuing F2 segregations would have been in a dihybrid ratio in which three or more of the parental patterns would have emerged among the same progeny. The genetic evidence shows that the zonation pattern is determined by multiple alleles of one gene, in which the presence of a zone is dominant over its absence. The most obvious expression is the dominance of the zonation pattern over its absence, where Zo is defined as any pattern:

$Zo > Zo^l$

Which may be simply expressed as:

$(Zo^m = Zo^p = Zo^w = Zo^n = Zo^b) > Zo^l$

If, however, one scores the position of the zone on the leaf, we have:

$(Zo^w = Zo^n = Zo^l) > (Zo^m = Zo^p = Zo^b)$

The complete role of Zo^l is still not very clear; there may well be more to find out about it. The marginal zone has only been crossed with the wide zone leaf so its position in the above scheme is only tentative, but it looks as if there are at least five zonation alleles present and one no zonation, a multiple allelic series of six alleles. Lastly, we still know very little about the role of the green zone; on the whole we favour a separate gene, but clearly further experimentation is necessary.

Double flowers

Along with the tendency for flowers to be more symmetrical, and larger, the double forms of the flower are very popular. No mention of double flowers occurs in Grieve's book of 1868. Victor Lemoine is reported to have observed the first mutation to semi-double flowers in 1864 (Clifford 1970; Craig 1971), so doubles were probably unknown to Grieve. Indeed, they are still quite rare among variegated plants.

The segregation among progeny, after selfing and crossing within and between singles and doubles, suggested genetic control (Ballard 1918). Barnhart (1957) observed that single flowers were true breeding, whereas semi-doubles segregated into progeny with single, semi-double and double flowers. Craig (1963) distinguished between singles with 5 petals, semi-doubles with 6 to 16 petals, and doubles with over 16 petals. He found that crosses between true breeding singles and doubles gave a uniform F1 semi-double progeny. On selfing these semi-double flowers, the progeny segregated into an apparent Mendelian 1:2:1 ratio of singles, semi-double and double flowers. On backcrossing the F1 to singles, the progeny segregated into a Mendelian 1:1 ratio of single and semi-double flowers. He came to the straightforward conclusion that single versus double flowers was determined by the alternative alleles of a gene S/s, with semi-dominance; singles were homozygous ss, semi-doubles were heterozygous Ss, and doubles were homozygous SS.

Double flowers are achieved partly by an increase in the number of petals, and partly through sepals becoming petaloid. The petaloid sepals are variable in number, abnormal in shape, and they bear green streaks where residual chloroplast containing cells are still present. The number of perianth parts is best understood by counting petals, petaloid sepals, and sepals together, as petals and sepals increased in integral multiples (Nugent and Snyder 1967). The base line of 5 petals plus 5 sepals, in a single flower, was doubled to 10 petals plus 10 sepals, of which up to 5 were petaloid, in a semi-double flower, and trebled to 15 petals plus 15 sepals, of which up to 10 were petaloid, in a double flower. Additional doubles existed that took the series up to 60 perianth parts, as in the rosebud varieties. After careful genetic analysis, Nugent and Snyder concluded that the formation of single flowers was determined by a gene D/d, when homozygous recessive dd. The recessive genotype dd, was epistatic to all other genes determining flower type. In the presence of the dominant allele DD or Dd, two changes occurred. Firstly, the presence of the D allele itself added 10 perianth parts to the base line of 10, and secondly it activated three modifying genes. Two modifying loci M1/m1 and M2/m2, each added a further 10 perianth parts when homozygous recessive m1m1 and m2m2, and a third modifying locus M3/m3, when homozygous recessive m3m3, added 20 perianth parts. The genotypes of the two parental cultivars used in their extensive analysis were 'Purple Heart', with single florets dd, M1m1, M2m2, M3m3 and 'Double White' with semi-double florets Dd, M1m1, M2M2, M3M3.

The more complicated explanation of Nugent and Snyder, compared with the simpler explanation of Craig, is essential if one is to understand how the rosebud varieties arose. But, as Nugent and Snyder proved, with their model it is also possible to obtain two different singles. The one gene model assumes that singles are all of one kind ss; in crosses with semi-doubles Ss, the progeny are expected to segregate in a ratio of 1 single: 1 semi-double. The two-gene model assumes that there are two kinds of single with genotypes dd,M1M1 and dd,M1m1. In crosses with semi-doubles Dd,M1m1, the progeny of the first cross dd,M1M1 × Dd,M1m1, are expected to segregate in a ratio of 1 single: 1 semi-double. In the progeny of the second cross dd,M1m1 × Dd,M1m1, the semi-double class is split and we obtain a ratio of 4 single: 3 semi-double: 1 double. The two-gene model was confirmed because the latter result was observed.

After crosses between the single 'Better Times' and the semi-double 'Rheinlands Gloria', Badr and Horn (1971) concluded that their results confirmed those of Craig, and Nugent and Snyder. This was not quite correct as Badr and Horn overlooked the additional data of Nugent and Snyder proving the existence of a second single genotype, and the 4: 3: 1 ratio to which it gave rise. Moreover, it follows from this model that the F1 hybrid is not a single heterozygote Ss, but a double heterozygote Dd,M1m1. This will give rise to the modified dihybrid ratio of 9 semi-double: 3 double: 4 single, and not the monohybrid ratio of 2 semi-double: 1 double: 1 single as predicted by the single gene model. In fact the probability of the single flowered plants is the same in both cases- 4 out of 16 and 1 out of 4. So the difference between them is between 9 D-,M1-: 3 D-,m1M1 on the one hand, and between 2 Ss: 1 SS on the other. The ratio of semi-double: doubles will have to be accurately scored, and even then, according to Mather (1951), we shall need as many as 319 plants after selfing the heterozygote in order to be 95% certain of distinguishing between these rather close ratios.

The number of plants needed to distinguish the ratios was not reached by any of the authors, and their data showed a reasonable fit with either. In an experiment involving a number of single cultivars, and 'Darlington Red' and four seedlings as a source of semi-double cultivars, Almouslem and Tilney-Bassett (1989) increased the population size. It was not enough, but when added to the three results of the previous authors the pooled chi-square value was 0.497 for agreement with the 9: 3: 4 ratio (P = 0.9 – 0.5) and 14.005 for agreement with the 2: 1: 1 ratio (P = < 0.001). They clearly fitted only the dihybrid segregation. The data received further support from Wu (1999) who looked at 20 semi-double cultivars. These she selfed, and their progeny segregated into singles, semi-doubles and double flowers. The flowers were scored as follows:

Singles. flowers with 10, or rarely 11, perianth parts consisting of 5 sepals and 5 petals or rarely 6 petals. Single extra petals were not uncommon, and so two samples with an average of 11 perianth parts were also scored as singles.

Semi-doubles. flowers with 12 to 20 perianth parts consisting of mostly 5 or 6 sepals and the remainder petals and petaloid parts. Sometimes the proportion of sepals was higher.

Doubles. flowers with 21 to 30 perianth parts consisting of from 5 up to 12 sepals and the remainder petals and petaloid parts.

If we take the score of these cultivars and add them to the previous total, we have 402 semi-doubles, 134 full doubles and 170 singles, a total of 706 altogether. The number of singles is very close to expectation. The chi-square for the 9: 3: 4 ratio is 0.319 (P = 0.9 – 0.5), and that for the 2: 1: 1 ratio is 17.275 (P = < 0.001). Hence the agreement is very good for the two-gene model, and very poor for the one gene model. Nevertheless, we suspect that other genes are needed to account for the differences between the cultivars, as for example between the numbers of sepals.

We did not score many plants from each cultivar, and we had to exclude some, and sometimes we scored too few plants to obtain other than singles and semi-doubles; these were 'Brazil', 'Esprit', 'Lilac Mist' and 'Pink Satisfaction'. There were three more cultivars with high counts, these were 'Duke of Devonshire', 'Henry Jacoby' and 'Kardino'; they were treated as semi-doubles. Among the doubles were plants from 'Arsona', 'Blues', 'Boogy', 'Cecille' and 'Regalia', with scores between 21 and 30. Finally, we had offspring from two cultivars producing scores of 32 to 37 perianth parts; these were 'Magic' and 'Red Satisfaction'. We may assume that the semi-double plants had the genetic constitution D-, M1-,M2-,M3- (9/16), the double plants D-,m1m1,M2-,M3- (3/16), and the two with over 31 perianth parts D-,m1m1,m2m2,M3- (3/64). We did not have any plants with the constitution D-,m1m1,m2m2,m3m3, which would have been expected with a probability of one quarter times the last frequency (3/256); this would have from 41 up to 60 parts or more, a real rosebud cultivar. As we scored only 706 plants, this was hardly surprising, but we might have obtained one or two even from our 141 plants.

We noted also that with semi-doubles the sepals hardly altered at all, but with an individual from 'Kardino' they reached 7 sepals, and with individuals from 'Cecille' and 'Magic' they reached 10 sepals. Generally speaking the sepals only increased their numbers in the full doubles, but with individual doubles from 'Magic' and 'Mayne' the sepals were completely stable, having 5 sepals in both. Thus different individuals among the offspring of 'Magic' had widely different stabilities with regard to increase in sepals when the flowers became semi-double, or double. It is obvious that the causes of the variability in parents between individuals of the same cultivar are not yet understood. Comparison between fewer cultivars with more flowers counted will help to throw light on the problem.

The feature that most clearly distinguishes the *Pelargonium* flower from the flowers of other genera of the same family, Geraniaceae (Moore 1971), is the spur. At the base of the uppermost sepal of the calyx of five sepals there is a nectariferous spur adnate to the pedicel (Chittenden 1951). Sometimes in the zonal pelargonium this nectar bearing tube is several cms long and runs almost the whole length of the pedicel, but in other cases it is of intermediate length, or is quite shallow (Clifford 1970; Moore 1971). Almouslem and Tilney-Bassett (1989) crossed the semi-double flowered 'Darlington Red' without spurs, with eight single flowered and spurred plants. They obtained an excellent fit with the 1:1 ratio ($\chi^2 = 0.083$, P = 0.9 – 0.5) by observing 219 spur-less semi-double plants and 213 spurred single flowered plants. The presence or absence of a spur exactly matched the presence of single flowered or semi-double flowered progeny. The presence or absence of a spur appears to be a pleiotropic effect of the locus D/d, or to factors closely linked to it. It will be interesting to know if any recombinant types have been observed. These may be either single flowers without a spur, or semi-double or double flowers with a spur.

Sections through the petioles of single flowers revealed two types of spur (Almouslem 1988). Either the nectary tube had a single bore, or there were closely parallel twin bores. The twin-bored type was the more common, but the genetic relationship awaits investigation.

References

Almouslem, A.B. (1988).
Qualitative and quantitative genetical studies in *Pelargonium x Hortorum* Bailey.
Ph.D. Thesis, University of Swansea, Wales.

Almouslem, A.B. and Tilney-Bassett, R.A.E. (1989).
The inheritance of flower doubleness and nectary spur in *Pelargonium x hortorum* Bailey. Euphytica 41, 23-29.

Amoatey, H.M. (1991).
Genetic studies in zonal pelargoniums. Ph.D. Thesis, University College of Swansea, Wales.

Amoatey, H.M. and Tilney-Bassett, R.A.E. (1993).
Multiple alleles and the control of leaf zonation patterns in zonal pelargoniums. Journal of Horticultural Science 68, 45-52.

Badr, M. and Horn, W. (1971).
Genetische Untersuchungen an diploiden und tetraploiden *Pelargonium zonale*-Hybriden. Zeitschrift fur Pflanzenzuchtung 66, 203-220.

Ballard, W.R. (1918).
Notes on geranium breeding. Proceedings American Society Horticultural Science 15, 62-65.

Barnhart, D. (1957).
Preliminary observations on a geranium breeding project. Geraniums Around the World 5, 15-16.

Chittenden, F.J. (1951).
Ed. The Royal Horticultural Society Dictionary of Gardening: A Practical and Scientific Encyclopaedia of Horticulture. Vol. III: JE-PT. Clarendon Press, Oxford.

Clifford, D. (1970).
Pelargoniums, including the popular geranium, a monograph. 2nd. ed. Blandford Press, London.

Clifton, R.T.F. (1990).
Geranium Family Species Check List. 4th ed. Part 4. *Pelargonium*. Compiled for the Geraniaceae Group of The British Pelargonium and Geranium Society.

Craig, R. (1963).
The inheritance of several characters in geranium, *Pelargonium × hortorum* Bailey. Ph.D. Thesis, Pennsylvania State University, USA.

Craig, R. (1971).
Cytology, genetics and breeding. In: J.W. Mastalerz (Ed). Geraniums. A Manual on the Culture, Disease, Insects, Economics, Taxonomy and Breeding of Geraniums, 2nd ed., 315-346. Pennsylvania Flower Growers, USA.

Imai, Y. (1936).
Geno- and plasmotypes of variegated pelargoniums. Journal of Genetics 33, 169-195.

Mather, K. (1951).
The measurement of linkage in heredity. Methuen and Co. Ltd., London.

Miller, D. (1996).
Pelargoniums a gardener's guide to the species and their cultivars and hybrids. B.T. Batsford Ltd. London.

Moore, H.E. (1971).
Taxonomy of pelargoniums in cultivation. In: J.W. Masterlerz (Ed.). Geraniums. A Manual on the Culture, Disease, Insects, Economics, Taxonomy and Breeding of Geraniums, 2nd ed., 14-52. Pennsylvania Flower Growers, USA.

Nugent, P.E. and Snyder, R.J. (1967).
The inheritance of floret doubleness, floret center colour, and plant habit in *Pelargonium hortorum* Bailey. Proceedings American Society Horticultural Science 91, 680-690.

Plavcova, O. (1988).
Vererbung einer engen Randzeichnung auf den Blättern bei *Pelargonium zonale* hort.
Acta Prühoniciana 55, 25-36.

Wu, G.F. (1999).
The genetics and biochemistry of flower pigments and flower patterns in *Pelargonium* × *hortorum*. Ph.D.Thesis, University of Wales Swansea.

11
Flower Colour

The genetics of full coloured flowers

The zonal pelargoniums are known, above all else, for their brilliant blooms flowering all through the summer and into the autumn. The variegated-leaved pelargoniums are, for the most part, equally floriferous. The breeder wants a good bloom as well as variegated leaves. Indeed, to create the great variety of plants, the breeder must select from among the very wide variation of flowers. My studies do not delve very far into the large numbers of different genes that must be involved, but they make a beginning upon which further progress will be made.

The American horticulturist Craig (1963) began the systematic investigation of flower colour by identifying two genes that in their dominant form produced red flowers. These he symbolised as P/p and Sa/sa because in their recessive state they produced pink and salmon flowers. Badr and Horn (1971) labelled them A/a and B/b. Almouslem *et al.* (1991) appreciated that the inheritance of red flower colour was controlled by the interaction of two complementary genes, and to emphasise the relationship we termed them R1/r1 and R2/r2 (Almouslem *et al.* 1991). These genes are equivalent to P/p (A/a) and Sa/sa (B/b). Almouslem (1988) could not agree that salmon and pink flower colours were determined by homozygous recessives to red. Instead he believed that dominant genes controlled salmon and pink. He believed that the homozygous recessives were inactive; so that when the genotype was r1r1 (pp or aa) a dominant gene Sa that determined the salmon phenotype was expressed. Similarly, when the genotype was r2r2 (sasa or bb) a dominant gene P that determined the pink phenotype was now expressed. At first he was uncertain whether the two dominant alleles R1 and R2 were the same as P and Sa, or additional to them, so we proceeded to analyse the results in terms of the R alleles alone (Almouslem *et al.* 1991).

We took 20 red flowered cultivars and 10 variegated, patterned or white cultivars plus a few hybrids. The non-red flowered cultivars included salmon, pink and some white flowers. The red flowered cultivars, after extensive self and cross pollinations, showed that there were four kinds of red cultivars as follows:
- (i)   All progeny red flowered.
- (ii)   All progeny red flowered, or they segregated into a monohybrid ratio of 3 red: 1 non-red.
- (iii)   All progeny red flowered, or they segregated into a monohybrid ratio of 3 red: 1 non-red. When the non-red progeny of groups (ii) and (iii) were crossed together, they complemented each

other producing red flowers proving that the parents were heterozygous for different genes.

(iv)   All progeny red flowered, or they segregated into a monohybrid ratio of 3 red: 1 non-red, or they segregated into a modified dihybrid ratio of 9 red: 7 non-red.

These results indicated that cultivars of the first kind were homozygous dominant; they included 'Eclipse' and 'Lass O'Gowrie'. The cultivars of the second kind were heterozygous for a single gene; they included 'Alde', 'Benedict', 'Dolly Varden', 'Dryden', 'Marmalade', and 'Mr Wren'. The cultivars of the alternative heterozygote were 'Foster's Seedling', 'Hills of Snow', and 'Vera Dillon'. The cultivars of the double heterozygote were 'Fleurette', 'Flower of Spring', 'Jennifer', 'Miss Burdette-Coutts', 'Mrs J.C. Mapping' and 'Pac Grosser Garten'.

The complementary nature of the two R genes was thus confirmed. The four groups were labelled red A R1R1,R2R2, red B R1r1,R2R2, red C R1R1,R2r2 and red D R1r1,R2r2. It is well known that if we have two genes each with two alleles they form nine genotypes. Four of these are the red genotypes, leaving five non-red. They were labelled non-red E r1r1,R2R2, F r1r1,R2r2, G R2R2,r1r1, H R2r2,r1r1 and I r1r1,r2r2. When the non-red patterned, variegated and pure white parental cultivars were selfed or inter-crossed, there was no segregation for red flowers among the progeny, which indicated that they contained no genotypes complementary to each other. When these non-red genotypes were crossed with plants of the red groups, we obtained frequencies of red: non-red progeny in good agreement with all red, 3 red: 1 non-red, 1 red: 1 non-red, 3 red: 5 non-red, and 1 red: 3 non-red ratios. In fact all the ratios that could be predicted. As the variegated, patterned or white cultivars were crossed with all four red groups, we obtained four kinds of result each of which contributed to the deduction of the non-red genotypes as follows:

(i)   Red A. All were red progeny. Therefore non-reds belonged to any group E to I.

(ii)   Red B. All segregated 1 red: 1 non-red ratio. Therefore non-reds belonged to groups E, F or I.

(iii)   Red C. Either they segregated 3 red: 1 non-red, or 1 red: 1 non-red ratio. Therefore non-red belonged to groups F, G, H or I.

(iv)   Red D. Either they segregated 3 red: 5 non-red, or 1 red: 3 non-red ratio. Therefore non-reds belonged to groups F, H or I.

The analysis shows that the only fit with the four reds is if the non-red groups belonged to group F or I. So we have 'Andromeda', 'Eggshell', 'Jay' and 'Lady Alice of Valencia' belonged to group F r1r1,R2r2 and the white cultivars 'Percival', 'Snowball' and 'Snowstorm' belonged to group I r1r1,r2r2. We also obtained some data from selfing pink cultivars, and crossing these with red A and red B. The resulting segregation patterns proved sufficient to indicate that the rose pink 'Verona' belonged to the non-red group G R1R1,r2r2 and the rose-pink male sterile hybrid MS1H belonged to group H R1r1,r2r2.

In the meantime, Kabwazi, a former MSc student (1986), who later moved to Cambridge, showed that there were only two genes involved, and not four, which he also symbolized as R1/r1 and R2/r2 (Kabwazi 1993). We now recognized the results of our selfs and crosses showing the characterisation of the non-reds into salmon, rose pink, and soft pink colours. Thus, when the genotype is homozygous r1r1 the dominant R2 is expressed making the salmon phenotype, and when the genotype is homozygous r2r2 the dominant R1 is expressed making the rose pink phenotype. This meant that E and F were salmon, G and H were rose pink, and I the double recessive r1r1,r2r2 was not totally inactive but had a soft pink colour. We set out a matrix showing all the 45 possible consequences of selfing or crossing these nine genotypes, and noting the various ratios and colours that we would expect (Fig. 11.1). We then analysed our data from 32 of the selfs and crosses. We found that we had all nine genotypes, and these confirmed reasonably well with the predicted results. In addition to the cultivars already mentioned we added data from five more cultivars and several hybrids. 'Paul Crampel' was red A, 'Single New Life' was red B, 'A Happy Thought' was red C, 'Preston Park' was salmon E, and 'Alpine Glow' was salmon F. In addition, we altered the green form of 'Foster's Seedling' to rose pink G, and the green form of 'Mrs J.C. Mapping' was now interpreted as soft pink I.

Thus red A R1R1,R2R2 on selfing gave only red progeny, while all the other reds segregated. Red B R1r1,R2R2 segregated 3 red: 1 salmon, red C R1R1,R2r2 segregated 3 red: 1 rose pink, and red D R1r1,R2r2 segregated 9 red: 3 salmon: 3 rose pink: 1 soft pink. On selfing the non-red colours salmon E r1r1,R2R2 gave all salmon, and salmon F r1r1,R2r2 segregated 3 salmon: 1 soft pink. Similarly, rose pink G R1R1,r2r2 gave all rose pink, and rose pink H R1r1,r2r2 segregated 3 rose pink: 1 soft pink. Finally, soft pink I r1r1,r2r2 gave all soft pink. The single backcrosses either did not segregate, or they segregated 1 red: 1 salmon, or 1 red: 1 rose pink, or 1 salmon: 1 soft pink, or 1 rose pink: 1 soft pink. The double backcrosses salmon F × red D segregated 3 red: 3 salmon: 1 rose pink: 1 soft pink, and rose pink H × red D segregated 3 red: 3 rose pink: 1 salmon: 1 soft pink. Finally, the backcrosses rose pink H × salmon F and soft pink I × red D segregated 1 red: 1 salmon: 1 rose pink: 1 soft pink (Fig. 11.1).

Phenotypes and Genotypes	Red A R1R1 R2R2	Red B R1r1 R2R2	Red C R1R1 R2r2	Red D R1r1 R2r2	Salmon E r1r1 R2R2	Salmon F r1r1 R2r2	Rose Pink G R1R1 r2r2	Rose Pink H R1r1 r2r2	Soft Pink I r1r1 r2r2
Red A R1R1 R2R2	All Red	All Red	All Red	All Red	All Red	All Red	All Red	All Red	All Red
Red B R1r1 R2R2	-	3 Red 1 Salmon	All Red	3 Red 1 Salmon	1 Red 1 Salmon	1 Red 1 Salmon	All Red	3 Red 1 Salmon	1 Red 1 Salmon
Red C R1R1 R2r2	-	-	3 Red 1 Rose-p	3 Red 1 Rose-p	All Red	3 Red 1 Rose-p	1 Red 1 Rose-p	1 Red 1 Rose-p	1 Red 1 Rose-p
Red D R1r1 R2r2	-	-	-	9 Red 3 Salmon 3 Rose-p 1 Soft pink	1 Red 1 Salmon	3 Red 3 Salmon 1 Rose-p 1 Soft pink	1 Red 1 Rose-p	3 Red 1 Salmon 1 Rose-p 1 Soft pink	1 Red 1 Salmon 1 Rose-p 1 Soft pink
Salmon E r1r1 R2R2	-	-	-	-	All Salmon	All Salmon	All Red	1 Red 1 Salmon	All Salmon
Salmon F r1r1 R2r2	-	-	-	-	-	3 Salmon 1 Soft pink	1 Red 1 Rose-p	1 Red 1 Salmon 1 Rose-p 1 Soft pink	1 Salmon 1 Soft pink
Rose-p G R1R1 r2r2	-	-	-	-	-	-	All Rose-p	All Rose-p	All Rose-p
Rose-p H R1r1 r2r2	-	-	-	-	-	-	-	3 Rose-p 1 Soft pink	1 Rose-p 1 Soft pink
Soft-p I r1r1 r2r2	-	-	-	-	-	-	-	-	All Soft pink

Fig. 11.1 Matrix of phenotypic ratios of red, salmon, rose-pink and soft-pink progeny after selfs and crosses according to the complementary gene model of flower colour inheritance. Adapted from Tilney-Bassett *et al.* (1995).

We can now interpret the genotypes of the cultivars used by Badr and Horn (1971) as 'Bergfeuer' red B, 'Better Times', 'Rheinlands Gloria' and 'Rheinlands Perle' as red C, salmon as salmon F, and the white as soft pink I. Badr and Horn had assumed that salmon and rose pink were both recessive genes instead of two dominant genes having complementary gene action. They also identified a third gene C/c that controls the colour intensity of the flowers, especially the rose coloured flowers. They obtained the segregation of 3 red: 1 pale rose; if pale rose is interpreted as soft pink I do not recognise it. The segregation should be 3 rose: 1 pale rose, or rather 3 rose pink: 1 soft pink. The third gene is probably the same gene as gives light red and dark red namely D/d.

Four of the variegated cultivars were also chimeras for flower colour. In these chimeras the epidermis, which is responsible for the colour of the petals, is different. The phenotype of the variegated plant appears equivalent to the genotype of the epidermis. It is red with 'Miss Burdette-Coutts', rose pink with 'Foster's Seedling' and 'Hills of Snow' and soft pink with 'Mrs J.C. Mapping'. But to account for their genotype, as gathered from breeding evidence, changes are necessary. 'Miss Burdette-Coutts' underwent a single mutation in L II of R2 to r2, so red B changes to red

D in L II. 'Foster's Seedling' and 'Hills of Snow' have undergone a single mutation in L I, so red C changed to rose pink G in L I. 'Mrs J.C. Mapping' has undergone two mutations, R2 to r2 and R1 to r1, so red D changed to soft pink I in L I. In every case we assume that the direction of mutation was from the dominant to the recessive allele (Tilney-Bassett *et al.* 1995) (Fig. 11.2).

W/G Cultivar	L I Epidermis Flower colour	L II Sub-epidermis Germ layer	Mutation Layer and gene
Miss Burdette Coutts	Red B	Red D	L II
	R1r1,R2R2	**R1r1,R2r2**	**R2 to r2**
Mrs. J.C. Mapping	Soft-pink I	Red D	L I
	r1r1,r2r2	**R1r1,R2r2**	**R1 to r1 & R2 to r2**
Foster's Seedling	Rose-pink G	Red C	L I
	R1R1,r2r2	**R1R1,R2r2**	**R2 to r2**
Hills of Snow	Rose-pink G	Red C	L I
	R1R1,r2r2	**R1R1,R2r2**	**R2 to r2**

Fig. 11.2. The four flower chimeras result from changes to the genotype of LII and LI causing the germ layer to be of a different genotype to the epidermal layer. Adapted from Tilney-Bassett *et al.* (1995)

We had some difficulty distinguishing the colours of the segregating progeny. There were several reasons for this. We were not using pure-breeding lines, so other colours sometimes caused some confusion, particularly whites. The white often lightened the colour so we were confused as to whether soft pink was really rose pink or salmon. Sometimes, we were confused as to whether rose pink was really salmon, or whether salmon was really red. Our difficulty was greatly eased when we realised that the colours either did not segregate, or they segregated for two colours, or four colours. They never segregated for three colours; salmon and rose pink never appeared together unless all four colours were segregating. Another difficulty was that we could not score all segregating progeny at the same time. These were seedlings, not cuttings, and often a plant would flower once and then no more. We had to score the colour often without reference to the other segregants coming to flower later. The RHS colour charts were very useful, but they were not always a good representation of the actual colours the flower presented.

Munchi and Tilney-Bassett (unpublished) made a number of selfs and crosses to investigate the inheritance of white flower colours. As coloured parents they used 'Preston Park' with salmon flowers [52C], 'Darlington Orange Red' with light red flowers [43C/D, 44D], and 'Flower of Spring' also with light red flowers [40A]. Selfing showed that 'Preston Park' was a salmon E r1r1,R2R2, 'Darlington Orange Red' was a red B R1r1,R2R2 and 'Flower of Spring' was a red D R1r1,R2r2 genotype. The white flowers were

Crosses	Salmon	Soft-Pink	White	Total	Ratio Tested	χ^2	d.f.	P
PP selfed	43	-	-	43	-	-	-	-
SS selfed	-	-	36	36	-	-	-	-
PP × SS: F1	41	-	-	41	-	-	-	-
PP × SS: F2 + F3	102	32	13	147	12: 3: 1	2.914	2	0.5-0.1
(PP × SS) F1 × SS	28	15	8	51	2: 1: 1	2.412	2	0.5-0.1
F2 salmon selfed	21	9	-	30	3: 1	0.400	1	0.9-0.5
F2 salmon × SS	25	24	-	49	1: 1	0.020	1	0.9-0.5
F2 soft-p selfed	-	18	11	29	3: 1	2.586	1	0.5-0.1
F2 soft-p × SS	-	25	31	56	1: 1	0.643	1	0.5-0.1
F2 white selfed	-	-	23	23	-	-	-	-
F2 white × SS	-	-	27	27	-	-	-	-

Table 11.1. Segregation data after crosses within and between salmon flowered 'Preston Park' and white flowered 'Snowstorm', and tests of goodness of fit between observed segregations and expected Mendelian ratios. From Munchi and Tilney-Bassett (unpublished).

the single flowered 'Snowstorm', and the double flowered 'Snowball', with the soft pink I genotype r1r1,r2r2. These produced pure white flowers on selfing. On selfing the coloured parents they segregated as expected from their genotypes.

The backcross between 'Snowstorm' and the F1 between 'Preston Park' and 'Snowstorm' segregated into a dihybrid ratio of 2 salmon: 1 soft pink: 1 white, while the F2 and a selection of the F3 segregated into a dihybrid ratio of 12 salmon: 3 soft pink: 1 white. Further selfing and backcrossing of selected salmon components segregated into 3 salmon: 1 soft pink and 1 salmon: 1 soft pink, and the selected soft pink component segregated into 3 soft pink: 1 white, and 1 soft pink: 1 white; all these ratios being obtained with a good fit (Table 11.1). Similarly, the F1 salmon between 'Darlington Orange Red' and 'Snowstorm' was selected, and segregated in a F2 dihybrid ratio of 12 salmon: 3 soft pink: 1 white, and a backcross to 'Snowstorm' in a ratio of 2 salmon: 1 soft pink: 1 white (Table 11.2). Likewise when 'Flower of Spring' was crossed with 'Snowball' a red F1 hybrid segregated in a trihybrid ratio of 36 red: 12 salmon: 12 rose pink: 3 soft pink: 1 white, while the backcross with 'Snowball' segregated into a trihybrid ratio of 2 red: 2 salmon: 2 rose pink: 1 soft pink: 1 white. Other tests were made using salmon F1 that resulted in a 12: 3: 1 ratio, and the backcross that resulted in a 2: 1: 1 ratio. Similarly, the self of the rose pink F1 resulted in a 12: 3: 1 ratio, and the backcross resulted in a 2: 1: 1 ratio (Table 11.3).

Crosses	Red	Salmon	Soft-Pink	White	Total	Ratio Tested	χ^2	d.f.	P
DOR selfed	18	3	-	-	21	3: 1	1.286	1	0.5-0.1
SS selfed	-	-	-	36	36	-	-	-	-
F1 salmon Selected Selfed	-	102	26	8	136	12: 3: 1	0.039	2	1.0-0.9
F1 salmon Selected × SS	-	25	18	14	57	2: 1: 1	1.421	2	0.5-0.1

Table 11.2. Segregation data after crosses within and between red flowered 'Darlington Orange Red' and white flowered 'Snowstorm', and tests of goodness of fit between observed segregation and expected Mendelian ratios. From Munchi and Tilney-Bassett (unpublished).

In each case the white segregates only as the most recessive of the genotypes. The trihybrid ratio 36:12: 12: 3: 1 is like the classical dihybrid 9: 3: 3: 1 ratio, except that the smallest class of progeny is subdivided into a ratio of 3 soft pink: 1 white progeny. Likewise, when the selected red plant was backcrossed to 'Snowball' the progeny segregated in a trihybrid ratio of 2: 2: 2: 1: 1, which is like the classical 1: 1: 1: 1 ratio, except that the soft pink class is subdivided into a ratio of 1 soft pink: 1 white progeny. The observation of these two trihybrid ratios, or the dihybrid ratios in this and the first two examples, or indeed the monohybrid ratios is confirmation for the existence of the W/w gene. The segregating ratios indicate that the selected red flowered plant had the genotype R1r1,R2r2,Ww and 'Snowball' or 'Snowstorm' the genotype r1r1,r2r2,ww with respect to the three genes.

Crosses	Red	Salmon	Rose-Pink	Soft-Pink	White	Total	Ratio Tested	χ^2	d.f.	P
FS selfed	44	(7	12	-)	-	63	9: 7	4.729	1	0.05-0.01
SB selfed	-	-	-	-	11	11	-	-	-	-
FS × SB: BC	10	8	9	7	-	34	1: 1: 1: 1	0.588	3	0.9-0.5
Red BC selfed	38	16	13	7	3	77	36: 12: 12: 3: 1	4.388	4	0.5-0.3
Salmon BC selfed	-	44	-	19	2	65	12: 3: 1	4.239	2	0.2-0.1
Rose-p BC selfed	-	-	29	16	4	49	12: 3: 1	5.823	2	0.1-0.05
Soft-p BC selfed	-	-	-	(21	-)	21	-	-	-	-
Red BC × SB	21	24	29	9	9	92	2: 2: 2: 1: 1	2.300	4	0.7-0.5
Salmon BC × SB	-	19	-	6	6	31	2: 1: 1	1.880	2	0.5-0.3
Rose-p BC × SB	-	-	37	(28	-)	65	1: 1	0.980	1	0.5-0.3
Soft-p BC × SB	-	-	-	(26	-)	26	-	-	-	-

Table 11.3. Segregation data after crosses within and between red flowered 'Flower of Spring' and white flowered 'Snowball', and tests of goodness of fit between observed segregation and expected Mendelian ratios. The brackets enclosing numbers indicate that both colours were present but they were not scored separately. From Munchi and Tilney-Bassett (unpublished).

It is worth mentioning that in the case of the trihybrid ratio only one white seedling is expected out of every 64 seedlings, so a fairly large progeny is required. On the other hand, with the backcross trihybrid ratio we expect one white seedling in every eight seedlings, so the progeny size need not be so large. The salmon flowers from the cross between 'Preston Park' and 'Snowstorm' were variable and ranged from a few with light red flowers [47D], a majority with the full salmon colour, and a minority of the "bull's eye" type with a salmon centre and a broad white rim to the petals. The soft pink flowers were a light pink [62D, 65D or 75D], or were white with traces of pink in the petals, and with red or lightly coloured stigmas. The white flowers had no colour at all, or merely traces of colour, particularly in the veins, developing with age, and they had white stigmas. On selfing these whites, the resulting white flowers showed no sign of colouration.

The salmon flowers from the cross between 'Preston Park' and 'Snowstorm' backcrossed to 'Snowstorm' again included a rare red [43B], strong salmon [52B], weaker salmon [52C], and a washy salmon [52D]. Presumably the latter weak salmon represent the effect of the homozygous white gene ww, and the stronger salmon the heterozygous white gene Ww. The rare red flower in this and other crosses represents the other extreme. Analysis of the pigments showed they had the same composition as the salmon, but were just a little denser. They were not of a distinct genotype to the salmon. The peduncles were often pigmented, likewise the petioles, and occasionally the sepals; the dark coloured vegetative parts appeared to be associated with the darker flowers or red zoning among the leaves.

Besides the four colours produced by the two genes of the red loci there were more colours to be accounted for. Orange flowers first entered the literature in 1990; they appeared in the F2 progeny from a cross between 'Maxim Kovalevski' and 'Robin Hood'. The orange flowers were selected until true breeding and then crossed with crimson, deep and light salmon, rose white and with pure white flower colours (Pan *et al.* 1990). F2 and backcross progenies were obtained; chi-square tests supported the segregation of all ratios. With crimson, or red, flowers the F1 were crimson [47B], and the F2 segregated 3 crimson [46B]: 1 orange [33B], and the backcross to orange segregated 1 crimson [47B]: 1 orange. Evidently a homozygous recessive gene determined orange, it was designated as the orange gene Or/or. When crossed with rose white flowers [57B], the F1 was red orange [40A] and the F2 segregated in a 1: 2: 1 ratio of orange, red orange and rose white flowers showing that under the influence of orange the R2r2 heterozygote [40A] could be distinguished from the homozygote R2R2 [33B]. These two orange colours are quite similar to each other and might easily be confused. I have replaced the P/p and Sa/sa symbolism with the R1/r1 and R2/r2 symbolism as appropriate.

When orange and white flowers were crossed the F1 was peach [52C], and the F2 segregated in a 1: 2: 1 ratio of orange, peach and white. The two backcrosses segregated in a ratio of 1 peach: 1 orange and 1 peach: 1 white. The segregation was interpreted as wholly owing to the white gene W/w. This appears justified as there was no appearance of rose pink, salmon and pale pink in the F2, which one would have expected if the white genotype was oror,r1r1,r2r2,ww and the orange genotype was oror,R1R1,R2R2,WW, and the F1 was oror,R1r1,R2r2,Ww. Instead they suggested the genotype oror,R1R1,R2R2,ww for the white parent. This means that this white gene, when homozygous recessive, is completely suppressing the two red genes in the white parent, and is therefore not the same as we have previously encountered. It may be a mutation of another gene, or perhaps it is a fourth allele of the white splash gene, full colour V, white splash V^{ws}, picotee V^p, and now white V^w, (see later) but this is merely speculation.

The cross between orange and deep salmon [39B], or between orange and light salmon [48C], both resulted in a single F1 with red orange flower colour [40A]. The backcrosses were 1: 1 ratios of red orange and orange, or red orange and deep salmon, or red orange and light salmon. The F2 resulted in two 9: 3: 4 ratios of red orange, orange and deep salmon, and red orange, orange and light salmon. These are modified dihybrid ratios with recessive epistasis, in which two genes are segregating. The authors proposed that a gene I interacts with the R1 gene to give red orange flowers R1-,I-, but when the I/i gene is homozygous recessive R1-,ii pure orange flowers result. In the absence of the dominant R1 gene r1r1,R2R2 recessive epistasis takes its effect and the I/i gene has no influence; the flower colour is salmon. Whether the salmon is deep [39B] or light [48C] is dependent upon alternative alleles of the salmon gene; r1r1,R2R2 is deep salmon and r1'r1',R2R2 is light salmon. This is a proposal for triple alleles at the R1/r1 gene. We do not know what is the relationship between r1r1 and r1'r1' as they have not been crossed with each other.

Purple flowers were known, but not well understood, and a gene for crimson was recognized first by Pan *et al.* (1990) and then by Kabwazi (1993). The five genes R1/r1, R2/r2, Cr/cr, Pu/pu and Or/or were responsible for ten colours, crimson, red, orange, magenta, light crimson, purple pink, rose pink, salmon, soft pink and pale pink (Fig. 11.3). If we take the soft pink group r1r1,r2r2 we see that the effect of the orange gene Or/or, is to make the difference between soft pink Or-, and pale pink oror. The salmon group r1r1,R2- is unaffected by the other genes present; R2- in the presence of r1r1 is epistatic to all the other genes. The pink group R1-,r2r2 is either purple pink, when dominant Pu is present, or rose pink when recessive pupu is present unless recessive oror is also present when the colour changes again to pale pink. When both dominant red genes are present R1-,R2-, the purple gene Pu/pu is responsible for the difference between crimson and red, and between magenta and light crimson; recessive r1r1 is epistatic to Pu in all circumstances. Again, when R1-,R2- is present, the colour of the flowers depends on whether the three alleles are dominant, or whether one or two are recessive, or indifferent. So we have crimson Cr-,Or-,Pu or Cr-,oror,Pu-, Or/or is indifferent; red Cr-,Or-,pupu; magenta crcr,Or-,Pu- or crcr,oror,Pu-, Or/or is again indifferent; light crimson crcr,Or-,pupu; and orange Cr-,oror,pupu or crcr,oror,pupu, Cr/cr is indifferent (Fig. 11.3). As a rough guide to the colours we found the RHS colour chart gives the following hints: orange 32A 33A; red 40A/B, 43A/B, 44A/B, 45A/B; salmon 43C/D; pale pink and rose pink 48D, 52D; crimson 45A/B, 50A/B/C; light crimson 52A/B/C; magenta 57A/B/C; rose pink 66A/B/C, 67B/C/D; and purple pink 68A/B, 73A/B, 74A/B. The range of variation in colours is quite considerable.

Genotypes at Cr/cr, Or/or and Pu/pu loci	Red Group R1-,R2-	Rose pink Group R1-,r2r2	Salmon Group r1r1,R2-	Soft pink Group r1r1,r2r2
Cr-,Or-,Pu-	Crimson	Purple pink	Salmon	Soft pink
Cr-,Or-,pupu	Red	Rose pink	Salmon	Soft pink
Cr-,oror,Pu-	Crimson	Purple pink	Salmon	Pale pink
Cr-,oror,pupu	Orange	Pale pink	Salmon	Pale pink
crcr,Or-,Pu-	Magenta	Purple pink	Salmon	Soft pink
crcr,Or-,pupu	Light crimson	Rose pink	Salmon	Soft pink
crcr,oror,Pu-	Magenta	Purple pink	Salmon	Pale pink
crcr,oror,pupu	Orange	Pale pink	Salmon	Pale pink

Fig. 11.3. It is the genotypes between the Cr/cr, Or/or and Pu/pu loci and the R1/r1 and R2/r2 loci that determines flower colour. The Fig 11.1 shows the possible phenotypes and genotypes of the "Red" line in full. After Wu (1999)

In addition to these main colours, at least three other genes interact to affect the colours. Kabwazi discovered a third allele of the R2/r2 gene, which he called R2^c because it modified crimson to magenta and magenta to light crimson; it was intermediate in dominance R2>R2^c>r2. A second gene D/d, controlled the intensity of the red colour; it was typically light red 40A/B, D-, but intensified to dark red 44A/B when the homozygous recessive dd, was present. Wu collected together the results of crosses involving several cultivars, which are either light red or dark red. They showed that light red is dominant and dark red is recessive (Table 11.4).

In addition there are some interesting results from 'Canasta'. This semi-double cultivar was selfed, and one of the single flowered progeny was selfed again. It produced 7 plants with red flowers and 3 with rose pink flowers, clearly segregating in a monohybrid ratio of 3: 1 (Fig. 11.1). One of the red flowered plants was selfed and it segregated 27 with light red flowers and 9 with dark red flowers, a perfect fit with the monohybrid 3:

Crosses	Light Red	Dark Red	Total	Ratio Tested	χ^2	d.f.	P
Dark red	-	79	79	-	-	-	-
Light red	35	-	35	-	-	-	-
Light red × Dark red: F1	31	-	35		-	-	-
Light red × Dark red: F2	26	10	36	3: 1	0.148	1	0.9-0.5
F1 × Dark red: BC	13	7	20	1: 1	1.800	1	0.5-0.1

Table 11.4. The dominance of light red is indicated in the segregation data. The carriers of the light genes were 'Canasta', 'Cecille', 'Duke of Devonshire' and 'Pink Satisfaction'; the carriers of the dark genes were 'Arsona', 'Magic', 'Boogy', 'Esprit', 'Henry Jacoby', 'Red Satisfaction', 'Dryden' and 'Regalia'. After Wu and Tilney-Bassett (unpublished).

1 ratio. They also segregated 29 full reds and 9 reds with a white splash, another near perfect fit. The white splash is discussed in more detail later. When the two genes were considered together they segregated with 21 light red and full coloured, 8 light red and splashed, 8 with dark red and full coloured, and 1 with dark red and splashed. They were segregating independently of each other with a good fit to the dihybrid ratio of 9: 3: 3: 1 [χ^2 = 0.947, df. = 3, P = 0.9-0.5]. The white gene W/w, controlled the existence of coloured versus white flowers (Badr and Horn 1971), but only if it was at least triple homozygous recessive. Kabwazi found that the dominant form WW, caused no dilution of the flower colour, but the heterozygote caused some dilution Ww, and the homozygous recessive brought about full dilution ww. This was the state of the white flower colour, which was homozygous recessive for the red genes as well as homozygous recessive for white r1r1,r2r2,ww. He confused the classification somewhat by also referring to the "W" diluter gene D^w/d^w, which to take an example of the salmon flower colour was unaffected in the homozygous recessive d^w/d^w, was diluted to light salmon in the heterozygote D^w/d^w, and fully diluted to blush salmon in the homozygous dominant D^w/D^w. Depending upon the reader's point of view, when the heterozygote differs from either homozygote, these alleles are either dominant or recessive depending on how they are described.

Kabwazi carried out his exemplary work using 14 accessions belonging to nine flower colour variants, which he selfed and crossed in many ways. Wu (1999) set out to verify these results by selfing and crossing 19, mostly semi-double, flower cultivars. She reasoned that she ought to be able to identify the colours, observe the Mendelian segregation patterns, and from them work out the genotypes. Failure to do so would suggest that Kabwazi's classificatory system was suspect. She selfed the semi-double flowers, and obtained from them plants with single, semi-double or full double flowers. She then selected the single flowered plants and used them in a wide range of further selfs and crosses scoring their flowers in F1 and F2 generations. These fitted into the enlarged colour range with Mendelian segregations of 3 purple: 1 non-purple, 3 crimson: 1 non-crimson, and both 3: 1 and 1: 1 ratios for combinations of the R2/R2^c/r2 segregation. To obtain the purple to non-purple segregation Wu grouped together crimson or purple pink flowers as opposed to red and rose pink flowers, or crimson, magenta and purple pink flowers as opposed to red, light crimson and rose pink flowers, or any other segregation with purple pink on one side and rose pink on the other. Similarly, to obtain the crimson to non-crimson segregation she grouped together red and magenta flowers as opposed to light crimson and magenta, or crimson and red as opposed to magenta and light crimson, or similar segregation. Likewise, she combined crimson and red as opposed to purple pink and rose pink, or other suitable combinations for the R2 > R2^c > r2 segregation (Table 11.5). We previously had identified plants with salmon and soft pink flowers, and we recognized the recessive nature of the orange flower colour in another context. We were therefore satisfied that Kabwazi's additional colours were good and the various interactions held.

Locus	Any colour of the Red Group R2 or R2^c	Any colour of the Rose-pink Group r2r2	Total	Ratio Tested	χ^2	d.f.	P
R2/R2^c/r2	196	74	270	3 : 1	0.242	1	0.9-0.5
BC	29	23	52	1 : 1	0.692	1	0.5-0.1
	Any colour which includes purple pink Pu-	**Any colour which excludes purple pink pupu**					
Pu/pu	119	41	160	3 : 1	0.033	1	0.9-0.5
BC	27	23	50	1 : 1	0.320	1	0.9-0.5
	Any colour which includes crimson Cr-	**Any colour which excludes crimson crcr**					
Cr/cr	40	18*	58	3 : 1	1.126	1	0.5-0.1

* Nine cases of magenta appeared, which are either Cr-,R2^{C}R2^C or crcr,R2^{C}R2^C, as R2^C modifies light crimson to magenta. Six were apportioned to the dominant and three to the recessive side.

Table 11.5. Crosses and backcrosses between many cultivars produced segregation for the three loci R2/R2^C/r2, Pu/pu and Cr/cr. After Wu (1999).

A tentative triple allelic series exists at the purple locus. When 'Ice Crystal' was selfed, it segregated into 11 purple violet and one purple pink, which suggested a monohybrid 3: 1 ratio with purple violet Pu^v dominant over purple pink Pu^p. The cross between a seedling of 'Magic' and a seedling of 'Ice Crystal' gave rise to a progeny with 9 crimson, 5 purple violet and

3 purple pink flowers. The seedling of 'Magic' was heterozygous for the red gene R2r2, and also for the purple pink gene Pu^{p}pu. The seedling of 'Ice Crystal' was homozygous recessive for r2r2, and heterozygous for the purple violet genes Pu^{v}Pu^p. The result was segregation in a ratio of 2 crimson: 1 purple violet: 1 purple pink [χ^2 = 0.059, df. = 2, P = 1-0.9]. This evidence suggests that this is another example of a triple allelic series Pu^v > Pu^p > pu (Wu 1999).

The genetics of patterned, white flash, picotee, white-eye, variegated, red spotted and cactus flowers

In 1992 Nasser and Tilney-Bassett examined the pattern markings on various plants of the salmon F genotypes r1r1,R2r2 that they examined by selfing and crossing with the pure white 'Snowstorm' r1r1,r2r2,ww. They identified five patterns. The bar pattern has pigment localised within a small zone on both sides near the base of each of the lower triplet of petals. The centre pattern has a V-shaped coloured zone in the basal half of all petals filling in the centre of the flower. The picotee pattern colours the edge of all petals. The ring pattern is a coloured zone running across the basal half of all petals. The vein pattern consists of two prominent coloured veins running from the base of the upper pair of petals. In our experiments the expression of these patterns is controlled by the dominant alleles of four genes; the bar, picotee and vein patterns by the genes Ba/ba, Ce/ce or Pi/pi, and Ve/ve respectively, and the centre and ring patterns by the interaction of the products of the two genes Ce with Ve and Ba with Ve respectively. In all cases the absence of the pattern gene is associated with the white petal phenotype so although formally it is treated as a recessive, the pattern is probably suppressed by the presence of the white gene ww. The colour of the markings showed segregation into dominant red and recessive pink, but the grouping showed that the cultivars crossed were all salmon F. It was therefore proposed that a separate gene Rm/rm determined the red and pink marks. This requires further investigation. Wu and Tilney-Bassett (unpublished) have since discovered another allele of the veined series. The feathery veins, in which the prominent veins on the two upper petals are pigmented in a herring bone pattern, is quite distinct from the visual pattern, in the which the veins have a lightly pigmented midrib, but no fine lateral veins. The normal vein pattern was symbolized as Ve in comparison with the apparent absence of veining veve. In a cross between the white flowers of 'Gala' with normal veins, and the purple violet flowers of 'Ice Crystal' with feathery veins, the F2 result was 29 flowers with feathery veins and 15 with normal veins [χ^2 = 1.939, df. = 1, P = 0.5-0.1], the purple violet flower colours were blush or coloured and white. The ratio is not significantly different from the monohybrid segregation of

3: 1, which suggests that the feathery veined character is dominant to the recessive normal vein. As normal vein is dominant over vein less, we may have a triple allelic series $Ve^f > Ve > ve$. At the same time the joint numbers of 22 blush with feathery veins, 11 blush with normal veins, 7 white with feathery veins and 4 white with normal veins fits a dihybrid ratio of 9: 3: 3: 1 showing the independent assortment of the two genes [$\chi^2 = 0.040$, df. = 3, P = 1-.9].

Picotee is the name given to near white flowers with a rim of colour at the margins of the petals. It may be a distinct band of colour, 1-2mm wide, clearly visible on every petal. Alternatively, the expression may be much reduced to a narrow band less than 0.5mm wide, and sometimes completely absent from some petals. Craig (1963) described picotee as an interaction between his variegated gene and his salmon gene when both were homozygous recessive sasa,vv. Nasser and Tilney-Bassett (1992) described a picotee in the flowers of 'Lady Alice of Valencia', which in crosses with the pure white 'Snowstorm' behaved as a dominant gene Pi/pi. The variegated gene of Craig (1963) v, is probably the same as we prefer to call the white splash gene. Its phenotype is a V-shaped splash of white arising from the base of the petal and spreading up towards the periphery. It varies from quite small to covering almost half the area of the upper petals, and it may affect the lower petals to a lesser degree. We have observed the manifestation of picotee as an extension of white splash without the necessary segregation of salmon and rose pink or soft pink flowers. In fact all the red genes may still be present, or these may be modified to orange, light crimson or even purple. They behave as if the white splash gene and the picotee gene were acting as suppressors of the colour genes.

We have used a number of cultivars in this investigation. 'Regalia' has semi-double, full dark red flowers [44B]. 'Canasta' has semi-double, full light red flowers [41C]. 'A.M.Mayne' has semi-double, purple pink flowers [74B] with white splashed petals. 'Dolphin' has single, light crimson flowers [52A] with white splashed petals. 'Dryden' has single, dark red flowers [43A] with white splashed petals. 'Duke of Devonshire' has semi-double, light red flowers [40A] with white splashed petals. 'Orange Appeal' has single, full orange flowers [33A].

After selfing the three cultivars 'Dolphin', 'Dryden' and 'Duke of Devonshire', the progeny segregated into 44 plants with white splashed flowers and 13 plants that were picotee. The frequency strongly suggested a Mendelian 3:1 ratio, in which the picotee flowers were recessive to white splash flowers. After selfing 'Orange Appeal' the progeny segregated into 10 plants with full orange flowers and 4 plants with white splashed orange flowers. It thus appeared that 'Orange Appeal' was heterozygous, in which the full coloured petals were dominant and the white splash were recessive. When we combined the two sets of information, it led us to think that there may be a triple allelic series with graded dominance operating here. We have taken Craig's gene for full colour, but the two alleles are represented by new symbols.

Full colour > White splash > Picotee. $V > V^{ws} > v^p$

After selfing, 'Orange Appeal' remained orange. 'Dolphin' segregated into red and crimson, 'Dryden' remained red, and 'Duke of Devonshire' segregated red and pink. The white splash gene needed only to be expressed. It was not dependent on the colour of the flowers. On further selfing the picotee from 'Duke of Devonshire', there were seven plants of which six were definitely picotee and one more a light blush. When 'A.M. Mayne', 'Dryden' and 'Duke of Devonshire', which all expressed the white splash, were crossed with 'Orange Appeal', which did not express the trait but which is heterozygous for it, the progeny segregated in the frequencies of 25 with the full colour and 24 with white splash in excellent agreement with the 1: 1 ratio expected. All the flowers were coloured red, as the reds are dominant over the recessive orange flower colour.

The crosses between first generation dark red 'Regalia' and light red 'Duke of Devonshire' produced six progeny with the full light red colour, and two dark red progeny. As 'Duke of Devonshire' had the white splash, the absence of this trait among the F1s implies that the full coloured parent is not a carrier of the white splash gene. This was confirmed by the absence of white splash among the 13 progeny of 'Regalia' after selfing. One of the light red F1 plants from the cross was selfed and it segregated 17 full colour light red, 4 full colour dark red, 2 white splashed light red, and 1 white splashed dark red. Evidently, as 'Regalia' lacked the white splash gene, it produced an F1 full coloured but carrying the gene from 'Duke of Devonshire'. The gene segregated again in the F2. A similar result was obtained when one of the progeny from 'Canasta' was selfed. There were 21 full colour light red, 8 full colour dark red, 8 white splashed light red, and 1 white splashed dark red. The segregations both agree with the expected dihybrid 9: 3: 3: 1 ratio, showing the independent assortment of the two genes; they were unlinked.

Selfing randomly selected individuals investigated the inheritance of white splash further among the progeny of 'Orange Appeal'. Three were heterozygous for the trait and segregated into 86 full coloured plants and 30 plants with white splashed flowers in good agreement with the 3: 1 ratio expected [$\chi^2 = 0.046$, df. = 1, P = 0.9-0.5]. Four of these white splashed progeny were grown on and the plants selfed. They produced 35 plants with wholly white splashed flowers. The fourth selected individual with full orange flowered plants produced 37 plants with full orange flowers and no white splashed flowers among them. These observations show that the original 'Orange Appeal' was heterozygous for white splash, but it did not carry the allele for picotee.

A cross between 'Dryden' and 'Orange Appeal' again showed that red was dominant over orange; it produced six plants with full red flowers and five plants with white splashed flowers. One of the white splashed plants was selfed; it produced three plants with red and two with orange flowers all with a white splash. Clearly the colour red versus orange was segregating as expected, but the picotee phenotype was lost. This was confirmed when one of the red, white splashed plants was selfed; it produced a further 20 plants all red and with white splashed flowers. Two of the white splashed plants from the cross between 'Duke of Devonshire' and 'Orange Appeal' were selfed. One of these produced a single white splashed plant, and on selfing this one, there were five more plants that produced white splashed plants but no picotee. The second plant, when selfed, produced 17 white splashed plants and 7 picotee in good agreement with the Mendelian monohybrid ratio [χ^2 = 0.222, df. = 1, P = 0.9-0.5]. Of the 17, there were 11 red and 6 with orange flowers. Evidently, picotee was transmitted in this instance, but it seems unlikely in the former case. Four plants were raised from the 17 white splashed plants, and they gave rise to 61 white splashed plants and 19 picotee plants; the frequencies again fitted the 3: 1 ratio [χ^2 = 0.067, df. = 1, P = 0.9-0.5]. A fifth white splashed plant produced two similar plants. A sixth produced eight more white splashed plants suggesting that the latter was true breeding. A single plant produced by selfing one of the seven original picotee plants, produced 40 picotee in the next generation showing that it was true breeding for the trait.

Wu and myself propose that there are three alleles determining full colour, white splash and picotee flowers. If they are true alleles, then only two of them can exist together in the same heterozygote. We have observed two examples of the backcross between a carrier of white splash and white splash itself; they each segregated in a ratio of 1 full colour: 1 white splash. Three examples are included of selfing the heterozygotes, and each segregated in a ratio of 3 full colour: 1 white splash. They did not subsequently segregate picotee. Finally, we gave three examples of selfing the white splash, and it segregated in a ratio of 3 white splash: 1 picotee. When the white splash was heterozygous with full colour, it never segregated picotee. When it was heterozygous with picotee, it never segregated full colour. The individual ratios and the sums of the three ratios all agree with the tests of goodness of fit. There can be no doubt about the existence of the three alleles.

We will now look at the individual genotypes of the cultivars involved. 'Regalia' contains only the full coloured allele; it also segregates rose pink flowers. Its genotype is R1R1,R2r2,VV. 'Orange Appeal' is full coloured and a carrier of the white splash allele. It carries the recessive gene for orange. Its genotype is oror,R1R1,R2R2,VV^{ws}. 'A.M. Mayne' is a white splash cultivar, either homozygous or heterozygous with picotee. It contains the genes for purple pink flowers. Its genotype is Pu^{p}Pu^p,R1R1,r2r2,V^{ws}V^{ws} or V^{ws}v^p. Finally, there are the plants 'Dolphin', 'Dryden' and 'Duke of Devonshire' that are heterozygous for white splash and picotee. 'Dolphin' is heterozygous for red and crimson, and for white splash. Its genotype is Pu^{p}pu,R1R1,R2R2,V^{ws}v^p. 'Dryden' carries the gene for dark red and is heterozygous for white splash and picotee. Its genotype is R1R1,R2R2,dd,V^{ws}v^p. 'Duke of Devonshire' is heterozygous for rose pink; it carries the gene for light red, and is heterozygous for white splash and picotee. Its genotype is R1R1,R2r2,DD,V^{ws}v^p. The white splash and picotee gene is clearly suppressing the normal activity of the many genes responsible for flower colour. If the breeder does not want white splashed flowers, or picotee ones, he or she must make sure they use stock containing only the full coloured allele.

Craig has said that since all pink flowers were variegated (white splash), it is assumed that the variegation is characteristic of these types and not the result of the V/v gene (1963). Almouslem (1988) found that although most pink flowers were variegated, 'Verona' was not. It was full pink. He called the trait pink white-eye. He investigated the trait using 'Flower of Spring', green and white-over-green 'Foster's Seedling', white-over-green 'Hills of Snow', green and white-over-green 'Mrs J.C. Mapping', 'MS1H', 'Pac Grosser Garten', 'Verona', W1 and W2, and a few hybrids of his own. When the white-eyed plants were selfed or crossed, the progeny segregated into plants having white-eyed pink flowers, and full pink flowers in agreement with a Mendelian 3: 1 ratio. When pink white-eyed and red and white flowered plants were crossed, the pink flowered progeny again segregated into white- eyed and full pink flowers in the same ratio. Hence all the plants were heterozygous with white-eyed pink dominant and the full pink trait recessive. When the red and white flowered plants were selfed or crossed, they segregated into non-pink and pink progeny. The pink flowered plants were again divided into those with a white-eye and full pink in agreement with a 3: 1 ratio. Altogether he observed segregation into 226 white-eyed pink and 77 full pink flowers [χ^2 = 0.132, df. = 1, P =0.9-0.5]. He next backcrossed the white-eyed pink flowers with the full pink plants, and obtained white-eyed pink and full pink flowered plants in agreement with a 1: 1 ratio. After crosses between white-eyed pink and non-pink flowered plants, the progeny again segregated in an approximately 1: 1 ratio. When he crossed the non-pink flowered plants with the full pink flowered plants, the pink progeny segregated into half with white-eyes and half full pink. Altogether he recorded 205 with the white-eye and 191 full pink; in good agreement with the 1: 1 ratio [χ^2 = 0.495, df. = 1, P = 0.5-0.1]. Collectively the results show that the white-eyed trait is dominant over the full pink trait, with no white-eyes. He suggests the symbol for the gene as Pwe/pwe, pink white-eyes versus full pink white-eyeless to represent the presence or absence of the pair of white-eyes on the two upper petals of pink flowers. Evidently Craig was incorrect in his assertion that pink plants always had white eyes.

'Eggshell' is a salmon F genotype r1r1,R2r2. It is a weak salmon diluted by white. The petals are not solid salmon but are extensively flecked by red, following cell lineages and varying in size from tiny pinpricks to whole petals. On selfing it segregated one plant with red flowers, 4 salmon with flecks, one salmon without flecks, 4 white flowers with flecks and 4 white flowers without flecks. Nasser (1990) made additional selfs and crosses, and backcrosses with 'Snowstorm'. He recognized four kinds of progeny. There were salmon and variegated, white and variegated, and salmon and white without variegation. I now believe the salmon without variegation should have been soft pink without variegation. In the crosses he obtained all the four kinds of progeny (Table 11.6). The ratio of variegated to non-variegated was 3: 1 after selfing 'Eggshell', and 1: 1 after crossing or backcrossing. The chi-square tests showed no significant deviation. The chi-square tests for independent assortment were also insignificant. The chi-square tests for coloured versus white were all high. An excess of white undoubtedly causes this, partly by not recognising soft pink at the time, and partly by not distinguishing true white from very pale coloureds. The Ww genotype is known to have a diluting effect on the colours and soft pink is already a very light colour, while the ww genotype turns salmon into white. Nasser admits that the background colours were weak and he could not give precise colours with confidence. The variegation makes it probable that 'Eggshell' is homozygous for a mutator gene Mu/mu, that induces the mutation of the r1r1 gene to R1r1 in a salmon or white background; hence the red colour. The red flowered plant is the result of an early mutation. The salmon is also heterozygous and segregates soft pink. One should look for traces of colour in the stigma, where only the true whites would be colourless. This is an interesting plant and needs further exploration.

Crosses	Variegated		Non-variegated		Total	Variegated Non-variegated	Independent Assortment	Coloured White
	Salmon	White	Soft-Pink	White		Ratio χ^2 test P	Ratio χ^2 test P	Ratio χ^2 test P
Eggshell self	51	37	18	15	121	3:1 0.333 0.9-0.5	1:1 0.405 0.9-0.5	3:1 20.851 <0.001
Eggshell × Snowstorm	22	38	20	56	136	1:1 1.882 0.5-0.1	1:1 2.941 0.1-0.05	1:1 19.882 <0.001
(ES × SS) × Eggshell	20	32	23	43	118	1:1 1.661 0.5-0.1	1:1 0.542 0.5-0.1	1:1 8.678 0.01-0.001
Genotype	R2r2Ww MuMu	R2r2ww MuMu	r2r2Ww MuMu	r2r2ww MuMu				

Table 11.6. Segregation data after selfing or crossing 'Eggshell', with variegated flowers, with 'Snowstorm'. After Nasser (unpublished).

'Verona' is an interesting cultivar because it is a rose pink G R1R1,r2r2, in which the rose pink petals have small red spots just visible on the upper epidermis. The red spots are more frequent in the lower three petals than the upper two, and they tend to be concentrated in the lower half of the petal. Microscopic examination reveals that the spots occur with the position of a trichome arising from the upper epidermis. Each trichome consists of a bright red, dense central cell, which is elongated into a glandular hair with a unicellular tip. Five to ten reddish epidermal cells, more strongly pigmented than other epidermal cells, surround the central cell. Trichomes occur on the lower as well as the upper epidermis, but except on pink flowers they are not associated with red spots. Hence, it the existence of red spots, rather than the existence of a trichome that is unique to 'Verona'. After self-pollinating 'Verona', its progeny segregated into plants having pink flowers with red spots and pink flowers without red spots. Self-pollinating a selected hybrid between 'Verona' and 'Dolly Varden', which had red spots, and crossing this spotted selection to 'Verona', gave a total of 56 pink plants with red spots and 21 pink plants without red spots [χ^2 = 0.212, df. = 1, P = 0.9-0.5]. The acceptable fit to a monohybrid 3: 1 ratio indicated that the presence of red spots was dominant over their absence. Dominance was confirmed by the 1: 1 ratio observed following backcrosses between 'Verona' and several spotless cultivars, 'Flower of Spring', 'Hills of Snow', 'Mrs J.C. Mapping', 'MS1H', and 'Pac Grosser Garten'. We have therefore symbolized the gene as Rst/rst to represent red-spotted versus spotless trichomes on the upper epidermis of pink petals (Almouslem and Tilney-Bassett 1989).

The 'cactus' type cultivars 'Fascination' and 'Fire Dragon' have a corolla of long, narrow petals, instead of the typical obovate petals. Crosses of cactus with normal gave a F1 of 218 with normal and 199 with cactus flowers (Robinson, unpublished). The F2 from cactus plants bred amongst themselves segregated into 76 normal, 138 cactus and 60 teratoid. The teratoid plants were grossly abnormal, very slow growing, with a squat, swollen stem giving off short, thin petioles terminating in small leaves that were folded back on themselves along the main rib. These survived for many months, slowly becoming larger, but never growing into a normal plant, nor flowering. Robinson designated the mutant gene cactus Ca. The 1:2:1 ratio, and the backcross 1:1 ratio, shows that it is semi-dominant; the heterozygote is different from either homozygote. Tilney-Bassett (unpublished) found that the petals of 'Fire Dragon' were semi-double, so he crossed it with one plant having a centre pattern and with 'Dolly Varden'. The resulting segregation of 24 single flowers and 16 semi-double flowers with broad, flat petals, and 14 single flowers and 15 semi-double flowers with narrow quill petals agrees with the 1:1:1:1 ratio proving that 'Fire Dragon' was heterozygous for both genes. I shall call the gene Ca^q indicating the narrow quill petal and Ca^b indicating broad petals. 'Fire Dragon' is therefore Ca^bCa^q while 'Dolly Varden' and the centre pattern plant are Ca^bCa^b with respect to the cactus genotype; the teratoid plant is Ca^qCa^q.

References

Almouslem, A.B. (1988).
Qualitative and quantitative genetical studies in *Pelargonium × Hortorum* Bailey. Ph.D. Thesis, University of Swansea, Wales.

Almouslem, A.B., Nasser, N.S. and Tilney-Bassett, R.A.E. (1991).
Complementary genes for red flower colour in zonal pelargoniums. Journal of Horticultural Science 66, 651-659.

Almouslem, A.B. and Tilney-Bassett, R.A.E. (1989).
Inheritance of red-spotted petals and golden leaves in zonal pelargonium. HortScience 24, 501-502.

Badr, M. and Horn, W. (1971).
Genetische Untersuchungen an diploiden und tetraploiden *Pelargonium zonale*-Hybriden. Zeitschrift fur Pflanzenzuchtung 66, 203-220.

Craig, R. (1963).
The inheritance of several characters in geranium, *Pelargonium × hortorum* Bailey. Ph.D. Thesis, Pennsylvania State University, USA.

Kabwazi, H.H.N. (1986).
Plastid inheritance studies in *Pelargonium x hortum* Bailey. MSc. Thesis, University of Swansea, Wales.

Kabwazi, H.H.N. (1993).
The genetics of flower colour and flavonoid pigments in the genus *Pelargonium*. Ph.D.Thesis, University of Cambridge, UK.

Nasser, N.S. (1990).
Flower colour inheritance in zonal pelargoniums. Ph.D.Thesis, University College of Swansea, Wales.

Nasser, N.S. and Tilney-Bassett, R.A.E. (1992).
The inheritance of patterned white flowers in zonal pelargoniums. Journal of Horticultural Science 67, 361-370.

Pan, S., Bacher, J. and Ewart, L.C. (1990).
Genetics of orange flower colour in *Pelargonium × Hortorum*. Acta Horticulturae 272, 53-57.

Tilney-Bassett, R.A.E., Munshi, A.A., Almouslem, A.B. and Nasser, N.S. (1995).
The inheritance of red, salmon, rose-pink and soft-pink flower colours in zonal pelargoniums. Journal of Horticultural Science 70, 499-508.

Wu, G.F. (1999).
The genetics and biochemistry of flower pigments and flower patterns in *Pelargonium x hortorum*. Ph.D.Thesis, University of Wales Swansea.

12
The Flower Colour Pigments

Full colours

When we describe the different flower colours we are using a simple descriptive terminology – red, salmon, crimson, magenta, light-crimson, orange, purple-pink, rose-pink, soft-pink and pale-pink. All these colours are distinguishable by eye. Underlying each is a variety of flower pigments, differing in number in a mixture, in type, and in concentration. How much do we know of these? In fact the flower pigments are a fraction of a much larger number of compounds found in plants known as plant phenolics. Munchi (1995) has summarised two classifications of these based on the Ribereau-Gayon (1972) and the Geissman (1963) classifications. A small part of these are the flavones, flavonols and related compounds, and the anthocyanins. Amongst the flavonols are quercetin, kaempferol and myricetin, and amongst the anthocyanins are pelargonidin, cyanidin, peonidin, delphinidin, petunidin and malvidin. These are the compounds we are interested in. The structure of the anthocyanins and flavonols is illustrated in figure 12.1. The compounds have been widely investigated, and they occur in many different plants often, as with *Petunia*, in considerable detail. They have been studied very little in *Pelargonium*.

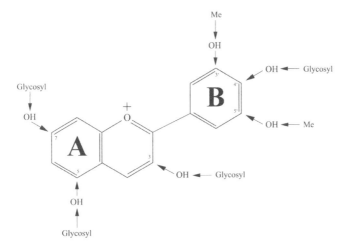

Fig. 12.1. Changes in the hydroxyl or the methyl group account for the anthocyanins. Hydroxylation at positions 5 and 7 throughout. At position 3' and 5' pelargonidin is H and H; cyanidin is OH and H; delphinidin is OH and OH; peonidin is OCH_3 and H; petunidin is OCH_3 and OH; malvidin is OCH_3 and OCH_3.
To make the flavonols there is no double bond and positive charge to the oxygen in position 1, and a second oxygen atom is attached at position 4. Hydroxylation at positions 3, 5 and 7 throughout. At positions 3' and 5' kaempferol is H and H; quercetin is OH and H; myricetin is OH and OH.

All six anthocyanins are known to occur in pelargoniums (Robinson and Robinson 1932; Craig 1982; Asen and Griesbach 1983), but rather little is known about the contents in individual cultivars. The petals of red, orange-red and salmon contain pelargonidin whereas pink flowers do not (Harborne 1961; Ahmedullah *et al.* 1963; Buswell 1978; Asen and Griesbach 1983). All flowers seem to contain cyanidin or peonidin (Harborne 1961; Ahmedullah *et al.* 1963; Asen and Griesbach 1983), but malvidin was also reported in a pink flower (Scott-Moncrieff 1936). Also flowers analysed by Asen and Griesbach (1983) contained the flavonols kaempferol and quercetin. None of these investigations take us very far. Asen and Griesbach (1983) are actually more concerned in establishing a method for flower cultivar identification by demonstrating the large numbers of compounds that occur. This is achieved with the technique of high-pressure liquid chromatography. In a similar way, Bauer and Treutter (1990a, b) used phenolic fingerprints for cultivar identification from the patterns of compounds present in leaves. All 52 cultivars of *P. zonale* and *P. peltatum* hybrids could be clearly distinguished by the phenolic pattern of their leaves, but the differences were mostly quantitative and only a few cultivars showed qualitative differences. It is a good method for the identification of cultivars under uniform conditions; unfortunately it uses equipment that is unlikely to be available to most pelargonium growers. It has not been used to investigate the anthocyanin content of a large number of coloured flowers. By using HPLC, Bissessur (1990) separated the anthocyanin pigments from seven cultivars. He made up solutions of pelargonidin chloride and malvidin from Sigma biochemicals as authentic compounds. From 'Benedict', 'Dolly Varden', 'Frank Headley' and 'Vera Dillon', he obtained three anthocyanins, and from 'Mrs J.C. Mapping', 'Preston Park' and 'Verona' he obtained four. In no case did he find evidence of malvidin, but he always found pelargonidin. So the other anthocyanins were presumably cyanidin, peonidin and delphinidin. They occurred in varying amounts, particularly pelargonidin which was a minor component in 'Preston Park' and 'Vera Dillon', but the major component in 'Frank Headley'. The retention times with his HPLC technique were all under ten minutes.

Kabwazi (1993) used paper chromatography, one and two-dimensional thin layer chromatography, and to answer some questions high-pressure liquid chromatography. The methods are all described in his thesis. I shall simply summarise the main results. He analysed the pigment composition of 171 cultivars and lines for anthocyanins (Table 12.1), and 79 of these, plus five white flowered lines, for flavonols. He confirmed that the 3,5-O-diglucosides of pelargonidin, cyanidin, peonidin, delphinidin and malvidin were the major anthocyanidins, while petunidin 3,5-diglucoside occurred only as a trace pigment. He estimated the concentration of pigments seen on a chromatograph plate on a relative scale from 10, the strongest concentration, to 1 the weakest, with a minor trace being expressed as +, and absence as 0. There were 13 patterns of anthocyanidin pigments as follows: -

Cultivars and Colours	
Red	**Magenta**
Black Prince	Parental
Breakaway Red	Picasso
Caroline Schmidt	Vera Dillon
Cheerio Coral	Will Rogers
Cherry Scarlet	**Orange**
Dark Red Irene	Orange Appeal
Dolly Varden	Orange Supreme
Flower of Spring	Reflex
Freak of Nature	Rousseuo
Friesdorf	Token
Gala Redhead	Treasure
Gala Sunbird	**Salmon**
Golden Crest	Deep Salmon
Golden Harem	Gala Amaretto
Harry Hieover	Harriet le Hair
Janet Tone	Mr H. Cox
Lass O'Gowrie	Quilter
Marechal MacMahon	**Light-salmon**
P. x stenopetalum	Gala Flamingo
Paul Crampel	Joan Fontaine
Quercus Folia	Joyce Headley
R. Flisk	Lady Spain
Red Streak	**Rose-pink & Purple-pink**
Sensational Coral	Avanti Rose
Sensational Scarlet	Camel
Tunisia	Cheerio Pink
Light-red	Dagata
Breakaway Salmon	Elite Pink
Frank Headley	Fenton Farm
Gala Lipstick	Gala Highlight
Phyllis	Gala Rose
Sensational Coral	Horizon Rose
Light-crimson	Kleine Liebling
Lines only	Lady Pink
Crimson	Mrs Everatts
Ashes	Pulsar Rose
Ashes Red	Rachel Fisher
Gala Bloodred	Sensational Rose
Happy Thought	Video Rose
Magenta	**Soft-pink & Pale-pink**
Gilbert West	Hills of Snow
Henry Jacoby	Multibloom Lavender
Holiday	Sensational Blush

Table 12.1 List of cultivars used for anthocyanidin analysis. Plus many unnamed accessions. Adapted from Kabwazi (1993).

(a)   Cyanidin types (cyanidin or peonidin)

Cyanidin types were present in all petals analysed. They differed in the presence, or absence, of peonidin and the ratios of cyanidin to peonidin. Three patterns were identified.

1.   Cyanidin occurred as a trace or minor pigment (+ - 2) and peonidin was plentiful (5 – 10).
2.   Peonidin occurred as a minor pigment (1 – 2) and cyanidin was plentiful (5 – 10).
3.   Peonidin was absent (0) and cyanidin was abundant (10).

(b)   Delphinidin types (delphinidin, petunidin and malvidin)

The plants varied in the presence or absence of delphinidin types. If the type was present, then three delphinidin patterns were identified.

4.   Delphinidin and petunidin were present as a minor or trace pigment (+ - 2) and malvidin was plentiful (5-10).
5.   Malvidin and petunidin were present as a minor or trace pigment (1 – 2) and delphinidin was plentiful (5 – 10).
6.   Delphinidin was an abundant pigment (10) and there was no petunidin or malvidin (0).

He found that the plants that contained more malvidin than delphinidin were also the plants that contained more peonidin than cyanidin. Conversely, plants that contained less malvidin than delphinidin also contained less peonidin than cyanidin. He also found in 'Happy Thought' that the absence of methylated delphinidin types (petunidin and malvidin) was accompanied by the absence of methylated cyanidin types (peonidin). These results suggest that one methylating system exists for cyanidin and delphinidin, and that at least three levels of O-methylation are present. The levels of O-methylation are as follows: -

(i)   No O-methylation (no OMt)
       Methylated anthocyanins were absent.
(ii)   Low level O-methylation (low OMt)
       There were more of the unmethylated (cyanidin 5 – 10) than methylated (peonidin 1 – 2) anthocyanins.
(iii) Full level O-methylation (full OMt)
       Both O-methylated (peonidin and/ or malvidin) and unmethylated (cyanidin and/ or delphinidin) were present, but there were more of the former (4 – 10) than of the latter (+ - 2).

The order full OMt > low OMt > no OMt corresponds to a decrease in the relative amount of the O-methylated anthocyanin accumulated.

(c)   Pelargonidin type

The plants accumulated significant amounts of pelargonidin. Three patterns were observed in the ratio of pelargonidin to cyanidin: -

7.   No pelargonidin (no Pg)
     Pelargonidin was absent or occurred in only trace amounts.

8.   High pelargonidin: cyanidin ratio (high Pg: Cy)
     The cultivars contained more pelargonidin than cyanidin types (cyanidin and peonidin). The flowers that exhibited this pattern could be divided into two categories on the basis of the amount of cyanidin types present. Some flowers contained significantly lower amounts of cyanidin types (Pg: Cy = 10: 1) than the rest (Pg: Cy = 10: 4 – 9).

9.   Low pelargonidin: cyanidin ratio (low Pg: Cy)
     The amount of pelargonidin was less than in the cyanidin types (cyanidin and peonidin).

(d)   Flavonol patterns

Kaempferol was always the major flavonol pigment, quercetin was present in lower concentration (2 – 3) or as a trace (+), myricetin occurred only as a trace (+). The following three patterns were identified: -

(1)   Kaempferol: quercetin (Km: Qu) = 10: 2 - 3
(2)   Kaempferol: quercetin (Km: Qu) = 10: +
(3)   Kaempferol: quercetin: myricetin (Km: Qu: My) = 10: 2 – 3: +

Myricetin only occurred in plants that also accumulate delphinidin types (delphinidin, petunidin, malvidin). Plants that contain quercetin in trace amounts were also the ones that contained significantly small amounts of cyanidin types (cyanidin and peonidin). The results confirm that quantitative and qualitative variation in hydroxylation and O-methylation patterns are the main sources of flavonoid variation in petals.

On the basis of qualitative variation of anthocyanin types and flavonols, four flavonol groups are identified, summarised in table 12.2. The presence of kaempferol in flowers that lacked pelargonidin shows that the enzymes or genes that control flavonol accumulation are independent of those that control pelargonidin accumulation.

Group	Anthocyanidin types	Flavonols
C	Cy types	Km & Qu
CD	Cy & Dp types	Km, Qu & My
PC	Pg and Cy types	Km & Qu
PCD	Pg, Cy & Dp types	Km, Qu & My

Table 12.2. The four groups based on the anthocyanidins and flavonols. Adapted from Kabwazi (1993).

On the basis of the observed variation in O-methylation pattern and Pg: Cy ratios, group PC and PCD were further subdivided into five and four flavonoid types respectively. Similarly, groups CD and C were subdivided into two groups each on the basis of the O-methylation pattern. These 13 flavonoid types are summarised in table 12.3. The chromatograms of these anthocyanin patterns are illustrated in the thesis of Kabwazi (1993).

Flavonoid Type	Flavonoid Group	Anthocyanidin Characteristics
C-1	C	No Pg; low OMt
C-2	C	No Pg; full OMt
CD-1	CD	No Pg; Dp types; low OMt
CD-2	CD	No Pg; Dp types; full OMt
PC-1	PC	High Pg: Cy ratio; low OMt
PC-2	PC	High Pg: Cy ratio; no OMt
PC-3	PC	High Pg: Cy ratio; full OMt
PC-4	PC	Low Pg: Cy ratio; full OMt
PC-5	PC	High Pg: Cy ratio; full OMt
PCD-1	PCD	High Pg: Cy ratio; Dp types; low OMt
PCD-2	PCD	High Pg: Cy ratio; Dp types; no OMt
PCD-3	-	-
PCD-4	PCD	Low Pg: Cy ratio; Dp types; full OMt
PCD-5	PCD	High Pg: Cy ratio; Dp types; full OMt

Table 12.3. The thirteen-flavonoid types, derived from the four groups, highlighting their characteristic anthocyanidin content. Adapted from Kabwazi (1993).

The magenta flowers were PCD-4, the orange flowers were PC-3, and the purple-pink flowers were CD-2. The remainder of the flower colours displayed more than one flavonoid pattern. Crimson flowers all displayed PCD-5, except the rare 'Happy Thought', which displayed PCD-2. Red flowers displayed two patterns, PC-2 and PC-5. The red- flowered cultivars 'Black Prince', 'Friesdorf' and 'Red Streak' were PC-2. All the light-red flowered plants were PC-5, except one line, which was PC-4. All the light-crimson flowered plants were PC-4, except one line, which was PCD-5. These anthocyanin patterns are set out in table 12.4. The majority of salmon and light salmon lines were PC-1, except two lines that were PC-3, and two lines that were PCD-1. Rose-pink flowers were C-2, except 'Gala Highlight', which was PCD-4. The soft-pink phenotypes contained four types. 'Hills of Snow' gave type PCD-4, one line was CD-1, one line was CD-2, six lines and 'Multibloom Lavender' were C-2, and the rest were C-1. Of the pale-pink flowers 'Sensational Blush' was C-2, and two lines were C-1. The presence of type PCD-4 flavonoid pattern in 'Hills of Snow' was attributed to its chimera structure, in which L II was genetically red although LI had pink flowers.

Flower Colours	Anthocyanidin Patterns
Crimson	PCD-2 & PCD-5
Magenta	PCD-4
Red	PC-2 & PC-5
Light-red	PC-4 & PC-5
Light-crimson	PC-4 & PCD-5
Orange	PC-3
Salmon	PC-1, PC-3 & PCD-1
Light-salmon	PC-1 & PCD-1
Purple-pink	CD-2
Rose-pink	C-2 & PCD-4
Soft-pink	C-1, C-2, CD-1 & CD-2
Pale-pink	C-1 & C-2

Table 12.4. The flower colours are correlated with the flavonoid patterns in the presence of diluters. Adapted from Kabwazi (1993).

Many of the flower colours and the resulting anthocyanidin patterns were thought to be the effect of flower colour dilution. Thus PCD-5 light crimson was a diluted form of crimson. Similarly, PC-5 light red was a diluted form of red; PC-4 light red was a diluted form of light-crimson; PC-1 light-salmon was a diluted form of salmon; PCD-4 rose-pink, C-2 soft-pink and C-1 pale-pink were diluted forms of magenta, rose-pink and soft-pink respectively. To sort this problem out a number of lines were crossed and the data analysed. The consequence of this analysis was that it became possible to correlate the list of the flavonoid patterns and groups with the flower colour phenotypes as in table 12.5.

Flavonoid Pattern	Flavonoid Group	Flower Colours	Flower Colour Group
C-1	C	Soft-pink	Pink
C-2	C	Rose-pink	Pink
CD-1	CD	Soft-pink	Pink
CD-2	CD	Purple-pink	Pink
PC-1	PC	Salmon	Salmon
PC-2	PC	Red	Red
PC-3	PC	Orange	Red
PC-3	PC	Salmon	Salmon
PC-4	PC	Light-crimson	Red
PC-5	PC	Red	Red
PCD-1	PCD	Salmon	Red
PCD-2	PCD	Crimson	Red
PCD-3	-	-	-
PCD-4	PCD	Magenta	Red
PCD-5	PCD	Crimson	Red

Table 12.5. The flavonoid pattern and group is closely correlated with the flower colour and group in the absence of diluters. Adapted from Kabwazi (1993).

Although the summary in table 12.5 suggests that most of the flavonoid patterns can be correlated with specific flower colour genotypes, most of the flower colour variants have more than one flavonoid pattern. This, together with the fact that PC-3 was displayed by two different flower colour phenotypes, suggests that the flower colour genes identified in chapter 11 determine not all of the thirteen- flavonoid patterns. The inheritance of the flavonoid patterns was therefore studied using semi-quantitative analysis of one-dimensional thin layer chromatography. As well as the use of 'Happy Thought' (PCD-2) and 'Gala Bloodred' (PCD-5), the study consisted of selfing and crossing some seventeen accessions. The inheritance was divided into the following parts: -

1. The inheritance of group C and group CD types.
2. The inheritance of group PC patterns.
3. The interaction between group PC and group C patterns.
4. The interaction between group PC and group CD plants.
5. The inheritance of group PCD types.
6. Interaction between type PCD-1 with group C, group CD and group PC flavonoid types.
7. Inheritance of type PCD-2: Interaction with group C and PC types.
8. Inheritance of type PCD-4 pattern: Interaction with group PC and group C plants.
9. Genotypes of the fourteen- flavonoid patterns.

Twelve of the thirteen patterns were studied, only PCD-3 was not. In addition some of the F1, F2 and backcross progenies that were used were obtained from the breeding programme involved in assigning genotype to flower colour in chapter 11. The resulting study occupies twenty pages and ten tables of Kabwazi's thesis, but ultimately it showed that most of the genotypes of almost all of the fourteen- flavonoid types correlate with flower colour genotypes. A summary of the flavonoid pattern, the genotypes, and the flower colours they give rise to is shown in table 12.6. We notice that the same flowers can often have two or three flavonoid groups, but each has a different genotype.

Flavonoid Pattern	Proposed Genotypes						Flower Colours
	R1/r1	M/m	R2/R2^c/r2	Cr/cr	Pu/pu	Or/or	
C-1	r1r1	M-	r2r2	-	pupu	Or-	Soft-pink
C-2	R1-	M-	r2r2	-	pupu	Or-	Rose-pink
C-2	r1r1	M-	r2r2	-	pupu	oror	Pale-pink
C-2	R1-	M-	r2r2	-	pupu	oror	Pale-pink
CD-1	r1r1	M-	r2r2	-	Pu-	Or-	Soft-pink
CD-2	R1-	M-	r2r2	-	Pu-	Or-	Purple-pink
PC-1	r1r1	M-	R2-	-	pupu	Or-	Salmon
PC-1	r1r1	M-	R2^c-	-	pupu	Or-	Salmon
PC-2	R1-	mm	R2-	Cr-	pupu	Or-	Red
PC-3	R1-	M-	R2-	Cr-	pupu	oror	Orange
PC-3	R1-	M-	R2^c-	-	pupu	oror	Orange
PC-3	R1-	M-	R2-	crcr	pupu	oror	Orange
PC-3	r1r1	M-	R2-	Cr-	pupu	oror	Salmon
PC-4	R1-	M-	R2-	crcr	pupu	Or-	Light-crimson
PC-4	R1-	M-	R2^c	-	pupu	Or-	Light-crimson
PC-5	R1-	M-	R2-	Cr-	pupu	Or-	Red
PCD-1	r1r1	M-	R2-	-	Pu-	Or-	Salmon
PCD-1	r1r1	M-	R2^c-	-	Pu-	Or-	Salmon
PCD-2	R1-	mm	R2-	Cr-	Pu-	Or-	Crimson
PCD-3	R1-	M-	R2-	crcr	Pu-	oror	Magenta
PCD-3	R1-	M-	R2^c-	-	Pu-	oror	Magenta
PCD-3	R1-	M-	R2-	Cr-	Pu-	oror	Crimson
PCD-4	R1-	M-	R2^c	crcr	Pu-	Or-	Magenta
PCD-4	R1-	M-	R2^c-	-	Pu-	Or	Magenta
PCD-5	R1-	M-	R2-	Cr-	Pu-	Or-	Crimson

Table 12.6. The flower colours are correlated with the proposed genotypes of the fourteen-flavonoid patterns. A – in the Cr/cr column indicates that the genotype was not important. Adapted from Kabwazi (1993).

In order to obtain a tighter grasp on the genetic control of flavonoid synthesis Kabwazi (1993) determined the concentration of anthocyanidin in arbitrary units of area per gram of fresh weight for each of the flavonoid types, using high-pressure liquid chromatography of the petals. He was thus able to determine more accurately the quantities of pigment produced. This enabled him to conclude rather more about the possible role of the flower colour genes in the control of flavonoid synthesis in flower as follows: -

Pu/pu Controls 5'-hydroxylation of both anthocyanins and flavonols. Recessive pupu lacks 5'-hydoxylated flavonoids (no delphinidin types and no myricetin).

Or/or Controls 3'-hydroxylation of anthocyanins and flavonols. Both alleles are functional. The recessive oror reduces the amount of cyanidin types and quercetin by 30 to 80%. The gene does not affect 5'-hydroxylation.

M/m Controls O-methylation of cyanidin and delphinidin types. The recessive mm is non-functional (no peonidin, petunidin or malvidin). The gene has no effect on flower colour.

R1/r1 Controls the O-methylation of both cyanidin and delphinidin types, and the concentration of both anthocyanin and flavonols. Both alleles are functional. The recessive r1r1 reduces the concentration of anthocyanins and the level of O-methylation by more than 79% and 90% respectively.

R2/R2^c/r2   Controls production of pelargonidin 3,5-O-diglucoside. Dominants R2 and R2^c produce, or accumulate, pelargonidin 3,5-O-diglucoside while the recessive r2r2 suppresses production.

Cr/cr   Seems to regulate the amount of pelargonidin 3,5-O-diglucoside produced by the allele R2 of the R2/R2^c/r2 gene.

Recessive oror is epistatic to R1/r1 such that R1-R2-oror and r1r1R2-oror have the same flavonoid pattern, type PC-3. Similarly, R1-r2r2oror and r1r1r2r2oror exhibit the same pattern, type C-2. The alleles cr and R2^c are epistatic to the genes R2/R2^c and Cr/cr respectively.

Diluted colours

The separation of flowers into ten colour types (Fig. 11.3) assumes that there is no dilution. Yet we know of two genes that can dilute the colours. These affect the colour by changing it to a weaker form, and in so doing the genotype of the flower is somewhat confused. Thus the colour soft-pink that is indicative of the genotype r1r1r2r2, may in fact be a diluted rose-pink R1-r2r2pupu, or a diluted purple-pink R1-r2r2Pu-. For white dilution "W" I will use the terminology of Kabwazi (1993) instead of the original designation. He used d^{w}d^w for undiluted, D^{w}d^w for partially diluted, and D^{w}D^w for fully diluted lines. The "B" dilution is completely dominant over the undiluted form so he calls the gene D^b/d^b. For his study of the "W" dilution he used the cultivars 'Gala Lipstick', 'Gala Flamingo', 'Gala Highlight' and 'Horizon Rosy Glow', and also a number of lines. He took as parents a number of undiluted coloured lines and crossed them with pure white lines. This created a number of semi-diluted F1 individuals. When the total concentration of anthocyanins was compared, the semi-diluted flowers had on average about half the undiluted concentration. The dilution had little or no effect on the structure and composition of the anthocyanins. He selfed the F1 and obtained a wide spread of colours in the F2 owing to the re-assortment of the underlying genes. This was accompanied by the segregation of flavonoid types. He found, for example, that type PC-5 plants R1-R2-were red if they were homozygous for the undiluted gene d^{w}d^w, light-red if heterozygous D^{w}d^w, and salmon if homozygous for the diluted gene D^{w}D^w. Type C-2 plants R1-r2r2 were rose-pink with the undiluted gene d^{w}d^w, soft-pink with the heterozygote D^{w}d^w, and pale-pink when homozygous for the diluted gene D^{w}D^w. Similarly, when the salmon genotype was a segregate r1r1R2- the series went salmon d^{w}d^w, light-salmon D^{w}d^w, and blush salmon D^{w}D^w. Finally, with C-1 plants, homozygous recessive for the two red genes r1r1r2r2, the series went soft-pink d^{w}d^w, pale-pink $D^w d^w$, and the homozygote, which could not be classified as a C-1 plant, was probably white $D^w D^w$. Thus in the F2, the main genes would segregate R1-R2-, R1-r2r2, r1r1R2-, and r1r1r2r2 and this could be shown by the flower colour and by the group segregation. The diluter gene could also show segregation as evidence by changes within the main colours, for example R1-r2r2 rose-pink, soft-pink and pale-pink. In order to confirm that his analysis of the F2 was right, particularly the finer differences in colour, he crossed or backcrossed these with suitable tester stocks. He expected that the two homozygotes $d^w d^w$ and $D^w D^w$ were true breeding, but the heterozygote $D^w d^w$ was segregating. The one homozygote $d^w d^w$ would not segregate any undiluted form, the other homozygote he expected to produce only diluted colours, and the heterozygote would be expected to segregate diluted and undiluted in agreement with a simple Mendelian ratio, 1: 1 or 1: 2: 1. The data confirmed his analysis and so demonstrated that the "W" dilution is a major source of flower colour variation, and that it affects all flower colours with an additive effect of flower colour phenotypes (Table 12.7).

Genotype	Undiluted Colours	Diluter	Diluted Colours
R1-R2-Pu-Cr-[a]	Crimson	$D^w d^w$	Light-crimson
R1-R2-Pu-Cr-[a]	Crimson	$D^w D^w$	Light-red
R1-R2-Pu-crcr[a]	Magenta	$D^w d^w$	Deep purple-pink
R1-R2-Pu-crcr[a]	Magenta	$D^w D^w$	Deep soft-pink
R1-R2-pupuCr-Or-	Red	$D^w d^w$	Light-red
R1-R2-pupuCr-Or-	Red	$D^w D^w$	Salmon
R1-R2-pupucrcrOr-	Red	$D^w d^w$	Light-red
R1-R2-pupucrcrOr-	Light-crimson	$D^w D^w$	Salmon ?
R1-R2-oror[b]	Orange	$D^w d^w$	Light-orange
R1-R2-oror[b]	Orange	$D^w D^w$	Salmon
R1-r2r2Pu-Or-[b]	Purple-pink	$D^w d^w$	Deep soft-pink
R1-r2r2Pu-Or-[b]	Purple-pink	$D^w D^w$	Pale-pink ?
R1-r2r2pupuOr-[b]	Rose-pink	$D^w d^w$	Soft-pink
R1-r2r2pupuOr-[b]	Rose-pink	$D^w D^w$	Pale-pink
r1r1R2-[c]	Salmon	$D^w d^w$	Light-salmon
r1r1r2r2[c]	Soft-pink	$D^w d^w$	Pale-pink

a Includes Or- and oror.
b Includes Cr- and crcr.
c Includes Cr- and crcr plus Pu- and pupu.

Table 12.7. Possible effects of "W" dilution on flower colour. After Kabwazi (1993).

When a light-red flower was selfed it segregated in a 3: 1 ratio indicating complete dominance of the light red allele D^b over the red allele d^b. On crossing these light-red flowered plants with red, salmon, rose-pink or soft-pink plants all the F1 segregated 1 light-red: 1 red. On backcrossing the light-red F1 $D^b d^b$ to the original light-red parent $D^b d^b$ the progeny segregated 3: 1. Thus all of the light-red F1 plants were heterozygous for the dilution. Further analysis showed that the "B" dilution was completely dominant in R1-R2- and in R1-r2r2 backgrounds, but he suggests that soft-pink genotypes r1r1r2r2, and also salmon genotypes r1r1R2-, are epistatic to "B" dilution. It was thought possible that the activity of the diluter was dependent on anthocyanin concentration. In which case, the dilution effect of dominant D^b on flower colour is easily noticeable in flowers that have a high anthocyanin concentration as in R1- flowers, compared to those that have a low anthocyanin concentration as in r1r1 flowers. Alternatively, higher levels of O-methylated anthocyanin as in R1- flowers might increase the activity of the diluter.

Kabwazi (1993) goes on to consider whether the two genes are part of a triple allelic series $D^w > D^b > d$, or are linked, but he comes to no definite conclusion. He also considers the possibility that the white flower locus D^w/d^w is also the diluter ($W/w = d^w/D^w$). Or that the diluter locus D^w/d^w and white flower colour genes W/w are tightly linked in repulsion. These are complicated notions that go beyond our present knowledge and experience, so I would still remain with the W/w for the "W" dilution and D/d for the "B" dilution.

Pigment content has also been investigated with *Pelargonium* × *domesticum*, the regal pelargonium and some zonals (Mitchell *et al.* 1998). This has involved column and high-pressure liquid chromatography, absorption spectroscopy, and nuclear magnetic resonance (NMR). The major anthocyanins identified were 3,5-digycosides and, in the regals, 3-glucoside-5- (6-acetyl) glucosides of pelargonidin, cyanidin, peonidin, delphinidin, petunidin and malvidin. The regal pelargoniums differ from the zonal pelargoniums in many ways particularly amongst the dark colours. There were quite high proportions of quercetin and myricetin, and also petunidin, while cyanidin and peonidin were generally low. There were also big differences between the outer and inner petals in the proportion of the pigments and their colours. No genetic analysis of these tetraploid cultivars accompanied these comparisons.

The deep purplish pink zonal 'Pink Multibloom' and 'Pink Elite Mix' have over 90% peonidin, 3% cyanidin and 1-2% pelargonidin, whereas the strong purplish pink 'Pink Multibloom Mix' has 43% peonidin and 50% malvidin. So these are probably in the C-2 and CD-2 categories. The 'Orange Appeal' and 'Salmon Multibloom Mix' contain 98% and 94% pelargonidin with the remainder either cyanidin or peonidin or both; they are probably both PC-3. The reds or reddish orange contain 64-76% pelargonidin, 21-34% peonidin and 2-3% cyanidin or malvidin. The cultivars are 'Red/Pink Multibloom', 'Red Multibloom' and 'Red Elite Mix'; they are probably in the PC-2 or PC-5 category. Finally, the vivid purplish red 'Karl Hageli' has no pelargonidin, 43% and 40% peonidin and malvidin and the remainder cyanidin, delphinidin and petunidin; it is probably in the CD-2 category. We thus see that while there are variations in the description of the colour, the anthocyanin content points fairly well in the direction of the right classification according to Kabwasi's scheme.

Recently, Japanese workers have investigated the production of purple flower colour in *Pelargonium* (Kobayashi *et al.* 1998). They found the main anthocyanins in purplish cultivars were pelargonidin, peonidin and malvidin. On selfing, these segregated into four types, the original type, a peonidin type, a peonidin malvidin type and a white type. Probably the original flower colour was magenta modified to a deep purple pink (Table 12.7). But their explanation is based on an entirely new system of genetic control, in which they suggest that there are separate genes for pelargonidin, Pg/pg, peonidin, Pn/pn, and malvidin, Mn/mn, as well as two further genes for the conversion of dihydro flavonol to leucoanthocyanin, E1/e1, and from leucoanthocyanin to anthocyanin, E2/e2. The approach has therefore been quite different from ours. It will be interesting to see how well it develops.

References

Ahmedullah, M., Carpenter, W.J. and Michell, H.L. (1963).
Identification of anthocyanidins in three cultivars of geranium (*Pelargonium* × *hortorum*) by chromatographic and spectrophotometric methods. Journal of the American Society for Horticultural Science 83, 769-771.

Asen, S. and Griesbach, R. (1983).
High pressure liquid chromatographic analysis of flavonoids in geranium florets as adjunct for cultivar identification. Journal of the American Society for Horticultural Sciences 108, 845-850.

Bauer, H. and Treutter, D. (1990a).
Identification of *Pelargonium* genotypes by phenolic 'fingerprints'. I. Separation and identification of phenolic compounds in leaves. Gartenbauwissenschaft 55, 113-118.

Bauer, H. and Treutter, D. (1990b).
Identification of *Pelargonium* genotypes by phenolic 'fingerprints'. II. Cultivar identification by HPLC analysis of leaf phenols combined with discriminant analysis. Gartenbauwissenschaft 55, 187-191.

Bissessur, D. (1990).
The HPLC analysis of flower pigments in zonal pelargoniums.
M.Sc. Thesis, University of Wales, Swansea.

Buswell, G.E. (1978).
Flower colour and anthocyanin inheritance of tetraploid *Pelargonium* × *hortorum* Bailey. Ph.D. Thesis, The Pennsylvania State University.

Craig, R. (1982).
Chromosomes, genes and cultivar improvements. In: Geranium III. (Eds. Mastalerz, J.W. and Holcomb, E.J.). 380-411. Pennsylvania Flower Growers.

Geissman, T.A. (1963).
Phenolic plant constituents. In: Comparative Biochemistry, ed. Florkin, M. and Stots, E.H., vol. 9C. Elsevier Publishing Company Ltd. Amsterdam, London & New York.

Harborne, J.B. (1961).
The anthocyanins of roses. Occurrence of peonin. Experientia 17, 72-73.

Kabwazi, H.H.N. (1993).
The genetics of flower colour and flavonoid pigments in the genus *Pelargonium*. Ph.D.Thesis, University of Cambridge, UK.

Kobayashi, K., Kakihara, F. and Kato, M. (1998).
Genetic analysis for the production of purple flower zonal Geranium (*Pelargonium* × *hortorum* Bailey). Breeding Science 48, 169-176.

Mitchell, K.A., Markham, K.R. and Boase, M.R. (1998).
Pigment chemistry and colour of *Pelargonium* flowers. Phytochemistry 47, 355-361.

Munchi,A.A. (1995).
Genetics and chromatography of anthocyanins in flowers of zonal pelargoniums. Ph.D. Thesis, University of Wales Swansea.

Ribereau-Gayon, P. (1972).
Plant phenolics. Oliver and Boyd, Edinburgh.

Robinson, G.M. and Robinson, R. (1932).
A survey of anthocyanins. II. Biochemical Journal 26, 1647-1664.

Scott-Moncrieff, R. (1936).
A biochemical survey of some Mendelian factors for flower colour. Journal of Genetics 32, 117-170.

13
Pigment Analysis

The weight of pigment in a sample

The use of the high performance liquid chromatography (HPLC) technique has provided the method of choice for the quantitative analysis of anthocyanins in plants. Wu (1999) has successfully developed an efficient method for the quantitative analysis of anthocyanin pigments from crude extracts of flowers. The method has not previously been used for pelargonium flowers. It relies on data obtained from isolated pure samples of each pigment. Once this has been done, the method may be used to determine the amount of any individual pigment in any plant, as long as the identity of the pigment is known, without further need to isolate the pigment from a complex mixture.

Fresh flower petals were heated in 50ml of 2M HCl in a flask for 40min at 100^0C. The coloured extract was cooled, decanted from the plant tissue remaining, and washed twice with 2 × 20ml of ethyl acetate. The process removed the flavones when the ethyl acetate layer was discarded. The remaining aqueous layer was extracted with 50ml of amyl alcohol, which was separated off and concentrated to dryness by gently heating on a rotary evaporator in a water bath at 40^0C. The flask plus crude dry extract was weighed and the weight of extract determined. The anthocyanidin in the residue was dissolved in methonolic HCl (0.1% v/v of 2M HCL in methyl alcohol). Samples were analysed further by HPLC.

Analytical HPLC was carried out on a 3.9mm × 150mm Waters Nova-pak C_{18} column. Two solvents were used for the elution.

Solvent A:	1.5% H_3PO_4 in H_2O.	
Solvent B:	1.5% H_3PO_4, 20% CH_3COOH, 25% CH_3CN in H_2O.	

Linear gradient elution was used with solvent B varying from 45 to 85% over 25min. The flow rate was 0.9ml/min. UV/V absorption spectra were recorded using a Hewlett-Packard detector HP 1050, and the elution profile determined at a wavelength of 530nm.

Wu (1999) decided to investigate just two anthocyanins – pelargonidin and malvidin, because both pigments were available from a commercial source. We will consider the case of pelargonidin that is present in the red flowers of the cross 'Canasta' × 'Ice Crystal'. She first ran a sample of the authentic compound from the commercial source, and noted it peaked at a retention time of 6.47min on the HPLC spectrum. She next ran a sample of the extract from the cross and noted a likely peak at 6.03min. She then ran the extract plus the authentic sample together, and now they produced a single and larger peak at a retention time of 6.45min.

Clearly the peak in the extract was the same as with the authentic sample; it was pelargonidin.

She once more prepared a standard solution of the authentic compound, which must be pure and dry, and which gave a single clear peak on the HPLC spectrum. The standard solution was prepared with 0.8mg of pelargonidin chloride in 2.0ml of methanol. She also made a standard solution of an internal compound, which she chose as phenol. It had a good response in the detection system, an appropriate retention time, and produced a single clear peak on the HPLC spectrum. It was prepared as 0.5mg phenol in 1.0ml methanol. After preparing each solution equal volumes were mixed immediately before co-injecting them into the HPLC column. These procedures were necessary for calculating the response factor R_f of the pelargonidin as follows: -

$$R_f = \frac{A_1}{A_2} \times \frac{C_2}{C_1}$$

R_f = the response factor for the authentic compound (e.g. pelargonidin).
A_1 = the peak area of the authentic compound on the HPLC spectrum of authentic compound plus internal standard.
A_2 = the peak area of the internal standard compound on the HPLC spectrum of authentic compound plus internal standard.
C_1 = original concentration of the authentic compound.
C_2 = original concentration of the internal standard compound.

The areas and the run time for the peaks were calculated by the computer and plotted out at the bottom of the spectrum.

A_1 = 120181, retention time 6.59min.
A_2 = 31128, retention time 3.13min.

We must now work out the concentration of the authentic compound. The molecular formula and the molecular weight of pelargonidin chloride is $C_{15}H_{11}O_5Cl$ = 306.7.

$$1M = 306.7 \text{ g/l} = 0.3067 \text{ g/ml}$$

Actual concentration $\quad$ = 0.8mg in 2.0ml CH_3OH = 0.0004 g/ml

$$C_1 = \frac{0.0004}{0.3067}$$

$$C_1 = 1.3 \times 10^{-3}M$$

Similarly, we must work out the concentration of the internal standard. The molecular formula and the molecular weight of phenol is C_6H_6O = 94.11.

$$1M = 94.11 \text{ g/l} = 0.09411 \text{ g/ml}$$

Actual concentration $\quad$ = 0.5mg in 1.0ml CH_3OH = 0.0005 g/ml

$$C_2 = \frac{0.0005}{0.09411}$$

$$C_2 = 5.3 \times 10^{-3}M$$

Equivalent volumes of C_1 and C_2 were used. Therefore the concentration of the solution of the authentic compound after mixing with the solution of the internal standard was: -

$$C_1' = \frac{C_1 \times V_1}{V_1 + V_2} = 0.65\text{mM}$$

Similarly, the concentration of the solution of the internal standard after mixing with the solution of the authentic compound was: -

$$C_2' = \frac{C_2 \times V_2}{V_1 + V_2} = 2.65\text{mM}$$

We can now calculate the response factor as follows: -

$$R_f = \frac{A_1 \times C_2'}{A_2 \times C_1'} = \frac{120181}{31128} \times \frac{2.65 \times 10^{-3}}{6.5 \times 10^{-4}}$$
$$= 3.8109 \times 4.077$$
$$R_f = 15.74$$

The average R_f for pelargonidin was 14.33 obtained by three independent experiments. Once a repeatable R_f value for certain individual compounds is established in HPLC, it can be used with confidence for the analysis of the corresponding compound in any plant under investigation. By the same process Wu obtained a response factor for malvidin of 17.22. We can now use the response factor for the weight and the yield of pelargonidin in a sample.

Wu took freshly opened red flowers from 'Red Satisfaction' and prepared the extract as she did originally. The extract was then dried under vacuum at room temperature for two days. A dark red plasma resulted. The plasma was weighed. The amount of solvent that was needed to dissolve this plasma depended on the peak area as determined by HPLC. For 'Red Satisfaction', with a dry sample weight of 14.77mg, it was necessary to add 0.6ml of methanol/TVA 0.1%, because at this concentration the HPLC produced an acceptable elution trace; the peak remained unbroken on the HPLC chart. The solution of the crude extract of fresh flowers is marked C_3.

The concentration of the internal standard is calculated as before: -
The internal standard solution was made up from 33mg phenol in 1ml of methanol.

$$= 33.00\text{mg per ml.}$$
$$= 0.033\text{g/ml.}$$
$$0.09411\text{g/ml} \quad (\text{Mr phenol})$$

Therefore concentration of internal standard, $C_{is} = 0.3506\text{M}$.
The concentration of both solutions after mixing is reduced by half.
Therefore concentration of $C_{is} = \frac{0.3506}{2} = 0.1753$.

The two solutions were mixed in equal volumes and 20µl injected into the HPLC column.

The value of the area for pelargonidin, A_3, under the peak at the retention time of 5.92 minutes was 422696.

The value of the area for the internal standard, A_2, was 169355.

$$C_3' = \frac{A_3}{A_2} \times \frac{C_2'}{R_{f\ (pelargonidin)}}$$

$$C_3' = \frac{422696}{169355} \times \frac{0.1753}{14.33}$$

$$= 30.53\text{mM}$$

But C_3' is the concentration of pigment in the crude extract after mixing with the internal standard solution.

$$C_3 = 2 \times C_3'$$
$$= 2 \times 30.53$$
$$= 61.06\text{mM}$$

If N_3 is the number of moles of pigment in the crude extract, and V_3 is the volume,

$$N_3 = C_3 \times V_3$$
$$= 6.106 \times 0.6 = 3.664 \times 10^{-2}\ \text{mM}$$

and W_3 is the mass of the pigment in the crude extract

$$W_3 = N_3 \times Mr_3$$
$$= 3.664 \times 10^{-2} \times 306.7$$
$$= 11.24\text{mg}$$

$$\text{Yield \%} = \frac{\text{Weight of pigment}}{\text{Weight of crude extract}}$$

$$= \frac{11.24}{14.77} \times 100 = 76.1\%$$

Thus the weight of pelargonidin in the crude extract from 'Red Satisfaction' is 11.24mg, and this represents 76.1% of the yield.

Wu found that the cross 'Arsona' × 'Kardino' produced purple-pink and rose-pink progeny; they contained malvidin but not pelargonidin. The malvidin had a yield of 0.5% and 0.1% suggesting they belonged to the CD-2 and CD-1 types respectively. With 'Red Satisfaction' selfed, the dark red flowers yielded about 76% pelargonidin and 15-24% malvidin, suggesting a PC-5 type. Crimson flowers yielded 29% pelargonidin and just over 2% malvidin, suggesting that it was a PCD-5 type. The dark red flowers from a second generation 'Canasta' selfed yielded 34-42% pelargonidin, but no malvidin, suggesting they were a PC-2 type. The light red flowers from the same parent yielded 2-6% pelargonidin and 0-3% malvidin. A dark red flowered plant with a white splash from the same self had a yield of 17% pelargonidin and no malvidin. Thus, even with only two pigments looked at, we are able to classify the plants at least approximately. Evidently the yield is very variable, and the minor component may sometimes produce too small a peak to be measurable. The technique needs to be developed further so that we can obtain an accurate R_f value for cyanidin, peonidin and delphinidin, and if possible petunidin. It should enable us to obtain an accurate assessment of the main pigments for any cultivar we wish to know.

We have seen in Kabwazi's classification that the five main pigments can exist in a number of different combinations. We cannot be certain that Kabwazi has identified them all. In fact there are 32 possible combinations of the five pigments as given by the combination formula ^nC_r where n = total number of pigments and r = number of pigments produced, and ^nC_r = n! / r!(n-r)!. The number of pigments produced may vary from all five down to none of them, with many combinations in between. These follow Pascal's triangle, which may be worked out as $^5C_5$, $^5C_4$, $^5C_3$, $^5C_2$, $^5C_1$ and $^5C_0$, which gives the frequencies of 1, 5, 10, 10, 5, and 1. For example, $^5C_2$ gives the number of combinations of the five pigments in which only two, any two, are being produced.

$$^5C_2 = 5! / 2!(5-2)!$$
$$= 5! / 2! \times 3!$$
$$= 10$$

In addition, Kabwazi included the gene M/m, which brings the number of combinations up to 64. Yet he based his classification on only 14 flavonoid patterns. This implies that many of the combinations do not occur. It follows that certain combinations of pigments are always produced together, or are not produced together, or as one increases the other decreases. The production of such pigments is correlated with each other.

The partial correlation between pigments

The correlation coefficient is a measure of interdependence or association that indicates the closeness or intensity of the association without defining it. To measure any relationship present, one uses a correlation coefficient (r) test, which depends on plotting the products of X measurements against Y, to look at the way they are related and the strength of the relationship. The coefficients are expressed as a number between + 1 and – 1, the stronger the positive or negative relationship between the variables respectively. Thus if r > 0, Y is positively correlated with X, but if r < 0, Y is negatively correlated with X. Finally, if r = 0, there is no evidence of either type of correlation and Y is considered to vary independently of X. The computing formula of the simple correlation coefficient is: -

$$\text{Correlation } r = \frac{\Sigma XY / n}{\sqrt{(\text{Variance } X)(\text{Variance } Y)}}$$

The fast computing formula (Erickson and Nosanchuk 1992) is sometimes called the Pearson coefficient: -

$$\text{Correlation } r = \frac{N\Sigma XY - (\Sigma X)(\Sigma Y)}{\sqrt{[N\Sigma X^2 - (\Sigma X)^2][N\Sigma Y^2 - (\Sigma Y)^2]}}$$

The coefficient focuses on the strength of the fit rather than on the fit itself; it is much used in biology.

Rather less well known is the situation where there is a third independent variable (X_2). The correlations may become divided unequally between the three $(X_1, Y$ and $X_2)$, because when any variable (X_1) is held constant or controlled, the relationship between the other two $(Y$ and $X_2)$ may change greatly, slightly or not at all. Similarly, the relationship between $(Y$ and $X_1)$ when (X_2) is controlled. Thus, we can obtain a comparable measure of the correlation with one variable controlled each time, and so this is called the first order partial correlation (Erickson and Nosanchuk 1992) as follows: -

$$\text{Partial correlation} \quad = rX_2YX_1 = \frac{rX_2Y - (rX_2X_1)(rYX_1)}{\sqrt{1 - r^2X_2X_1} \sqrt{1 - r^2YX_1}}$$

Where

1   rX_2YX_1 = the partial correlation of X_2 and Y with X_1 controlled.

2   $rX_2Y - (rX_2X_1)(rYX_1)$ = the correlation between X_2 and Y before controlling for X_1 – the correlation of X_1 with X_2 multiplied by the correlation of X_1 with Y (to remove the effects of X_1).

3   $\sqrt{1 - r^2X_2X_1} \sqrt{1 - r^2YX_1}$ = the amount of X_2 that X_1 does not explain, and the amount of Y that X_1 does not explain. This is a kind of normalizing or standardizing of the factors that ensures that our partial correlation will run from + 1 to – 1 as in the simple correlation.

This form of statistical control is enormously useful for examining and interpreting the causal relationship between variables by controlling one variable each time. Munchi (1995) looked at four pigments, pelargonidin, cyanidin, peonidin and malvidin, so he was able to make comparisons between the four variables. He ran the test of the partial coefficients as follows: -

1   Zero order partial correlation coefficients. Correlation between any two variables without taking into account possible effects of other variables.

2   First order partial correlation coefficients. Correlation between two variables after maintaining a third variable constant.

3   Second order partial correlation coefficients. Correlation between two variables after maintaining the third and fourth variable constant.

He chose flowers from a range of flower colours and measured the quantities of the four pigments by HPLC. He used a slightly different method from that of Wu, and he worked out the amount of each pigment from the area under the peak, and the concentration and area of the standard, in terms of µg/g. He did not calculate the R_f values or the exact weights of each pigment. From the many concentrations of the pigments taken from different flowers he was able to calculate the partial coefficients using the SPSS (Statistical package for social scientists) and Microsoft Windows computer programme.

The most common pigments found were pelargonidin, malvidin, and peonidin, which accounted for 93.1% of all pigment, which was found in 98.4% of the samples. Cyanidin, which was found in 6.9% of total pigments, was found in 93.4% of the samples. The small amount of pigment that was not accounted for was probably delphinidin and a trace of petunidin. The partial correlation coefficients are set out in figures 13.1 to 13.3. Each result is expressed as the partial coefficient, and below the probability of it being significant. Values greater than $P = 0.05$ are assumed to be insignificant; all other values are significant ($P < 0.05, 0.01$) or highly significant ($P < 0.001$). The partial coefficients showed the following relationships among the pigments.

First correlated Pigment	Correlation coefficient and significance level Second correlated pigment		
	Cyanidin	Peonidin	Malvidin
Pelargonidin	- 0.028	0.579	0.425
	P = 0.840	P = < 0.001	P = < 0.001
Cyanidin	-----	- 0.426	- 0.081
		P = < 0.001	P = 0.555
Peonidin	-----	-----	0.469
			P = < 0.001

Fig. 13.1. Zero order partial coefficients displayed with the probability levels

First correlated Pigment	Controlled pigments, Correlation coefficient and significance level Second correlated pigment					
	Cyanidin		Peonidin		Malvidin	
Pelargonidin	[Pn] 0.287	[Mv] 0.007	[Mv] 0.475	[Cy] 0.627	[Pn] 0.212	[Cy] 0.424
	P = 0.027	P = 0.957	P = < 0.001	P = < 0.001	P = 0.119	P = < 0.001
Cyanidin	-----		[Pg] - 0.503	[Mv] - 0.441	[Pg] - 0.076	[Pn] 0.150
			P = < 0.001	P = < 0.001	P = 0.581	P = 0.275
Peonidin	-----		-----		[Pg] 0.303	[Cy] 0.482
					P = 0.025	P = < 0.001

Fig. 13.2. First order partial correlation coefficients displayed with the probability levels.

First correlated pigment	Controlled pigments, Correlation coefficient and significance level Second correlated pigment		
	Cyanidin	Peonidin	Malvidin
Pelargonidin	[Pn + Mv] 0.275	[Mv + Cy] 0.533	[Pn + Cy] 0.178
	P = 0.044	P = < 0.001	P = 0.198
Cyanidin	-----	[Pg + Mv] - 0.506	[Pg + Pn] 0.093
		P = < 0.001	P = 0.505
Peonidin	-----	-----	[Pg + Cy] 0.307
			P = 0.024

Fig. 13.3. Second order partial correlation coefficients displayed with the probability levels.

1. Pelargonidin with cyanidin.
    1 Zero order negative and not significant.
    2 First order positive and not significant with malvidin fixed, but just significant with peonidin fixed.
    3 Second order positive and just significant with both malvidin and peonidin fixed.

Hence there is a slight positive relationship between pigments when peonidin is fixed. Without fixing peonidin the relationship between pelargonidin and cyanidin is masked by the strong relationship that exists between pelargonidin and peonidin and between cyanidin and peonidin.

2. Pelargonidin with peonidin.
    1 Zero order positive and highly significant.
    2 First order positive and highly significant when cyanidin or malvidin are fixed.
    3 Second order positive and highly significant when cyanidin and malvidin are both fixed.

Hence the relationship between pelargonidin and peonidin is positive and highly significant.

3. Pelargonidin and malvidin.
    1 Zero order positive and highly significant.
    2 First order positive and highly significant with cyanidin fixed, but not with peonidin fixed.
    3 Second order positive but not significant with cyanidin and peonidin both fixed.

Hence the relationship between pigments is not significant. Zero order correlation is spurious owing to the highly significant correlation between pelargonidin and peonidin and between peonidin and malvidin.

4. Cyanidin and peonidin.
    1 Zero order negative and highly significant.
    2 First order negative and highly significant with either pelargonidin or malvidin fixed.
    3 Second order negative and highly significant with both pelargonidin and malvidin fixed.

Hence there is a strong negative correlation between cyanidin and peonidin.

5. Cyanidin and malvidin.
    1 Zero order negative and not significant.
    2 First order negative and not significant with pelargonidin fixed, but positive and not significant with peonidin fixed.
    3 Second order positive and not significant with both pelargonidin and peonidin fixed.

Hence there is no relationship between cyanidin and malvidin.

6. Peonidin and malvidin.

    1   Zero order positive and highly significant.
    2   First order positive and highly significant with cyanidin fixed, but only just significant with pelargonidin fixed.
    3   Second order positive and just significant with both pelargonidin and cyanidin fixed.

Hence there is a slight positive relationship between the pigments. The initial correlation appears to be uninfluenced by cyanidin, but is greatly diminished by fixing pelargonidin, which exhibits a strong positive zero order correlation with both peonidin and malvidin.

The strong positive or negative correlations are very interesting, but we need to introduce the fifth pigment. Moreover, the correlations are the result of comparing the pigments under a particular set of conditions. They may not be true under all conditions. In future, we shall need to ask particular questions and take samples from particular groups of plants. The method is a good one, and we may expect to see useful comparisons made in the future.

References

Erickson, B.H. and Nosanchuk, T.A. (1992).
Understanding data. 2nd ed. St. Edmundsbury Press, Great Britain.

Kabwazi, H.H.N. (1993).
The genetics of flower colour and flavonoid pigments in the genus *Pelargonium.*
Ph.D.Thesis, University of Cambridge, UK.

Munchi,A.A. (1995).
Genetics and chromatography of anthocyanins in flowers of zonal pelargoniums.
Ph.D.Thesis, University of Wales Swansea.

Wu, G.F. (1999).
The genetics and biochemistry of flower pigments and flower patterns in
Pelargonium × hortorum. Ph.D.Thesis, University of Wales Swansea.

14
Linkage

At present less than 40 genes are known in zonal pelargoniums (Table 14.1).

Gene Symbols	Description of the Genes
Aur/Aur+	Aurea or golden leaf. **AurAur** green; **Aur+Aur+** cotyledons white.
Ba/ba	Bar pattern on flowers. Pigment localised on both sides near base of each of the lower triplet of petals.
Ca^b/ca^q	Broad petal versus narrow quill shaped petal. Cactus flowered.
Ce/ce	Picotee pattern on flowers. A narrow coloured band on edge of petal.
Cr/cr	Crimson coloured petals.
D/d, also **S/s**	Double versus single flowers. **Dd** semi-double flowers.
D/d	Lightens, or darkens flower colour. Not the same gene as above.
Dw/dw	Dwarf growth, **Dwdw** semi-dwarf and **dwdw** tall growth.
G/g	Purple versus green leaf colour.
I/i	The **I** gene interacts with the **R1** gene to give red orange flower colour in the presence of **oror**. With **ii** pure orange flowers result.
M1/m1 **M2/m2** **M3/m3**	Gene modifying the number of petals in double flowers. The recessives **m1m1** and **m2m2** add 10 perianth parts, and **m3m3** adds 20 perianth parts.
Ms1/ms1 **Ms2/ms2**	Male fertile versus male sterile.
Ms3/ms3	Male fertile versus male sterile. Independent origin from above.
Mu/mu	Mutator gene invoked to explain flower variegation.
Or/or	Or needed for red flowers, **oror** gives orange flowers.
P/p	Green versus pale green leaves.
Pi/pi	Picotee pattern on flowers. It may be different from **Ce/ce**.
Pr1/pr1 **Pr2/pr2**	Plastid replication. When both dominants are present a type II segregation results. When either dominant is absent a type I segregation results.
Pu^v/Pu^p/pu	Triple alleles for violet or purple flower colour.
Pwe/pwe	Pink white-eye versus full pink flower.
R1/r1/r1^l, also **P/p** or **A/a** **R2/R2^c/r2**, also **Sa/sa** or **B/b**	Triple alleles of the **R1** gene. The two genes are complementary and when both dominants are present, the flower colour is red. Triple alleles of the **R2** gene.
Rm/rm	Red or pink marking on pattern genes.
Rst/rst	Red spotted trichomes versus spotless trichomes on petals.
V/V^{ws}/v **V/v**	Triple alleles for full colour, white splash or picotee. Red zone versus green zone. Full colour or variegated gene.
Ve^r/Ve/ve	Triple alleles for vein marking on the upper pair of petals.
W/w	Full colour **WW**, diluted colour **Ww** and white **ww**, but only if the **r1r1r2r2** genotype is present.
W/w (needs changing)	White flowers in which the white gene suppresses the activity of **R1R1R2R2**.
Zo/Zo^p/Zo^w/Zo^m **Zo^b/Zo^l**	Multiple alleles affecting the zonal pattern of the leaves.

Fig. 14.1. A list of genes known to the author is given in the left column, and a brief description of them is given in the right hand column.

Yet we know that many more characters with alternative traits may be found among over a thousand cultivars. These can be analysed, it is not difficult to do. It takes just a few years and some careful recording. Furthermore, all of the existing known genes are examined with relatively few others. We know that the gene for double flowers D/d acts with the genes R1/r1, Ca^b/Ca^a, Ms3/ms3 and Pr1/pr1, but not how it acts with thirty other genes. With these four it assorts independently, there is no linkage. We know also that with nine pairs of chromosomes ($2n = 2x = 18$) there are nine linkage groups. So D/d will surely turn out to be linked with one or more of the genes tested. I have drawn up a table in which I have tested for independent assortment 22 pairs of genes taken from various sources (Table 14.2). These are based on 9: 3: 3: 1, 3: 3: 1: 1 or 1: 1: 1: 1 ratios in which the recombinant genotypes are clearly distinguished from the parental genotypes. I have excluded a few based on 9: 7: 9: 7 ratios or 12: 3: 1 or 9: 3: 4 ratios in which some of the parental and recombinant progeny have the same phenotype. Linkage can only be estimated by assuming the unobserved recombinant group is the same size as the observed recombinant group. Often there were more than two genes involved when the cross was made, but only two genes contributed. For example, when I looked at the semi-double red flower Dd,R1r1,R2r2 crossed with the single red flower dd,R1r1,R2R2 I was able to eliminate the R2/r2 gene because it does not segregate any r2r2 progeny, and therefore although present it does not matter.

Parents	Recombinants		Total		χ^2		Sum
F1 (Flower of Spring x Snowball) x Snowball. R1r1,R2r2 × r1r1,r2r2							
1R1-R2-	1 r1r1r2r2	1 R1-r2r2	1 r1r1R2-		R1: r1	R2: r2	P: R
31	25	38	32	126	1.143	0	1.556	1.699
F1 (Flower of Spring x Snowball) selfed. R1r1,R2r2							
9 R1-R2-	1 r1r1r2r2	3 R1-r2r2	3 r1r1R2-		R1: r1	R2: R2	P: R
38	7	16	13	77	0.974	3.156	2.426	6.556
Semi-double, red flower x Single, red flower. Dd,R1r1 × dd,R1r1							
3DdR1-	1 ddr1r1	1 Ddr1r1	3 ddR1-		D: d	R: r	P: R
30	11	10	29	80	0	0.067	0.050	0.117
Soft pink, type I x Red, type II. r1r1,pr2pr2 × R1r1,Pr2pr2							
1 R1r1 Pr2pr2	1 r1r1 pr2pr2	1 R1r1 pr2pr2	1 r1r1 Pr2pr2		R1: r1	Pr2: pr2	P: R
11	14	23	25	73	0.342	0.014	7.247*	7.603
Blush, feathery veins selfed. R1r1,Ve^{f}Ve							
9 R1-Ve^f-	1 r1r1Ve-	3 R1-Ve-	3 r1r1Ve^f-		R1: r1	Ve^f: Ve	P: R
22	4	11	7	44	0	1.939	0.040	1.979
Red flower, golden leaf x Soft-pink flower, green leaf. R2r2,AurAur$^+$ × r1r2,AurAur							
1 R2r2 Aur$^+$Aur	1 r2r2 AurAur	1 R2r2 AurAur	1 r2r2 Aur$^+$Aur		R2: r2	Aur$^+$: Aur	P: R
71	80	91	84	326	0.017	0.785	1.767	2.569
Non-red, male fertile x Red, male fertile. r2r2,Msms × R2r2,Msms							
3 r2r2 Msms	1R2r2 msms	3 R2r2 Msms	1r2r2 msms		R2: r2	Ms: ms	P: R
102	35	108	42	287	0.003	0.512	0.589	1.104
Crimson selfed. R2r2,Pupu							
9 R2-Pu-	1 r2r2 pupu	3 R2- pupu	3 r2r2 Pupu		R2: r2	Pu: pu	P: R
52	3	20	27	102	1.059	0.327	4.187*	5.573
Red, normal veins x Soft pink, veinless. R2r2,Veve × r2r2,veve*							
1R2r2Vve	1 r2r2veve	1 r2r2Vve	1 R2r2vev		R2: r2	Ve: ve	P: R
18	12	7	6	43	1.140	0.581	6.721*	8.442
Red, normal veins selfed. R2r2,Veve*							
9 R2r2Vv	1r2r2vv	3 r2r2Vv	3 R2r2vv		R2: r2	Ve: ve	P: R
79	14	12	23	128	1.500	1.042	8.680*	11.222
Salmon, medium wide zone selfed. R2r2,Zo^{w}Zo^p							
9 R2r2 Zo^{w}Zo^p	1 r2r2 Zo^{p}Zo^p	3 r2r2 Zo^{w}Zo^p	3 R2r2 Zo^{p}Zo^p		R2: r2	Zo^w: Zo^p	P: R
42	3	10	12	67	1.119	0.244	0.015	1.378

*Incomplete genotypes shown.

Semi-double, quill shaped flower x Single flower, normal. $Dd,Ca^bCa^q \times dd,Ca^bCa^b$

1 Dd Ca^bCa^q	1 dd Ca^bCa^b	1 Dd Ca^bCa^b	1 dd Ca^bCa^q		D: d	Ca^b: Ca^q	P: R	
15	24	16	14	69	0.710	1.754	1.174	3.638

Semi-double, male fertile selfed. $Dd,Msms$

9 Dd Msms	1 dd msms	3 Dd msms	3 dd Msms		D: d	Ms: ms	P: R	
80	7	21	27	135	0.002	1.306	0.001	1.309

Semi-double, male fertile x Single, male fertile. $Dd,Msms \times dd,Msms$

3 Dd Msms	1 dd msms	1 Dd msms	3 dd Msms		D: d	Ms: ms	P: R	
68	26	26	60	180	0.356	1.452	0.355	2.163

Semi-double, type II x Semi-double, type I. $Dd,Pr1pr1 \times dd,pr1pr1$

3 Dd Pr1pr1	1 dd pr1pr1	3 Dd pr1pr1	1 dd Pr1pr1		D: d	Pr1: pr1	P: R	
22	11	22	12	67	3.109	0.015	0.015	3.139

Light red, full flower selfed. Dd,VV^{ws} (Not semi-double)

9 Dd VV^{ws}	1dd $V^{ws}V^{ws}$	3 Dd $V^{ws}V^{ws}$	3 dd VV^{ws}		D: d	V: V^{ws}	P: R	
21	1	8	8	38	0.035	0.035	0.947	1.017

Golden, pink white eyeless x Green, pink white eye. $Aur^+Aur,pwepwe \times AurAur,Pwepwe$

1 Aur^+Aur pwepwe	1 AurAur Pwepwe	1 Aur^+Aur Pwepwe	1 AurAur pwepwe		Aur^+: Aur	Pwe: pwe	P: R	
50	59	68	60	237	0.004	1.219	1.523	2.746

Golden, red spotted trichome x Green, spotless. $Aur^+Aur,Rstrst \times AurAur,rstrst$

1 Aur^+Aur Rstrst	1 AurAur rstrst	1 Aur^+Aur rstrst	1 AurAur Rstrst		Aur^+: Aur	Rst: rst	P: R	
77	77	69	73	296	0.054	0.054	0.486	0.594

Golden, male fertile x Green, male fertile. $Aur^+Aur,Msms \times AurAur,Msms$

3 Aur^+Aur Msms	1 AurAur msms	1 Aur^+Aur msms	3 AurAur Msms		Aur^+: Aur	Ms: ms	P: R	
115	52	36	126	329	2.216	0.536	0.076	2.828

Golden, type II x Green, type I. $Aur^+Aur,Pr1pr1 \times AurAur,pr1pr1$

1 Aur^+Aur Pr1pr1	1 AurAur pr1pr1	1 Aur^+Aur pr1pr1	1 AurAur Pr1pr1		Aur^+: Aur	Pr1: pr1	P: R	
38	38	26	42	144	1.777	1.777	0.444	3.998

Male fertile, red spotted trichomes x Male fertile, spotless. $Msms,Rstrst \times Msms,rstrst$

3 Msms Rstrst	1 msms rstrst	3 Msms rstrst	1 msms Rstrst		Ms: ms	Rst: rst	P: R	
64	21	65	26	176	0.273	0.091	0.204	0.568

Red spotted trichomes, eyeless x Spotless, pink white eye. Rstrst,pwepwe × rstrst,Pwepwe

1 Rstrst pwepwe	1 rstrst Pwepwe	1 Rstrst Pwepwe	1 rstrst pwepwe		Rst: rst	Pwe: pwe	P: R	
58	65	62	52	237	0.038	1.219	0.342	1.599

Red spotted trichomes, type II x Spotless, type I. Rstrst,Prlprl × rstrst,prlprl

1 Rstrst Prlprl	1 rstrst prlprl	1 Rstrst prlprl	1 rstrst Prlprl		Rst: rst	Prl: prl *	P: R	
15	5	8	20	48	0.083	10.083	1.337	11.503

Pink white eye, male fertile selfed. Pwepwe,Msms

9 Pwepwe Msms	1 pwepwe msms	3 Pwepwe msms	3 pwepwe Msms		Pwe: pwe	Ms: ms	P: R	
61	7	19	24	111	0.508	0.147	0.025	0.680

Pink white eyeless, male fertile x White eyed, male fertile. pwepwe,Msms × Pwepwe,Msms

3 pwepwe Msms	1 Pwepwe msms	3 Pwepwe Msms	1 pwepwe msms		Pwe: pwe	Ms: ms	P: R	
64	26	71	15	176	1.841	0.273	0.091	2.205

Pink white eyeless, type I x White eyed, type II. pwepwe,prlprl × Pwepwe,Prlprl

1 pwepwe prlprl	1 Pwepwe Prlprl	1 pwepwe Prlprl	1Pwepwe prlprl		Pwe: pwe	Prl: prl	P: R	
12	11	6	18	47	2.574	3.596	0.021	6.191

Table 14.1. The segregation is tested for a number of different genes according to the 1:1:1:1 ratio, or the 9:3:3:1 or the 3:3:1:1 ratio. The gene pairs are tested for their agreement with the chi-square ratio, and the frequency of parent to recombinant is also tested. Individual chi-square values above 3.841 are regarded as significant at the 5 per cent level, above 6.635 at the 1 per cent level. One value indicates that the recombinants were more frequent than the parents in this experiment. Two values strongly indicate that there is linkage between R2/r2 and Ve/ve, and a third value indicates that there may be linkage between R2/r2 and Pu/pu. Otherwise the data demonstrate that the gene pairs are assorting independently of one another.

If we were to take any two genes at a time, how many combinations would we require to include 30 gene pairs? The answer is given by the combination formula $^{n}C_{r}$ where n = the number of pairs and r = two genes per pair, and $^{n}C_{r} = n!/r!(n-r)!$

$$^{n}C_{r} = 30!/2!(30-2)!$$
$$= 30!/2! \times 28!$$
$$= 435$$

Thus if we took as the model the double heterozygote Aa,Bb crossed with the double homozygous recessive aa,bb for 30 pairs of genes, we would need to make 435 crosses. There are plenty of crosses for everyone. Some crosses may not be very practical, but if the crosses were chosen at random by several people there is a fair chance that there would be no overlap. Even if there were overlaps a similar result would be useful confirmation.

The detection of linkage is by analysing the data according to the method of orthogonal contrasts. As indicated in the table, the F2 or backcross ratio segregates into four genotypes each with a different combination of two genes. The three contrasts are therefore the first dominant gene against its alternative allele, the second contrast the second dominant gene against its alternative allele, and the third contrast the parental genotypes against the recombinant genotypes. Each of these contrasts has one degree of freedom, and produces a chi-square value for which the probability value may be read from a table. Thus if the first contrast is 1 + 2 against 3 + 4, and the second contrast is 1 + 3 against 2 + 4, the third and final contrast is 1 + 4 against 2 + 3, there is no alternative. This is not necessarily the order in which they are written. The arrangement makes no difference. If needed suitable multiples are used to make the two sides of the equations equal. In one contrast a chi-square value greater that 3.841 is shown by one of the two pairs of genes segregating. This is the Pr1/pr1 gene in which the pr1 is clearly in considerable deficit, but it does not affect the other two contrasts. In four cases the parental: recombinant ratio is greater than our critical value at the 5% level. These values therefore detect linkage, but they do not estimate it. They indicate the value at which linkage may be estimated.

The estimate of linkage is measured by the frequency of recombinants over the total. This value is subject to a variance, which is dependent upon the total size of the population. The smaller the population size the greater the variance.

$$V_p = p(1 - p)/n$$

Where V_p = Variance, p = linkage estimate/ 100 and n = population size. The standard deviation S_p is equal to the square root of the variance; hence the smaller the population size the greater is the variance.

$$S_p = \sqrt{V_p}$$

If the estimate of linkage plus its variance overlaps 50% then there is no linkage, as the value is the same as independent assortment. This is what happened to the value of 4.187, it suggested we measure linkage but the estimate was inconclusive. The value of 7.247 gave an estimate for the linkage of 34.25% between R1/r1 and Pr2/pr2, with a standard deviation of 5.35% (Mather 1951). Hence, we may be 95% confident that the distance between them is between 28.7% and 39.8%. The two remaining chi-square values of 6.721 and 8.680 are for the same pair of genes. The first estimate is for 30.23% with a standard deviation of 7.0% that is between 23.23% and 37.23%; this is quite wide because of a relatively small total population size. The second estimate from a larger total is 27.34% with a standard deviation of +/- 3.93%, in other words for an estimated distance of 23.41% to 31.27% for the distance between the genes R2/r2 and Ve/ve. When the population is larger, the variance is less than that of the smaller population, and falls inside the limits of the smaller population.

In addition to the tests with two genes, Kabwazi (1993) analysed examples of multiple colour segregation involving several genes. These he tested for linkage, and for the segregation of individual genes, by the method of orthogonal contrasts. In no one was it necessary to estimate the recombination values, as all were apparently unlinked. His methods and results are summarised in table 14.2.

Orthogonal contrasts	Ratio segregating genes	χ^2
R1r1,Pupu,Crcr: Data: 32 crimson, 10 magenta, 6 red, 3 light-crimson, 19 salmon		
Overall ratio	27:9:9:3:16	1.862
$[(a+b+c+d)-(3e)]^2/3n$	3 **R1**-:1 **r1r1**	0.171
$[(a+b)-3(c+d)]^2/2.25n$	3 **Pu**-:1 **pupu**	1.429
$[(a+c)-3(b+d)]^2/2.25n$	3 **Cr**-:1 **crcr**	0.006
$[(a+9d)-3(b+c)]^2/6.75n$	Linkage **Cr-Pu**	0.256
R2r2,R1r1,Pupu,Crcr: Data: 30 crimson, 13 magenta, 6 red, 2 light-crimson, 6 salmon, 12 purple-pink, 3 rose-pink, 4 soft-pink.		
Overall ratio	81:27:27:9:48:36:12:16	10.394
$[(a+b+c+d+e)-3(f+g+h)]^2/3n$	3 **R2**-: 1 **r2r2**	0.000
$[(a+b+c+d+f+g)-3(e+h)]^2/3n$	3 **R1**-: 1 **r1r1**	5.684*
$[(a+b+f)-3(c+d+g)]^2/2.25n$	3 **Pu**-: 1 **pupu**	2.830
$[(a+c)-3(b+d)]^2/1.6875n$	3 **Cr**-: 1 **crcr**	0.632
$[(a+b+c+d+9h)-3(e+f+g)]^2/9n$	Linkage **R1-R2**	0.842
$[(a+b+9g)-3(c+d+f)]^2/6.75n$	Linkage **R1-Pu**	0.195
$[(a+9d)-3(b+c)^2/5.0625n$	Linkage **Pu-Cr**	0.211
R2r2,Pupu: Data: 13 magenta, 4 light-crimson, 6 purple-pink, 2 rose-pink		
Overall ratio	9:3:3:1	0.670
$[(a+b)-3(c+d)]^2/3n$	3 **R2**-: 1 **r2r2**	0.653
$[(a+c)-3(b+d)]^2/3n$	3 **Pu**-: 1 **pupu**	0.013
$[(a+9d)-3(b+c)^2/9n$	Linkage **R2-Pu**	0.004
Oror,Pupu,Crcr: Data: 56 crimson, 20 magenta, 16 red, 4 light-crimson, 10 orange		
Overall ratio	36:12:9:3:4:	2.204
$[(c+d)-3(e)]^2/0.75n$	3 **Or**-: 1 **oror**	1.258
$[(a+b)-3(c+d+e)^2/3n$	3 **Pu**-: 1 **pupu**	0.616
$[(a+c)-3(b+d)]^2/2.8125n$	3 **Cr**-: 1 **crcr**	0.000
$[(a+9d)-3(b+c)]^2/7.3125n$	Linkage **Cr-Pu**	0.330

Table 14.2. The orthogonal contrast method of establishing linkage, or not, for four genes affecting flower colour. *The individual segregation of the R1/r1 gene is significant at the 95% level, but this does not affect the other values. Adapted from Kabwazi (1993).

References

Kabwazi, H.H.N. (1993).
The genetics of flower colour and flavonoid pigments in the genus *Pelargonium*.
Ph.D.Thesis, University of Cambridge, UK.

Mather, K. (1951).
The measurement of linkage in heredity. Methuen and Co. Ltd., London.

15
Conclusions

In my experience the best source of variegated seedlings is the white-over-green 'Miss Burdette-Coutts' when crossed with green 'Dolly Varden' as the male parent. This gave 84 per cent variegated progeny, from which several white-over-green chimeras would have arisen. Unfortunately these progeny would be all rather alike and so alternative parents must also be sought. These might not be so easy to find. The female zygote is extraordinary versatile in its ability to encourage the biparental transmission of plastids. Indeed, we have found a great many green parents that transmit no white plastids at all after type I crosses. A great many more transmit only rarely and are extremely unlikely to give rise to stable chimeras. Relatively few transmit plastids approximately evenly, a requirement for stable chimeras. The situation is just as bad after type II crosses that produce large numbers of white seedlings as well as green, but very few and sometimes no variegated seedlings. The wisest course is to choose a white-over-green variegated plant and after crossing examine a good sample of embryos. This is best done under a × 10 hand lens or a low power stereo-microscope some three weeks after pollination, when the colour of the embryos is clear and the variegated embryos can easily be picked out. A number of variegated females can be assessed and the ones that produce the highest proportion of variegated embryos chosen. Providing the fertility is good they should produce a useful number of variegated seedlings. The male parent is usually of minor importance as far as plastid transmission is concerned, but may be carefully chosen to introduce other traits. If one is after a precise combination of variegation, flower colour and form, one may need to enter the crossing programme on several occasions.

Historically plastid inheritance in pelargonium is biparental, both normal and mutant plastids contributing through both parents. There is an element of chance, if a mutant plastid is chosen to replicate at the expense of the normal plastid a mutant embryo is produced. Equally likely, in many cases, the green plastids replicate and only the green embryos are formed. After G × W plastid crosses the plastid inheritance is maternal. If both plastids are transmitted the inheritance is biparental. But it is not all chance. The pattern of behaviour, whether type I or type II segregation, is proof that they are under overall nuclear control. This may be entirely maternal when the G × W cross gives only green progeny. This is not so very different from the situation in many plants where it has been shown that plastid inheritance is purely maternal.

In the case of maternal transmission of plastids, electron microscope studies, and DNA tracking studies, have shown that, at least in many cases, plastids fail to enter the generative cell at the time the developing pollen grain divides into a vegetative and generative cell. As the generative cell has no plastids, its two daughter cells, the two male gametes, have no plastids either and so carry none into the zygote at fertilisation. Hence the control of plastid inheritance is determined by the development phenomenon in which the plastids are excluded from the generative cell. The question of the mode of inheritance is thus reduced to the problem of deciding where is the gene located that controls this important developmental step? Is it more likely to be in the nucleus, in which case the inheritance is Mendelian, or outside the nucleus, in which case the inheritance is extra-nuclear and non-Mendelian?

Nobody has discovered a gene within the plastid genome that might be a candidate for the control of the restricted movement of all plastids within the developing pollen grain. On the contrary, it is widely agreed that mRNAs coded and transcribed by chloroplast DNA and translated on chloroplast ribosomes produce polypeptides that remain within the chloroplasts. No polypeptides have been produced that pass out through the chloroplast double membrane envelope to function outside the organelle. Hence there is no reason to believe that there are any chloroplast enzymes that function outside the chloroplast. Thus it seems highly probable that the control of maternal inheritance, or rather the control of male plastid removal, is under nuclear gene control, and so should not be referred to as non-Mendelian.

The difficulty is that the trait, which the gene controls, is lost at the moment of pollen grain mitosis. It passes through the female line but not the male line. Numerous other traits controlled by nuclear genes are not lost by one sex, but are transmitted unaltered as seen in the Mendelian ratios. It is the loss of this trait, in which the male plastid is removed from circulation that determines the purely maternal inheritance. As we have seen in the case of pelargonium, it is the nuclear genes that control plastid inheritance, but it is the plastid organelle that is inherited in a non-Mendelian fashion.

Another important subject is flower colour inheritance. Now we have good evidence for five genes controlling a wide range of flower colours, it is tempting to think that the analysis of flower genes is largely over. It is not; we have a number of problems still to be unravelled. We have a white colour that is only expressed when the two red genes are recessive and the white gene is also recessive. We also have a hint of a white gene that completely inhibits the two red genes; this gene is perhaps allelic with the full, white splash, picotee series. Further investigation is definitely needed. The gene that is a suppressor of colour may lurk in the population causing all kinds of problem for future investigators. We have a triple allelic series of the second red gene, but also it seems a possible third allele in the first red gene. Can this be true? We need to explore the possibilities. Is violet really the result of triple alleles at the purple locus or can it be shown that violet is controlled by a separate gene? My limited results need more tests. Similarly, we have an interesting series of triple alleles affecting the veins. Are the feathery veins really distinct from the normal and from vein less? More information is needed. Another problem relates to eye colours. There are many situations in which the eye colours are different from the main flower colour. These need careful investigation. Do different genes control them, and do they have an independent existence? Similarly is the red marking gene used in the formation of the flower patterns on a white background really different from the gene that gives the red flower colour? I think it is, but I should be glad of independent confirmation. All these and many more problems await keen investigators.

The flower doubling genes have escaped our attention so far, but now that double flowers are so common among our cultivars they must be looked into. There are plenty of problems. Some of the semi-double cultivars have a greater range than others. Is this a subject for quantitative studies, or are there simple gene differences between them? In some cultivars the calyx parts seem to double as well as the perianth parts, in other cultivars only the perianth parts seem to be affected. Why is this? Could other genes affect them?

There are in fact comparatively few colours compared with the number of combinations of genes that could control them. So many combinations of genes may be having the same effect. Before we are in a position to say exactly how the pigments react together we will need to know rather more details about the precise combination with each colour. Do certain pigments always increase when others decrease, or are the pigments really independent of each other? Are certain pigments always formed before the others, or are they time independent? The methods needed to explore these problems have been outlined, but much more investigation will be needed in the future.

The leaf zones are at present controlled by as many as six alleles of a multiple allelic series. Will this be increased still further or has the limit been reached? The leaf colour is divided into two types, green and purple. Will we not find some more? Besides the anthocyanins that show themselves in the leaf, they are also present in the main stem, the peduncles of the inflorescence, and the individual pedicels of each flower. Is this all the effect of one gene, or are these multiple effects which can be separated and subject to future genetic analysis? A similar in depth analysis is needed into the growth and habit of the whole plant. One can clearly see differences, but the division between them is not sharp enough for the simple genetic analysis. Can major differences be separated, or must we leave all to quantitative analysis?

I have not touched on the problem of the various steps in the pathway of pigment synthesis. Kabwazi looked at this, but he did not take us very far. We need much more information, in particular the many genes that are involved in the early stages. These have yet to be identified. The lack of knowledge we see repeated in the absence of all but the very beginnings of linkage groups. It will require the assistance of many amateur pelargonium breeders to fill this gap. The identification of all kinds of genes is a task for the future.

On the more positive side, the recognition of how chimeras are formed, how they are controlled, and how they may alter during development is now fairly clear. They caused a lot of enquiry in the past, but now most of the mysteries are solved. The knowledge is there. Now we have ample warning of the effect of chimeras on the different layers, and how these can affect the breeding results to give unexpected consequences. This is truly a success story.

Hybrid variegation is another success story, but this time at the beginning. It enables chimeras to be made from certain green species, and embryo culture methods may allow the delicate embryos to develop. These experimental methods allow new combinations of genes into the gene pool from which, by careful selection, new and interesting plants should arise. No doubt much crossing will be needed, but the eventual outcome seems assured, a really challenging new field.

The pelargonium is the basis of a huge commercial enterprise employing thousands of people in many parts of the world. They have not shown themselves to be particularly interested in genes, but rather they pursue new cultivars with great zeal. We owe them much. The amateur breeder will have to remain the main contributor to the basic knowledge of pelargonium that I have outlined in this book.

16
Mendelian Genetics

As the main text of this book uses genetic analysis, I felt I should write this additional section to illustrate some of the main principles. This should be especially helpful to those among you with minimal understanding of genetics, but who are sufficiently interested to want to improve their knowledge. For the most part I have taken data from original papers and modified it, and interpreted it, to make my own view clear.

I begin with Mendel's famous paper, but I have changed the tables a little and have ignored the rest of the paper, but I believe I have covered the important details. This is followed by the Punnett Square method of explaining the Mendelian ratios for the main crosses. Afterwards I introduce the use of symbols for representing genes.

I introduce the chi-square test for the goodness of fit between observed and expected results, and the associated concepts of degrees of freedom and probability. The chi-square value is frequently referred to in the main text; its importance cannot be over-estimated. It is a great confidence booster to learn that a ratio is not too far from the normal. I look at the standard method of calculating chi-square, and show how the alternative methods are both more precise and easier to use. There follows a brief account of partial dominance and partial lethality leading into the calculation of the heterogeneity chi-square when dealing with many varied results of repeating crosses.

A section on permutation and combination leads into the binomial distribution. This may seem incongruous, but in fact I show how they can all be used when asking various kinds of questions in genetics. They help to show how the Mendelian ratios are related to the known mathematical laws. They show how one can develop more complicated ratios simply by expanding the existing ones.

In the section on partial lethality, and on dominant epistasis, I consider the effect on the chi-square value, and on one kind of gene interaction. This leads to two cases of how we can partition the chi-square value with two degrees of freedom into orthogonal contrasts each with a single degree of freedom. This is not normally considered in genetic texts, although it is particularly useful for understanding the structure of the genetic cross. Breaking down the chi-square value into its orthogonal contrasts is especially useful when looking for linkage.

It often happens that one is not too sure which of two alternatives the data fit best. How to decide, with a known probability of being correct, is shown. This leads into the problem of what family size must one choose in order to be reasonably certain of obtaining at least one, or a number of them, of say known recessives. A problem that may regularly face the plant breeder, but one he is unlikely to find in the standard genetic textbook. The solution is not too difficult if we only want a single plant; we have only to know the fraction expected and the probability level. But if we want more plants then additional methods need applying.

There follows several sections on linkage, firstly simple cases between the F1 backcrossed to the recessive. An estimate of the map distance and how to calculate the standard error is given. Further examples include the three-point test cross, which plots the position of and the recombination between three linked genes, and the situation with incomplete dominance. Finally, there is the special formula for calculating linkage between two genes in coupling or repulsion after selfing the double heterozygote, and how this compares with the backcross. Lastly, there is an example of how to order four linked genes after crosses between them.

There are additional examples in the main text, but these sections should give a good indication of the genetic analysis involved. Some of these may be hard to find, yet they are all relevant to the kind of analysis that is performed with zonal pelargoniums.

Mendel's paper

Near the beginning of his paper, Mendel (see Stern and Sherwood 1966) pointed out that the selection of plants must be made with great care in order not to jeopardize all possibility of success from the outset. He suggested that the experimental plants must possess constant differing traits, they must be fully protected against interference from foreign pollen, and there should be no serious disturbance in the fertility of the hybrids and their offspring through successive generations. He realised that contamination by foreign pollen would lead to erroneous results, and that reduced fertility or sterility would render the experiments difficult or defeat them entirely.

Mendel recognized peas as having the qualifications demanded to a sufficient degree. He had collected forms possessing constant and differing traits, and the peas were naturally self-pollinating, and protected by their flower structure from foreign pollen, yet capable of being crossed when required. He achieved cross-pollination by opening the flower bud, removing the keel, and pulling out the unripe stamens with forceps, after which he dusted the stigma with foreign pollen. Additionally, the peas were easily cultivated either in pots or on open ground, and they had a relatively short life cycle. One might add that there were many flowers per plant, they did not open all at once, the seeds set well with several seeds per pod, and they were easily collected and stored until the next season.

Mendel began with 34 cultivars mostly from P. *sativum* plus a few from P. *quadratum*, P. *saccharatum* or P. *umbellatum*. Of these, 22 cultivars were selected for fertilization and planted annually throughout the entire experimental period. The peas showed differences in the length and colour of the stem; in the size and shape of leaves; in the position, colour and size of flowers; in the length of flower stalks; in the colour, shape and size of pods; in the shape and size of seeds; and in the colour of seed coats and cotyledons (endosperm). Some of these traits did not express a sufficiently sharp separation and so he finally reduced his experimental material to seven characters each with a pair of alternative traits (Table 16.1). From these stocks, he chose only the most vigorous plants for fertilization. Weak plants gave uncertain results, because of offspring that failed to flower or gave just a few inferior seeds both in the first and subsequent generations. Among his final selection, he maintained potted plants in the greenhouse as controls for the less well protected outdoor plants; however, he observed no significant disturbances.

Characters	Dominant trait	Recessive trait
Shape of ripe seeds in seed pod	Round, or nearly round with shallow depressions, if any, on surface	Irregularly angular and deeply wrinkled
Colour of albumen (cotyledons) in seed pod	Pale yellow, bright yellow, or orange	Intense green
Colour of seed coat	Grey, grey-brown, leather brown; associated with violet/purple flowers	White; associated with white flowers
Shape ripe pods	Smoothly arched, no constrictions	Deeply constricted and more or less wrinkled
Colour unripe pod	Light to dark green	Vivid yellow
Position of flowers	Axillary, along the main stem	Terminal, bunched at end of stem
Main stem length	Long stem, 6 to 7 feet	Short stem, 3/4 to 1 1/2 feet

Table 16.1. The seven characters chosen by Mendel.

Mendel's first result, over many years of testing, was the demonstration that the cultivar traits bred true. Secondly, when he made reciprocal crosses between the pair of alternate traits for each character, the hybrid progeny (we now call the F1) always expressed the trait of one parent while the trait from the other parent was undetected. The trait that passed unchanged into the hybrid, he called the dominant trait, and the one which remained hidden in the association, he called the recessive trait; the latter trait receded or disappeared entirely in the hybrids, but reappeared unchanged in their progeny. The same trait was dominant irrespective of the cross direction, and so Mendel was able to sum the data from reciprocal crosses.

Mendel grew his F1 hybrid plants and allowed them to self-pollinate, from which he collected abundant seeds that he scored directly, or which he grew up into the next generation of plants for scoring when mature (Table 16.2). In every pair of reciprocal crosses and for all experiments, along with individuals of the dominant trait there were now others in which the recessive trait had reappeared. The ratio of the frequency of dominant to recessive traits within these F2 segregating generations always varied around 3:1. Out of every four plants, on average, 3 received the dominant and 1 the recessive trait. Transitional forms were not observed. In the first two crosses he observed that the pods usually contained both round and angular seeds, or both yellow and green seeds Occasionally a pod contained seeds all of the dominant kind, but there were never more than five of the recessive, angular or green ones. Extreme examples of deviation were single plants producing 43 round and 2 angular seeds, and producing 14 round and 15 angular seeds. Similarly, he sampled plants with 32 yellow and 1 green seed, and with 20 yellow and 19 green seeds. Mendel attributed these deviations to chance. This is justified. The deviations occur either side of the expected segregation to give ratios >3:1 and <3:1, and even the large deviations are small enough to be expected occasionally from the large population of peas sampled.

| Characters | Traits | | Total | Ratio |
	Dominant	Recessive		D: R traits
Seed shape [253 hybrids]	5474 round	1850 angular	7324	2.96: 1
Cotyledon colour [258 hybrids]	6022 yellow	2001 green	8023	3.01: 1
Seed coat colour	705 grey	224 white	929	3.15: 1
Shape of pods	882 smooth	299 constricted	1181	2.95: 1
Colour unripe pods	428 green	152 yellow	580	2.82: 1
Position of flowers	651 axillary	207 terminal	858	3.14: 1
Length of stem	787 long	277 short	1064	2.84: 1

Table 16.2. The segregation frequencies of F2 seeds on F1 plants, or of F2 plants, after selfing the F1 hybrids between the pairs of traits for each of the seven characters.

Mendel's next step was to test the F2 generation by selfing samples of peas with the dominant and with the recessive traits. He found that plants with the recessive traits remained constant, whereas those with the dominant traits either remained constant or segregated again. For the first experiment, he tested 565 round seeded plants, and for the second experiment, he tested 519 plants that had yellow cotyledons. For the other five experiments, he tested 100 plants from each of the dominant traits. His results for this F3 generation showed that for all seven characters the plants from the F2 generation with the dominant traits divided, on average, into one constant for every two that again segregated (Table 16.3). Half the ratios were > 2:1 and half < 2:1. Hence, the original F2 had segregated in a ratio of 1 dominant and constant: 2 dominant and segregating: 1 recessive and constant.

| Characters | F3 Generation | | Ratio |
	F2: Dominant trait constant	F2: Dominant trait segregating	C: S
Seed shape	193 round	372 round & angular	1: 1.93
Cotyledon colour	166 yellow	353 yellow & green	1: 2.13
Seed coat colour	36 grey	64 grey & white	1: 1.78
Shape of pods	29 smooth	71 smooth & constricted	1: 2.45
Colour unripe pods [Repeat]	40 green 35 green	60 green & yellow 65 green & yellow	1: 1.50 1: 1.86
Position of flowers	33 axillary	67 axillary & terminal	1: 2.03
Length of stem	28 long	72 long & short	1: 2.57

Table 16.3. When the F2 with the dominant trait were selfed, the F3 generation shows a ratio in the F2 of about 1 constant: 2 segregating.

At this point Mendel felt that it would be useful to develop a model in order to present his observations in a simple form. He suggested that:

If A denotes the dominant, constant trait, and

If a denotes the recessive, constant trait, and

If Aa denotes the hybrid in which both are united, then the expression

A + 2Aa + a or   AA + 2Aa + aa (current usage)

gives the series for the progeny of plant hybrids in a pair of differing traits. I will use the current formation with every parent having two of each letter, which may be AA, aa or hybrid Aa.

In the first experiment, he combined the characters for seed shape and cotyledon colour, and in the second experiment he added a third character for seed coat colour. To simplify the description of his data, he designated the three characters by AA, BB and CC for the dominant traits, by aa, bb and cc for the recessive traits, and by Aa, Bb and Cc for the hybrid forms. When he combined the two dominant traits, round seed and yellow cotyledons [AABB], and crossed them with the two recessive traits, angular seeds and green cotyledons [aabb], the cross-fertilized seeds were all round with yellow cotyledons. From 15 plants raised from them, and allowed to set seed naturally by self-fertilization, he obtained 556 seeds of which there were 315 round and yellow; 101 angular and yellow; 108 round and green; and 32 angular and green (Table 16.4).

F2 Seeds		Segregation traits of the F3 seed born on F2 plants		
Frequency	Traits	F2 plants	Traits of F3 seeds	Designation
315 [301] *	Round & yellow	38	Round & yellow	**AABB**
* Scored		65	Round & yellow / Round & green	**AABb**
* Survived		60	Round & yellow / Angular & yellow	**AaBB**
		138	Round, yellow & green / Angular, yellow & green	**AaBb**
101 [96]	Angular & yellow	28	Angular & yellow	**aaBB**
		68	Angular & yellow / Angular & green	**aaBb**
108 [102]	Round & green	35	Round & green	**AAbb**
		67	Round & green / Angular & green	**Aabb**
32 [30]	Angular & green	30	Angular & green	**aabb**

Table 16.4. The frequencies of the F2 plants grown up from the F2 seed, as measured by the segregation patterns of their F3 seeds, which were derived from selfing the four pairs of traits of the F2 generation of plants. The F2 seeds were derived from selfing the F1 hybrids following the cross between parental plants true-breeding for round seeds with yellow cotyledons AABB, and plants true-breeding for angular seeds and green cotyledons aabb.

All these F2 seeds were planted in the following year and most reached maturity, so Mendel was able to score the segregation traits of the F3 seeds that developed in their pods. These are tabulated according to the F2 traits from which they came. The table shows that the F3 seed of the F2 hybrids appeared in nine different forms, which may be classified into three groups. In one group, with designation and frequencies AABB [38], aaBB [28], AAbb [35] and aabb [30] the traits are constant. In a second group AABb [65], AaBB [60], aaBb [68] and Aabb [67] one character is constant, and the other hybrid segregates for both traits. Finally, a third group AaBb [138] is hybrid for both characters and segregates for both pairs of traits, just like the hybrid from which it descended. When the frequencies for the three groups were summed, they averaged 32.5: 65.0: 138 for each type within a group. To Mendel, it was clear that these frequencies fitted the proportion of 1: 2: 4. Hence, the series consists of nine terms according to the expression:

AABB + AAbb + aaBB + aabb + 2 AABb + 2 aaBb + 2 AaBB + 2 Aabb + 4 AaBb

This is a combination series in which the two series for the traits A and a, B and b are combined term by term:

AA + 2Aa + aa
BB + 2Bb + bb

these combine as:

(AA+ 2Aa + aa)(BB + 2Bb + bb).

In his next experiment, Mendel combined three characters in which the seed parent had the dominant traits round seed shape, yellow cotyledons, and grey-brown seed coat, while the pollen parent had the recessive traits angular seed shape, green cotyledons, and white seed coat. The 24 hybrids expressed the dominant traits, and from them 687 F2 seeds were obtained of which 639 bore fruit in the following year. Further investigation showed that they comprised a series of 27 members (Table 16.5). Of these, 8 constant for all traits occurred 10 times on average; 12 constant for two traits and hybrid for the third averaged 19 times; 6 constant for one trait and hybrid for the other two averaged 43 times; and one form occurred 78 times and was hybrid for all traits. The ratios 10:19:43:78 were close to 10:20:40:80 which simplified to a ratio of 1:2:4:8, which Mendel interpreted as the correct values. Hence, the development of hybrids whose parent differed in three traits occur according to the expression:

AABBCC + AABBcc + AAbbCC + AAbbcc + aaBBCC + aaBBcc + aabbCC + aabbcc + 2AABBCc + 2AAbbCc + 2aaBBCc + 2aabbCc + 2AABbCC + 2AABbcc + 2aaBbCC + 2aaBbcc + 2AaBBCC + 2AaBBcc + 2AabbCC + 2Aabbcc + 4AABbCc + 4aaBbCc + 4AaBBCc + 4AabbCc + 4AaBbCC + 4AaBbcc + 8AaBbCc

This too, is a combination series in which the series for the traits A and a, B and b, C and c are combined with each other in the expression:

(AA + 2Aa + aa)(BB + 2Bb + bb)(CC + 2Cc + cc)

Frequency F2 plants	Segregation traits of the F3 seed born on F2 plants	Designation
	Constant for all traits	
8	Round, yellow & grey	AABBCC
14	Round, yellow & white	AABBcc
9	Round, green & grey	AAbbCC
11	Round, green & white	AAbbcc
8	Angular, yellow & grey	aaBBCC
10	Angular, yellow & white	aaBBcc
10	Angular, green & grey	aabbCC
7	Angular, green & white	aabbcc
	Constant for two traits, hybrid for one	
22	Round, yellow, grey & white	AABBCc
17	Round, green, grey & white	AAbbCc
25	Angular, yellow, grey & white	aaBBCc
20	Angular, green, grey & white	aabbCc
15	Round, yellow & green, grey	AABbCC
18	Round, yellow & green, white	AABbcc
19	Angular, yellow & green, grey	aaBbCC
24	Angular, yellow & green, white	aaBbcc
14	Round & angular, yellow, grey	AaBBCC
18	Round & angular, yellow, white	AaBBcc
20	Round & angular, green, grey	AabbCC
16	Round & angular, green, white	Aabbcc
	Constant for one trait, hybrid for two	
45	Round, yellow & green, grey & white	AABbCc
36	Angular, yellow & green, grey & white	aaBbCc
38	Round & angular, yellow, grey & white	AaBBCc
40	Round & angular, green, grey & white	AabbCc
49	Round & angular, yellow & green, grey	AaBbCC
48	Round & angular, yellow & green, white	AaBbcc
	Hybrid for all three traits	
78	Round & angular, yellow & green, grey & white	AaBbCc

Table 16.5. The frequencies of the 27 classes of F2 plants, as measured by the segregation patterns of their F3 seeds, which were derived from 639 F2 seeds obtained from 24 F1 hybrids, following the cross between parents bearing the alternative pairs of traits for three characters. The seed parent was AABBCC and the pollen parent aabbcc for the three pairs of traits - round versus angular seeds A/a; yellow versus green cotyledons B/b; and grey versus white seed coat colour C/c.

After these experiments, Mendel argued that as selfing the hybrid AaBb produced four kinds of constant forms, then it must be capable of producing four kinds of pollen or eggs in equal frequency - AB Ab aB and ab whereas any parental pure line produced only one kind of pollen or eggs. Hence, he predicted, that by making the backcrosses between the F1 hybrid AaBb and either pure parent, he would obtain four kinds of progeny (1 × 4). He tested this hypothesis by making the two backcrosses between the F1 hybrid for yellow and round peas and the pure breeding parents. All the progeny of the hybrid crossed with the dominant parent were again yellow and round, whereas the hybrid crossed with the recessive parent gave rise to four kinds of progeny (Table 16.6). The data clearly indicate that these occur in about equal frequency in the ratio of 1: 1: 1: 1. Reciprocal crosses are alike. By germinating the backcross seeds, growing up the plants, and examining the seeds of the next generation, it became apparent that the yellow and round seeds of the first pair of backcrosses also consisted of four kinds of progeny occurring in about equal frequency. For both pairs of backcrosses, the segregation of the progeny in the generation following the backcross revealed the exact constitution of each of the four kinds just as the F3 generation had done for the F2 segregants obtained from selfing the F1 hybrids (Tables 16.4; 16.5). So these results fully supported his predictions. Moreover, he gained supporting evidence by similar tests with the alternate traits of the characters for flower colour and stem length, as did further small scale experiments with other combinations of characters.

In order to summarize his work, Mendel concluded that in the simplest series AA + 2Aa + aa, with constant forms A and a, the hybrid Aa was able to produce two corresponding kinds of pollen or eggs - A or a, and these occurred in equal frequency. Thereafter, fertilization between them was random so that an A or a pollen grain had an equal chance of fertilizing an A or a egg. So, out of every four individuals one could expect an average of 1 AA, 1 Aa, 1 aA and 1 aa, which simplifies to 1AA: 2Aa: 1aa, which is the average course of self-fertilization of hybrids differing in two traits. Owing to chance, isolated values would be subject to fluctuations, and even extreme deviations would be possible. The larger the number of progeny scored, the greater the likelihood for chance effects to be eliminated and for the calculated means to approach the true ratios.

Crosses	Backcross progeny		Following generation		Designation
	Cross 1 / 2	Traits	Cross 1 / 2	Traits	
1 / 2	98 / 94	All round & yellow	20 / 25	Round & yellow	**AABB**
			23 / 19	Round, yellow & green	**AABb**
			25 / 22	Round & angular, yellow	**AaBB**
			22 / 21	Round & angular, yellow & green	**AaBb**
	Cross 3 / 4	Traits			
3 / 4	31 / 24	Round & yellow		Round & angular, yellow & green	**AaBb**
	26 / 25	Round & green		Round & angular, green	**Aabb**
	27 / 22	Angular & yellow		Angular, yellow & green	**aaBb**
	26 / 27	Angular & green		Angular, green	**aabb**

Table 16.6. The seed frequencies of the backcross plants further classified according to the segregation patterns of their next generation of seeds. The backcrosses were between the F1 hybrids for two characters and the pure breeding dominant or recessive parents. There are two sets of data n / n.
Cross 1: Female hybrid round & yellow x male pure round & yellow
Cross 2: Female pure round & yellow x male hybrid round & yellow
Cross 3: Female hybrid round & yellow x male pure angular & green
Cross 4. Female pure angular & green x male hybrid round & yellow

The same line of reasoning was now extended to the hybrid differing in two pairs of traits. When the double hybrid AaBb was selfed, the expectation was of nine different forms for every 16 individuals of which there were four constant combinations. Hence, this hybrid would produce four kinds of pollen or eggs – AB, Ab, aB or ab in equal frequency. At fertilization, every pollen grain would unite, on average, equally often with every egg (4 × 4) to give 16 individuals in the combination series (AA + 2Aa + aa)(BB + 2Bb + bb). Similarly, the triple hybrid AaBbCc, that produced eight constant forms, would produce eight kinds of pollen and egg and so combine at random to produce 64 (8 × 8) individuals in the combination series (AA + 2Aa + aa)(BB + 2Bb + bb)(CC + 2Cc + cc).

The Punnett Square

The expected genotypes arising from a cross between two individuals of known genotype may be illustrated by the Punnett Square. The cross is written in the top left corner, the expected gametes arising from the two genotypes are written vertically in the bottom left side for the female parent, and horizontally in the top right side for the male parent. The genotypes of progeny arising from the random fusions between these gametes occupy the bottom right corner. Illustrations of the concept are found in a variety of designs. Instead of using the model symbols A/a, the real symbols for the alleles (alternative letters) are often used. By making the square larger, it is simple to enter the phenotypes corresponding to each of the progeny genotypes.

Parental Genotypes Aa × Aa		Male Gametes	
		A	**a**
Female	**A**	**AA**	**Aa**
Gametes	**a**	**Aa**	**aa**

The result of the cross is segregation among the progeny in the monohybrid genotypic ratio of 1 AA: 2 Aa: 1 aa. We shall assume that A is dominant over a in all the following figures; this corresponds to a monohybrid phenotypic ratio of 3A-: 1aa, or simply 3: 1.

We may now make a Punnett Square illustrating the backcross between a female heterozygous for a single gene Aa, and a male homozygous recessive aa.

Parental Genotypes Aa × aa		Male Gametes	
		a	
Female	**A**	**Aa**	
Gametes	**a**	**aa**	

The result is segregation among the progeny in the monohybrid genotypic ratio of 1Aa: 1 aa, and also a monohybrid phenotypic ratio of 1: 1.

We illustrate next the cross between two individuals heterozygous for two genes located on separate chromosomes with genotype Aa,Bb.

Parental Genotypes		Male Gametes			
Aa,Bb × Aa,Bb		AB	Ab	aB	ab
	AB	AA,BB	AA,Bb	Aa,BB	Aa,Bb
Female	Ab	AA,Bb	AA,bb	Aa,Bb	Aa,bb
Gametes	aB	Aa,BB	Aa,Bb	aa,BB	aa,Bb
	ab	Aa,Bb	Aa,bb	aa,Bb	aa,bb

The result is segregation among the progeny into nine classes in the dihybrid genotypic ratio of 1 AA,BB: 2 AA,Bb: 2 Aa,BB: 4 Aa,Bb: 1 AA,bb: 2 Aa,bb: 1 aa,BB: 2 aa,Bb: 1 aa,bb. The ratio follows the expectation of the combination series (1AA + 2Aa + 1aa)(1BB + 2Bb + 1bb). This corresponds to a dihybrid phenotypic ratio of 9 A-,B-: 3 A-,bb: 3 aa,B-: 1 aa,bb, or simply 9: 3: 3: 1.

The next Punnett Square illustrates the cross between a female heterozygous for two genes with genotype Aa,Bb, and a male homozygous recessive with genotype aa,bb.

Parental Genotypes		Male Gametes
Aa,Bb × aa,bb		ab
	AB	Aa,Bb
Female	Ab	Aa,bb
Gametes	aB	aa,Bb
	ab	aa,bb

The result is segregation among the progeny into four classes in the dihybrid backcross genotypic ratio of 1 Aa,Bb: 1 Aa,bb: 1 aa,Bb: 1 aa,bb. The ratio follows the expectation of the combination series (1Aa: 1aa)(1Bb: 1bb). This corresponds to a dihybrid phenotypic ratio of 1: 1: 1: 1.

The Punnett Square now illustrates the partial backcross between a female heterozygous for two genes with genotype Aa,Bb, and a male homozygous recessive with genotype Aa,bb.

Parental Genotypes		Male Gametes	
Aa,Bb × Aa,bb		Ab	ab
	AB	AA,Bb	Aa,Bb
Female	Ab	AA,bb	Aa,bb
Gametes	aB	Aa,Bb	aa,Bb
	ab	Aa,bb	aa,bb

The result is segregation among the progeny into six classes in the dihybrid genotypic ratio of 1 AA,Bb: 2 Aa,Bb: 1 AA,bb: 2 Aa,bb: 1 aa,Bb: 1 aa,bb. The ratio follows the expectation of the combination series (1AA: 2Aa: 1aa)(1Bb: 1bb). This corresponds to a dihybrid phenotypic ratio of 3 A-,Bb: 3 A-,bb: 1 aa,Bb: 1 aa,bb, or 3: 3: 1: 1.

The final Punnet Square illustrates the alternative partial backcross cross between a female heterozygous for two genes with genotype Aa,Bb, and a male homozygous recessive with genotype aa,Bb.

Parental genotypes		Male gametes	
Aa,Bb × aa,Bb		aB	ab
	AB	Aa,BB	Aa,Bb
Female	Ab	Aa,Bb	Aa,bb
Gametes	aB	aa.BB	aa,Bb
	ab	aa,Bb	aa,bb

The result is segregation among the progeny into six classes in the dihybrid genotypic ratio of 1 Aa,BB: 2 Aa,Bb: 1 aa,BB: 2 aa,Bb: 1 Aa,bb: 1 aa,bb. This corresponds to the expectation of the combination series (1Aa: 1aa)(1BB: 2Bb: 1bb). This corresponds to a dihybrid phenotypic ratio of 3 Aa,B-: 3 aa,B-: 1 Aa,bb: 1 aa,bb, or 3: 3: 1: 1.

Gene symbols

One character that Mendel observed was the height of pea plants. He found that the cultivars were of two kinds - tall or dwarf. His genetical analysis proved that these were alternative traits of the character height - tall was dominant and dwarf recessive. Mendel used the capital letter A to represent the dominant trait and the lower case letter a to represent the recessive trait. The symbols were used to represent the genes controlling the traits, not the traits themselves. When modelling a cross, simple letters A/a, B/b and C/c are very useful, but they clearly cannot be used again and again as permanent gene symbols. Each gene has to have its own unique symbol. The same symbol may be used for homologous characters in different organisms, like peas and beans, but not for dissimilar characters within the same organism.

The pea cross between homozygous dominant tall and homozygous recessive dwarf is modelled as AA × aa. If we are using genetic symbols, the cross is represented as DD × dd, where D and d are the symbols for the dominant and recessive alleles of the gene for tall versus dwarf height, or perhaps DwDw × dwdw, if a two letter symbol Dw/dw is used. The F1 hybrid between tall and dwarf has the genotype Dd, or Dwdw respectively. Even though the symbol represents the gene and not the alternative traits, it is usually chosen from the name given to one of them. This is commonly the recessive trait, so in the case of the alternative traits tall and dwarf, the gene becomes known as the dwarf gene and is given the symbol dw that best recalls the name. It follows that the dominant allele for the dwarf gene becomes Dw, yet the gene is still known as the dwarf gene even though its dominant trait is tall. The recessive trait is usually chosen for the name because this is most often the uncommon or abnormal condition, whereas the alternative dominant trait is most often the common or normal condition.

In fungi, bacteria, and many other organisms, the common condition is known as the wild type and is given the symbol +, whereas the mutant allele, arginine requiring for example, is given the symbol arg. To make it even clearer a cross is written arg+ × arg-, and the heterozygote arg+arg-. The + may be written on its own, and is then a simple, quick abbreviation for the wild type, especially helpful when writing out long crosses.

A three-letter symbol is often chosen when this recalls the name better than a two-letter symbol. For example, when a mutation makes the plant foliage variegated it is given the symbol var, and the normal green plant Var. Even four letter symbols are sometimes used; an example is the sulphurea mutant producing sulphur coloured leaves in the tomato, which is given the symbol Sulf/sulf.

In this book, when indicating that there are two known alleles for the dwarf gene, it is written as Dw/dw, but when referring specifically to the heterozygote, the genotype is written as Dwdw, and the alternative homozygotes as DwDw and dwdw. When referring to a double heterozygote, such as for the characters normal versus dwarf plant height together with normal versus variegated foliage, the two genes are separated by a comma, and the genotype becomes Dwdw,Varvar. Sometimes, however, one knows that the heterozygote arose from a cross between one tall plant with green foliage and a second dwarf plant with variegated foliage. In these circumstances it is better to keep together the genes that were associated in their parents, and so the double heterozygous genotype is written as DwVar,dwvar. If the genes are linked on the same chromosome, then one uses a stroke to represent the chromosome and so the genotype is written in coupling as DwVar/dwvar, or with the opposite arrangement, the genotype is written in repulsion is Dwvar/dwVar.

Many genes control plant characters and on mutation each produces, at least superficially, the same trait. There are many genes associated with the complex development of flowers, and a mutation that is easy to spot is a defect in the anthers resulting in male sterility. Frequently the alternative traits of normal versus male sterile are symbolized as Ms/ms. When there are several genes producing this character, it is not convenient to think up new symbols so the genes are referred to as male sterile 1, male sterile 2 and so on. This is indicated by a numerical sub fix to give Ms_1/ms_1 and Ms_2/ms_2.

Another kind of symbol modification is used when there proves to be several alleles of the same gene. The genes associated with the self-incompatibility mechanisms of plants are given the symbol S, and so the different alleles are distinguished by their super fixes as S^1, S^2, S^3....S^n. With the multiple allelic series affecting the V-leaf markings on white clover, the super fixes are more variable expressing the different traits of which a few are the low mark V^l, the high mark V^h, and the broken mark V^b.

A regrettable practice that used to be taught in schools, and perhaps still is, is to refer to the tall plant by the letter T and the dwarf plant by the letter d, so that the cross between alternative true-breeding lines of pea becomes TT × dd, and the consequent F1 hybrid becomes Td. This is very naughty because although, correctly, a capital and small letter are used to represent the dominant and recessive traits, it is wrong to use abbreviations for symbols corresponding to each trait; different letters are intended to be symbols for unrelated genes. Seeing the cross TT × dd, a geneticist sees two unrelated letters and understands that the two unrelated symbols represent two independent genes, one T/t and the other D/d. Hence, a geneticist interprets the cross TT × dd as short for

TT,DD × tt,dd leading to the F1 as Tt,Dd. When one is dealing with a simple single gene situation, the mistaken use of the symbols may not seem to matter, but this is a mistake in the basic language of genetics. Once the bad habit is installed, the perpetrator tries to extend it to more complex situations, and when crosses become more complicated with two or three genes each symbolized by two or three letters, and each with two or more alleles, the result of the misuse of symbols leads to total confusion. At this stage, it is not surprising that many students now find genetics too complicated.

Chi-square Analysis of Goodness of Fit

Whenever we obtain an expected monohybrid, dihybrid, or any other Mendelian ratio, among the progeny of a segregating family, we want to know how good is the fit. How close are the frequencies of the progeny observed to the progeny expected on the assumption of the ratio? When the observed and expected frequencies are close, the fit is good, and we conclude that the Mendelian ratio is correct. When the observed and expected frequencies are too divergent, the fit is poor, and so the ratio assumed is probably incorrect.

The test we use in order to compare observed and expected frequencies, and to help us to decide on the goodness of fit is the chi-square test. The universal symbol for the chi-square statistic is the Greek letter chi χ, with an exponent of 2, that is χ^2. We calculate the value of χ^2 from the experimental data, and compare it with critical values of the distribution of χ^2, which are associated with the appropriate degrees of freedom. With a fixed total of 100 progeny, once we count 88 with the dominant trait, the remainder is bound to be 12 with the recessive trait. Within such a fixed total, as the size of one-class increases, the size of the other class compensates by decreasing to the same extent. Thus only one class is able to vary freely; the other class is constrained by the constant sum. Accordingly, there is one degree of freedom. By the same argument, had we four classes, any three of them could vary freely, but the fourth would be fixed as the difference between the total and the sum of the first three. So when there are n classes, there are n-1 degrees of freedom.

When the χ^2 values are larger than the critical value for a specified probability level, the goodness of fit is regarded as inadequate, and we conclude that the data does not fit the expectation on the basis of the hypothesis under test. When the χ^2 values are smaller than the critical value, the goodness of fit is good, and the hypothesis is accepted.

An example will illustrate the calculations and make the statistical terms clearer. Let us suppose that we cross two F1 individuals Aa × Aa and obtain a total of 100 F2 progeny with counts of 88 having the dominant trait, and 12 having the recessive trait. If the genotypes really are as indicated, we would expect to obtain progeny segregating in a 3: 1 monohybrid ratio. The observed ratio of 7.3: 1 appears way out, but this exaggerates the deviation from 3:1. By dividing 88 by 12, the ratio falsely assumes that 12 are the expected number of recessives. Instead, we need to determine the expected number of recessives and dominants from the total sample according to the hypothesis of a 3: 1 [3/4: 1/4] ratio as follows:

Expected number of dominants = 100 × 3/4 = 75
Expected number of recessives = 100 × 1/4 = 25

Hence, the real comparison is between 88 dominants, when we expect 75 on average, and 12 recessives, when we expect 25 on average. Relatively speaking, the deviation of the recessive class from its expectation is much greater than the deviation of the dominant class from its expectation. With the chi-square test, we measure all the deviations between the observed (o_i) and expected (e_i) frequencies, make them positive by squaring them to yield a measure of the magnitude of the deviation from expectation, divide each by its expected frequency, and finally sum (Σ) all the quantities obtained. The equation is:

$$\chi^2 = \Sigma(o_i\text{-}e_i)^2 / e_i \qquad\qquad i = 1, 2, 3...k$$
$$\chi^2 = (88\text{-}75)^2 / 75 + (12\text{-}25)^2 / 25$$
$$\chi^2 = (13)^2 / 75 + (\text{-}13)^2 / 25$$
$$\chi^2 = 2.2533 + 6.7600$$
$$\chi^2 = 9.0133$$

Before continuing, we notice that both observed frequencies deviate from their expected frequencies by the same amount, but as the expected frequencies for the recessive class, the divisor, is one third of that for the dominant class, the final χ^2 value for the recessive class is three times larger than for the dominant class.

We compare next the value of χ^2 with tables of the sampling distribution of chi-square in order to determine what is the probability of obtaining such a value. The sampling distribution of chi-square is dependent on the number of degrees of freedom as there is a different distribution for each number. For low degrees of freedom the distributions are strongly skewed, but as the degrees of freedom increase, the curves gradually approach and finally reach normal at about 30 degrees of freedom. The distribution is independent of the sample size and of the parameters measured. A limitation is the assumption that the possible observed values in any one class form a normal distribution with the mean equal to the expected values. It follows that when the expected values are small, the distribution of possible observed values do not sufficiently approximate a normal distribution owing to the limitation imposed by zero. Hence, as a guideline, the expected value in any one class should not be less than 5, or preferably not less than 10. It should also be emphasized that chi-square is calculated using actual numbers, not percentages or proportions.

We need to judge the value of our χ^2 against the sampling distribution for one degree of freedom. The probability (P) of obtaining the observed χ^2 value or larger values for the appropriate degrees of freedom (df) is determined by measuring the area under the distribution curve to the right of any given χ^2 value and dividing it by the total area, which is made equal to one. Normally, these probabilities are read directly from a chi-square table. From such a table, the value of 9.013 with 1 degree of freedom has a value for P < 0.005. Hence, the chance of the observed frequencies differing from the expected frequencies by as much as they do is between 1:100 and 1:1000. It is more probable that the progeny are not segregating in a 3: 1 ratio. With such a poor fit it is safer to reject the hypothesis, and to seek another explanation for the segregation data. As a rule, geneticists regard as giving an acceptable fit a probability, P > 0.05, or 5%, or 1 in 20; this corresponds to a χ^2 value of 3.841 for 1df. A perfect fit occurs when χ^2 is 0, and P = 1. The table 16.7 shows a selection of the more common Mendelian ratios, with the critical chi-square value at three probability levels. Whether accepting or rejecting a hypothesis, it is useful to be able to quote the region of probability; the chance of a χ^2 value of 9.013 fitting the 3:1 ratio falls between P = 0.01 to 0.001, often written as 0.01 < P < 0.001.

Mendelian Ratio	Number of Classes (i)	Degrees of Freedom (df)	P = 0.05 1:20	P = 0.01 1:100	P = 0.001 1:1000
Monohybrid					
1:1	2	1	3.841	6.635	10.827
3:1	2	1	3.841	6.635	10.827
1:2:1	3	2	5.991	9.210	13.815
Dihybrid					
1:1:1:1	4	3	7.815	11.345	16.266
9:3:3:1	4	3	7.815	11.345	16.266
3:3:1:1	4	3	7.815	11.345	16.266
Trihybrid					
1:1:1:1:1:1:1:1	8	7	14.067	18.475	24.322
27:9:9:3:9:3:3:1	8	7	14.067	18.475	24.322

Table 16.7. Critical values of the Chi-square distribution are given for some common Medelian ratios at three probability levels.

The equation used in the traditional method of calculating a chi-square value can be substituted by the following:

$$\chi^2 = \Sigma(o_i)^2 / e_i - n$$
$$\chi^2 = [88^2 / 75 + 12^2 / 25] - 100$$
$$\chi^2 = [103.2533 + 5.7600] - 100$$
$$\chi^2 = 9.0133$$

A disadvantage of the traditional method is that the expected number often has to be rounded off, which introduces small errors especially when the deviations are squared. An advantage of the second method is that it removes the need to calculate the deviations between observed and expected results. In the special case where there are two classes, n1 and n2 = n, and the expected ratio is r: s then:

$$\chi^2 = (n_1s\text{-}rn_2)^2 / rsn$$
$$\chi^2 = [(88 \times 1)\text{-}(3 \times 12)]2^2/ 3 \times 1 \times 100$$
$$\chi^2 = [88\text{-}36]^2 / 300$$
$$\chi^2 = 52^2 / 300$$
$$\chi^2 = 2704 / 300$$
$$\chi^2 = 9.0133$$

The expectation, with this method, is that $[n_1s\text{-}rn_2] = 0$. The chi-square value enlarges as the sum increasingly deviates from zero. The method has the advantage that neither the expected numbers nor the deviations are calculated, and so there are no rounding-off errors. It is an excellent method to use with a hand calculator. In the simple case where $r: s = 1: 1$, the equation reduces to:

$$\chi^2 = (n_1\text{-}n_2)^2 / n$$

The special case is regularly used when more complex ratios are partitioned into simpler ratios; the chi-square values for these may then be summed to give the total chi-square value for the original ratio.

Partial, incomplete or semi-dominance

In the second edition of his excellent little book on "A history of ornamental-foliaged pelargoniums", Peter Grieve writes in 1869:

That after a cross between a scarlet-flowered and a white-flowered zonal pelargonium the seedlings vary with respect to the shade or colour of their blooms, some of them bearing more resemblance to one parent than to the other. But most probably no individual amongst them will be found to produce either scarlet or white flowers, but all of them intermediate colours - that is to say lighter shades of red - showing that the seedlings have inherited more or less from both parents.

Peter Grieve does not mention Mendel, and there is no reason to suspect that he was aware of his work, so he presents the observation without further interpretation. In fact it is typical of what we find sometimes when two true-breeding lines for the alternative traits of the same character are crossed together; neither trait expresses dominance or recessiveness. Instead the hybrid between the two traits has an intermediate phenotype. Several terms are commonly used to define this condition, all of which retain the concept of dominance to some extent. In the case of the light red flower, we might argue that some colour is dominant over no colour and therefore the light red flower shows some dominance in comparison with the white flower. The dominance in the hybrid does not go as far as the full scarlet, and so it is partial or incomplete. Quantitatively, the amount of anthocyanin pigment produced in the hybrid is more than in the white flower and less than in the scarlet flower; the concept of a measurable difference between the traits with the hybrid somewhere between the two is often expressed by the term semi-dominance.

If we symbolize the white gene as W/W, the initial cross may be shown as follows:

Scarlet	×	White	→	Light red
WW		ww		Ww

The further inheritance is now testable by selfing the F1, or by backcrossing the F1 to either parent. When the F1 is selfed, the F2 progeny segregate in a monohybrid 1:2:1 ratio.

F1 Light red selfed   →   1 Scarlet: 2 Light red: 1 White
    Ww × Ww   →   WW   Ww   ww

When the F1 is backcrossed to the scarlet parent, the progeny segregate in a monohybrid ratio of 1 scarlet: 1 light red.

F1 Light red × Scarlet   →   1 Scarlet: 1 Light red
    Ww × WW   WW   Ww

Similarly, when the F1 is backcrossed to the white parent, the progeny segregate in a monohybrid ratio of 1 light red: 1 white.

F1 Light red × White   →   1 Light red: 1 White
    Ww ×   ww   Ww   ww

From a biochemical point of view, it is assumed that the anthocyanins are produced in a reaction in which an enzyme converts a colourless precursor into coloured anthocyanins. In the true-breeding scarlet line, two copies of the gene control the synthesis of more enzymes, and so produce more pigment, than occurs when there is only one copy. Just one copy of the gene is limiting the reaction, and so a significant portion of the colourless precursor remains unconverted. By contrast, in situations when there is complete dominance, the hybrid is assumed to produce enough, or more than enough, enzymes to fully accomplish the synthesis on its own; just one copy of the gene is not limiting.

The occurrence of partial dominance is generally useful. Not only does it provide the breeder with an extra phenotype intermediate between the homozygous lines, but also it enables the breeder to distinguish between all three F2 genotypes. When the breeder has crossed two lines homozygous for alternative traits, he knows exactly which is the F1 heterozygote. Often he wants to use, or is obliged to use, a heterozygote segregating in an F2 generation. When the character under investigation has complete dominance, and he is unable to separate heterozygous plants from the identical homozygous plants amongst the progeny, he is obliged to choose five or more plants with which to make crosses in order to be 95 per cent confident that the required heterozygote is one of them; an inefficient, time-consuming process which partial dominance avoids. The improved separation of genotypes with partial dominance, compared with full dominance, also improves the measurement of the recombination frequency between linked genes.

The monohybrid 3:1 ratio with a deficit of the homozygous recessive trait

Sometimes it is discovered that there are rather more progeny with the dominant and rather fewer progeny with the recessive trait than expected. In the sweet pea, *Lathyrus odoratus*, Punnett (1932) noticed that when full coloured flowers were selfed, and they segregated into full coloured and marbled progeny, the marbled were often fewer than expected. He collected from 29 families spread over eight years (Table 16.8). For each family, he calculated the ratio of full: marbled flowers. The expected ratio was 3: 1, yet in all but five families it was greater than 3: 1, which suggested that marbled were under represented. Yet, only three families have a chi-square value greater than the critical value of 3.841 at the 5% probability level. As most families actually had a good fit with the expected ratio, was there really a deficit of marbled?

One family, 1922/1, with a ratio of 6.21: 1, produces a chi-square value of 9.053. This fit is much poorer than that of any other family [P < 0.005], so we should treat it as an outlier and discard it. The remaining 28 families have an average family size of 175 with ratios varying from 2.48 to 4.43 around a mean of 3.53; they appear reasonably uniform and so suitable for further analysis.

Year	Family	Full	Marbled	Total	Ratio	χ^2 value
1919	1	202	49	251	4.08:1	4.017
	2	113	33	146	3.42:1	0.447
	3	83	21	104	3.95:1	1.282
	4	109	32	141	3.40:1	0.399
	5	83	21	104	3.95:1	1.282
	6	109	31	140	3.52:1	0.609
	7	120	32	152	3.75:1	1.263
	8	102	25	127	4.08:1	1.913
1920	1	133	45	178	2.96:1	0.007
	2	104	42	146	2.48:1	1.050
	3	75	28	103	2.68:1	0.262
	4	93	21	114	4.43:1	2.632
1921	1	88	21	109	4.19:1	1.911
{1922	1	118	19	137	6.21:1	9.053}
	2	184	46	230	4.00:1	3.067
	3	112	28	140	4.00:1	1.867
	4	140	34	174	4.12:1	2.766
1923	1	109	31	140	3.52:1	0.609
1926	1	143	44	187	3.25:1	0.217
	2	199	51	250	3.90:1	2.821
	3	73	27	100	2.70:1	0.213
	4	232	56	288	4.14:1	4.741
1927	1	237	66	303	3.59:1	1.673
	2	434	139	573	3.13:1	0.168
	3	114	34	148	3.35:1	0.324
	4	103	34	137	3.03:1	0.002
	5	143	48	191	2.98:1	0.002
	6	104	24	128	4.33:1	2.667
1928	1	93	22	115	4.23:1	2.113
Totals	28 df	-	-	-	-	40.327
Pooled	1 df	3834	1085	4919	3.53:1	22.717
Hetero-geneity	27 df					17.610

Table 16.8. Analysis of the goodness of fit of 28 F2 families in sweet peas showing monohybrid segregation into full coloured flowers and marbled flowers. Adapted from Punnett (1932).

The chi-square value for the pooled data is 22.717, which gives an extremely poor fit with the expected 3: 1 ratio [P < 0.001]. Hence, even though most individual families do not have a significant deviation from 3: 1, over a large enough population the deficit of marbled is real. Is this deficit spread across all the families, or is there evidence of differences among them? We can answer this question by testing for the heterogeneity or, conversely, the homogeneity of the data.

The total chi-square value is obtained by summing all the 28 individual values. When we subtract the pooled chi-square value from the total, the remainder is the heterogeneity chi-square value. Similarly, for the degrees of freedom, the total 28 is the sum of all the individual degrees of freedom, the pooled chi-square has one, and the difference 27 is the degrees of freedom for heterogeneity. In sweet pea, the heterogeneity chi-square value comes to 17.610, with 27 degrees of freedom, which gives a probability value of 1 to 0.9. Hence, the data are not heterogeneous, the families are highly homogeneous and there is no evidence of differences among them. The conclusion that there is a small but real deficit of marbled flowered plants is now all the more convincing because the families are so homogeneous.

Permutations and combinations

In many different situations, we often ask ourselves the question, what are all the possibilities? Supposing that we knew that a set of three genes ABC were linked on the same chromosome but we did not know their order. What are the possible orders? Each ordering or arrangement of all or a part of a set of objects is called a permutation. There are six permutations of the three genes, which are worked out, in our heads, as follows:

> A in the middle: BAC and CAB
> B in the middle: ABC and CBA
> C in the middle: ACB and BCA

Another way of looking at the same problem is to choose the letters in the order first, second and third. There are three choices for the first letter A, B or C. Whichever letter we choose, there are now two choices for the second letter, because the first letter is not repeated, and one choice for the last letter, because the first and second letters are not repeated. Hence, the choices are 3 × 2 × 1. The general permutation formula for 'n' things taken 'r' at a time, where r is < or = n, is nPr.
Hence, in the example:

$$^nP_r = {}^3P_3 \text{ or } 3! \text{ [3 factorial]} = 3 \times 2 \times 1 = 6$$

Were we to ask what are the permutations for ordering of four genes? This would take longer to work out in our heads, and so the formula would be really useful.

$$^nP_r = {}^4P_4 \text{ or } 4! = 4 \times 3 \times 2 \times 1 = 24$$

On another occasion, we might want to know what were the possible permutations of any three genes from a set of four ABCD; here it is useful to use the expression:

$$^nP_r = {}^4P_3 = n! / (n-r)!$$
$$= 4! / (4-3)!$$
$$= [4 \times 3 \times 2 \times 1] / 1!$$
$$= 24$$

Using the new formula, ${}^4P_4$, becomes n! / (n-r)!, which is 4! / (4-4)!, or 4! / 0!. This is not zero, however, as 0! = 1. Similarly, the permutations of three genes at a time from a set of five ABCDE, is:

$$^nP_r = {}^5P_3 = 5! / (5-3)!$$
$$= 5! / 2!$$
$$= 60$$

For two genes at a time from a set of five ABCDE, the permutations are:

. $^nP_r = {}^5P_2 = 5! / (5-2)!$
        $= 5! / 3!$
        $= 20$

These 20 permutations consist of 10 back-to-back pairs:

AB BA, AC CA, AD DA, AE EA, BC CB, BD DB, BE EB, CD DC, CE EC, DE ED

Each of these back-to-back pairs is a single combination of two letters, or two genes. With a permutation, the order is important - AB is different from BA; whereas with a combination, the order is unimportant - AB and BA are the same. The number of combinations of 'n' things taken 'r' at a time is written as ^nC_r or ^nC_n-r .

In general, $^nC_r = {}^nP_r / r!$, so $^nC_r = n! / r!(n-r)!$

Thus the number of combinations of two genes at a time from a set of five ABCDE, is

        $^nC_r = {}^5C_2$
        $^nC_r = n! / r!(n-r)!$
        $= 5! / 2!(5-2)!$
        $= 5 \times 4 \times 3 \times 2 \times 1 / 2 \times 1 \times 3 \times 2 \times 1$
        $= 120 / 12$
        $= 10$

In this case the number of combinations is half the number of permutations. In another example, there are 24 permutations of three genes from a set of four ABCD. The number of combinations is:

        $^nC_r = {}^4C_3$
        $^nC_r = n! / r!(n-r)!$
        $= 4! / 3! (4-3)!$
        $= 4! / 3!$
        $= 4$

In this instance the number of combinations is one-sixth the number of permutations; each gene is represented in three of the four combinations:

        ABC, ABD, ACD, and BCD

The number of combinations in a class can also be found by using Pascal's triangle. This is obtained by adding two numbers adjacent to each other to give the number placed between them on the line below, starting with 1.

0					1				
1				1		1			
2			1		2		1		
3		1		3		3		1	
4	1		4		6		4		1
5	1	5		10		10		5		1

The fifth row is the same sequence as is obtained by working out:

$$^5C_5, {}^5C_4, {}^5C_3, {}^5C_2, {}^5C_1, {}^5C_0$$

As an example of the use of this triangle, we can determine the number of different crosses that we can make between nine genotypes. As one parent has one genotype, and the second parent another genotype, the problem is to determine the number of crosses from a set of nine genotypes taken two at a time. Were we to extend the triangle to the ninth row, we would find the following line:

1 9 36 84 126 126 84 36 9 1

From which we would choose $^9C_2 = 36$

$$^9C_2 = n! / r!(n\text{-}r)!$$
$$= 9! / 2! (9\text{-}2)!$$
$$= 9! / 2! (7!)$$
$$= 36$$

Nine is the number of F2 genotypes that we obtain when we self or intercross an F1 double heterozygote between two genes Aa,Bb. Hence, were we to cross all the nine F2 genotypes with each other in all possible ways, we would have 36 crosses to make. If we made reciprocal crosses, there would be another 36, and if we selfed the nine genotypes as well, that would be a further 9, in total 81. This is sometimes referred to as a full matrix of crosses - 9 × 9 = 81. Usually, there is no reason to expect the reciprocal crosses to differ, and so we would probably settle for the 36 combinations, plus the nine selfs, for a total of 45 selfs and crosses.

Binomial distribution

When we wish to study populations in which objects occur independently in only two classes - coloured and white, tall and short, fertile and sterile, and so on, we make use of the expansion of the binomial term:

(p + q)k
where
k = the sample size
p = the probability of occurrence of the first class
q = the probability of occurrence of the second class

By definition, p + q = 1, and so, if appropriate, p = 1-q, or q = 1-p.

For a sample of size 1	$(p + q)^1 = p + q$
For a sample of size 2	$(p + q)^2 = p^2 + 2pq + q^2$
For a sample of size 3	$(p + q)^3 = p^3 + 3p^2q + 3pq^2 + q^3$

The reader will observe that the three expressions are the same as lines 1, 2 and 3 of the Pascal triangle. The numbers before p and q, termed the coefficients, express the number of ways a particular outcome is obtained. An example will illustrate the use of the binomial distribution.

After a backcross, in peas, between an F1 heterozygous for a gene determining yellow versus green seeds Yy, and the homozygous recessive yy, the progeny are expected to segregate in a ratio of 1 yellow: 1 green seed. If there were six seeds per pod, how often would one expect to find a pod with all six seeds green?
The binomial expression is $(p + q)^6$ Let p = yellow and q = green seeds
This expands to
$$1p^6 + 6p^5q^1 + 15p^4q^2 + 20p^3q^3 + 15p^2q^4 + 6p^1q^5 + 1q^6$$

In this example, p and q are both 0.5 as the two classes are expected to occur with equal frequency. In table 1.9, we have worked out the seven parts of this expression as a proportion of the total one. It is easier, however, to multiply each part by one thousand in order to see how often we obtain pods with from zero up to six yellow seeds or, for the other colour, from zero to six green seeds. The distribution shows us that the most frequent class, rounded off, is 312 pods out of 1000, in which both yellow and green seeds occur with equal frequency. The least frequent class, rounded off, is just 16 pods out of 1000 with either all 6 seeds green or all 6 six seeds yellow. Evidently, the chance of obtaining a pod with seeds all of one colour is not great. If the colour of the pea is not defined, the chance is about 31 per 1000, or just over 3 per cent.

How would these expectations be modified, if instead of making a backcross we had selfed the heterozygote Yy? As the yellow trait is dominant and the green trait recessive, the progeny now segregate in a ratio of 3/4 yellow: 1/4 green.

The binomial expression is $(p + q)^6$, where p = 0.75 and q = 0.25

This expands to $1p^6 + 6p^5q^1 + 15p^4q^2 + 20p^3q^3 + 15p^2q^4 + 6p^1q^5 + 1q^6$

We now need to enter 0.75 for p and 0.25 for q [. = ×]:

$1.75^6 + 6.75^5.25^1 + 15.75^4.25^2 + 20.75^3.25^3 + 15.75^2.25^4 + 6.75^1.25^5 + 1.25^6$

Table 16.9 shows the result of this expression, firstly as a proportion of one, and secondly after multiplying by 1000. The results are now quite asymmetrical. The most frequent class is for pods with 5 yellow and 1 green seed, expected 356 times per 1000 pods sampled. Pods with six yellow seeds are quite frequent, with an expectation of 178 per 1000 pods. By contrast, pods with all six seeds green are extremely rare. So rare that not a single one is expected; we might obtain just one such pod in a sample of 4000 pods. It is not surprising that Mendel claimed never to have obtained a pod with more than five seeds of the recessive kind amongst his F2 progeny; it was not chance, he just did not score enough. What is perhaps quite surprising is that although the ratio of p: q is 3:1, the number of pods with six yellow seeds is not 3 times the number of pods with six green seeds, but just over 729 times as many!

Peas in pods Y = yellow G = green	Binomial terms	1: 1 Ratio p = q = 0.5		3: 1 Ratio p = 0.75, q = 0.25	
		Proportion	1000 Pods	Proportion	1000 Pods
6 Y, 0 G	$1p^6$	0.015625	15.625	0.177976	177.976
5 Y, 1 G	$6p^5q^1$	0.093750	93.750	0.355957	355.957
4 Y, 2 G	$15p^4q^2$	0.234375	234.375	0.296631	296.631
3 Y, 3 G	$20p^3q^3$	0.312500	312.500	0.131836	131.836
2 Y, 4 G	$15p^2q^4$	0.234375	234.375	0.032959	32. 959
1 Y, 5 G	$6p^1q^5$	0.093750	93.750	0.004395	4.395
0 Y, 6 G	$1q^6$	0.015625	15.625	0.000244	0.244
		1.000000	1000.000	0.999998	999.998

Table 16.9. The expected frequencies of green and yellow peas in a six-pea pod as a proportion of one, and as a sample of 1000 pods, when the alternative traits are segregating in either a 1:1 ratio or a 3:1 ratio.

It is not essential always to work out all the terms of the binomial distribution. In pelargoniums, red flower colour is dominant over orange flower colour, so that if we selfed a heterozygous red flowered plant Oror, we would expect the progeny to segregate in a monohybrid ratio of 3 red: 1 orange [3 Or-: 1 oror], assuming all other flower colour genes were homozygous. So what is the chance of obtaining from ten seeds, 8 plants with red flowers and 2 plants with orange flowers?

$P = k! / r!(k-r)! \times p^r \times q^{k-r}$

$P = 10! / 8! (10-8)! \times 0.75^8 \times 0.25^2$

$P = 45 \times 0.75^8 \times 0.25^2$

$P = 0.281$, hence the chance is about 28%

What is the chance of obtaining from ten seeds, 2 plants with red flowers and 8 plants with orange flowers?

$$P = k! / r!(k-r)! \times p^r \times q^{k-r}$$
$$P = 10! / 2! (10-2)! \times 0.75^2 \times 0.25^8$$
$$P = 45 \times 0.75^2 \times 0.25^8$$
$$P = 0.000386, \text{ hence the chance is about } 0.04\%$$

These two examples remind us that the chance of obtaining an actual segregation close to the expected segregation is high, whereas the chance of obtaining a segregation far removed from expectation is very low. In the former case, we would be very happy with the result, in the latter case, we would probably be quite concerned that we had not selfed a single heterozygote at all, or that our hypothesis that red was dominant to orange was at fault. Or maybe we would be consoling ourselves that rare events are possible and do sometimes happen.

Another question that we might ask is what is the chance of obtaining at least two plants with orange flowers? In this case, we should need to add to the possibility of obtaining two orange flowers, the additional and decreasing possibilities of obtaining 3, 4, 5, 6, 7, 8, 9 and 10 orange flowers.

The monohybrid 1: 2: 1 ratio with a partial lethal

When Almouslem (1988) repeated an early experiment of Baur (1907) and selfed the pelargonium cultivar 'Verona', he obtained 47 green, 109 golden and 21 white seedlings (Table 16.10a). This appears to be a 1: 2: 1 ratio with the white seedlings under-represented (x^2 = 17.135, df. 2, P < 0.001).

Green (a)	Golden (b)	White (c)	Total	Ratio	χ^2	df.	P
47	109	21	177	1: 2: 1	17.135	2	< 0.001
156	(47+109)	21	177	3: 1	16.288	1	< 0.001
47	109	-	156	1: 2	0.847	1	0.9-0.5

Table 16.10a. The ratios of green, golden and white seedlings and the χ^2 values, the degrees of freedom, and the probability values associated with each.

$$x^2 = \Sigma(o_i)^2 / e_i - n = 47^2 / 44.25 + 109^2 / 88.5 + 21^2 / 44.25 - 177 = 17.135$$

The two degrees of freedom enables us to make two tests. The first is a 3 green + golden: 1 white ratio (Table 16.10b). The high x^2 value (x^2 = 16.288, df.1, P = < 0.001) again reveals a highly significant deficit of white seedlings.

$$x^2 = [(a+b)-(3c)]^2 / 3n = [(156)-(3\times21)]^2 / 3\times177 = 16.288$$

The second degrees of freedom are used up in the x^2 test for the ratio of 1 green: 2 golden (Table 16.10b). The low x^2 value (x^2 = 0.847, df.1, P = 0.5-0.1) is not significant.

$$x^2 = [(b-2a)]^2 / 1.5n = [(109-94)]^2 / 1.5\times177 = 0.847$$
The two traits are perfectly in agreement with the expected 1: 2 ratio.

The two chi-square values for one degree of freedom add up to the initial chi-square value with two degrees of freedom, which is a property of orthogonal contrasts. The deficit in the overall ratio may be attributed entirely to the poor germination of white seedlings. All the white seedlings died soon after germination, as they could not support themselves in the absence of chloroplasts; this is a case of a zygotic lethal.

How is the original chi-squared value partitioned between two individual degrees of freedom? We can partition the χ^2 value in two ways. For a full analysis of the 1: 2: 1 ratio, we need to take account of the expected proportion or weight, w, of each of the three phenotypes and multiply each weight by an appropriate coefficient, c, such that for each contrast the sum of products of weight and coefficients is equal to zero ($\Sigma wc = 0$). From the table (Table 16.10b), we can write out two equations for determining the correct χ^2 value for each of the two orthogonal contrasts. They do not have the same denominator. We determine this as the sum of the products of each weight multiplied by the square of its coefficient, and then divide the sum by the total ratio size.

Letter used in the χ^2 equation	a	b	c	Products
Genotypes	AA	Aa	aa	-
Expected frequency	1/4	1/2	1/4	4n
Weight, w	1	2	1	-
		Orthogonal Contrast 1 AA: 2 Aa		
Coefficient, c	2	-1		-
Product wc	1×2	2×-1		$\Sigma wc = 0$
Σwc^2	$1 \times (2)^2$	$2 \times (-1)^2$		$= 6/4n = 1.5n$
		$\chi^2 = [(2a-b)]^2 / 1.5n$		
		Orthogonal Contrast 3 (AA + Aa): 1 aa		
Coefficient, c	-	1	-3	
Product wc	-	3×1	1×-3	$\Sigma wc = 0$
Σwc^2	-	$3 \times (1)^2$	$1 \times (-3)^2$	$= 12/4n = 3n$
		$\chi^2 = [(a+b) - 3(c)]^2 / 3n$		

Table 16.10b. The method of partitioning the chi-square with two degrees of freedom into two individual contrasts each with one degree of freedom.

The ability to split, in this way, chi-square values with two or more degrees of freedom is an important statistical tool, which we will turn to again when we analyse the action of two or more genes.

Interaction of gene products

Two genes that are independently assorting combine in the series:
(AA + 2Aa + aa)(BB + 2Bb + bb)
Usually the homozygous dominant and the heterozygote act as if they have the same phenotype, in which case they combine in the series:
(3A- + 1aa)(3B- + 1bb)

This gives us the classical dihybrid 9: 3: 3: 1 phenotypic ratio. Thus in the example from Mendel's experiments, we obtain in the F2 9 round and yellow, 3 round and green, 3 angular and yellow and 1 angular and green coloured seeds. The combinations of colour and shape do not interact. In many cases the products of two genes that segregate in the F2 do interact, and so the dihybrid ratio becomes modified. There are two or three phenotypes according to the modification.

When the action of one gene prevents the action of a second, the first is said to be epistatic to the second. Alternatively, the second gene is hypostatic to the first. Clearly a lethal gene causing death must be epistatic to any other gene affecting the life it cuts short. Similarly, a gene removing an organ must be epistatic to any gene modifying the organ. A gene suppressing, or failing to produce, a substance, must be epistatic to one modifying it. There are six main types of modification.

Dominant epistasis, 12: 3: 1 ratio.
The gene A is inactive and epistatic to B/b. In the case of the summer squash this results in colour appearing only in aa genotypes.

9 A-,B-	White squash
3 A-,bb	White "
3 aa,B-	Yellow "
1 aa,bb	Green "

Recessive epistasis, 9: 3: 4 ratio.
The homozygous recessive aa is inactive and epistatic to gene B/b. The effect is seen in the colour of onion skins.

9 A-,B-	Red skin
3 A-,bb	Yellow "
3 aa,B-	White "
1 aa,bb	White "

Additive genes, 9: 6: 1 ratio.
The genes A and B produce the same product in semi-sufficient amount. In the case of the squash the two dominants produce a disc shaped fruit, either dominant on its own produces a spherical shaped fruit, and the two homozygous recessives produce a long shaped fruit. The two genes are sometimes said to be semi-epistatic.

9 A-,B-	Disc shaped fruit
3 A-,bb	Spherical shaped "
3 aa,B-	Spherical shaped "
1 aa,bb	Long shaped "

Complementary genes, 9: 7 ratio.
Both recessive genes are inactive and epistatic to the dominant genes.
So in sweet peas both dominants produce a purple flower while either of
the homozygous recessives result in a white flower.

9 A-,B-	Purple flower
3 A-,bb	White "
3 aa,B-	White "
1 aa,bb	White "

The genes are said to be complementary because when the two whites
aa,B- and A-,bb are crossed together, the two dominants complement
each other in the production of the purple flowered progeny A-,B-.

Duplicate genes, 15: 1 ratio.
Both dominant genes produce the same phenotype. In peas only the
double recessive produces elongated pods, while all the other genotypes
produce triangular-shaped pods.

9 A-,B-	Triangular pods
3 A-,bb	Triangular "
3 aa,B-	Triangular "
1 aa,bb	Elongated pods

Complementary action of dominant and recessive genes, 13: 3 ratio.
The gene A and b are inactive and epistatic to B and A respectively. The
action is found in certain genotypes of maize.

9 A-,B-	White cobs
3 A-,bb	White "
3 aa,B-	Coloured cobs
1 aa,bb	White cobs

When the F1 genotypes are backcrossed to the homozygous recessive
parents they will produce a modified 1: 1: 1: 1 backcross ratio. Similarly,
when they are backcrossed to the two semi homozygous recessive
parents they will produce a modified 3: 3: 1: 1 ratio.

All six types of modification have not yet been reported in Pelargonium. I
shall now describe an example of dominant epistasis in more detail.

Dominant epistasis

Variegated leaves of the Japanese Morning Glory have white or whitish patches, which also occur on other green parts. The patches arise in coarse or fine patterns of irregular sizes. A marked variegation frequently results in disordered or crooked leaves. The cotyledons are sometimes variegated. Another form, termed variegated-reduced, results in less conspicuous variegation with fine whitish netlike mottling that occurs irregularly on otherwise green leaves (Miyake and Imai 1934).

On selfing, both the variegated and the variegated-reduced forms bred true. When variegated was crossed with green, the F1 progeny were green, and the F2 segregated into 8,405 green and 2,795 variegated progeny in excellent agreement with a monohybrid 3: 1 ratio [χ^2 = 0.012]. In the F3, from the normal F2 plants:
48 plants, about one third, bred true and produced 9890 green seedlings.
95 plants, about two-thirds, segregated into 12,860 green and 4,222 variegated seedlings: a good fit with the 3:1 ratio [χ^2 = 0.734].
22 variegated F2 plants bred true and produced 2,175 variegated seedlings.
Clearly the trait for normal colour was dominant and the trait for variegated foliage was recessive; the gene for variegation was symbolized as V/v.

When variegated and variegated-reduced plants were crossed together, the F1 were variegated and the F2 segregated into 443 variegated and 142 variegated-reduced, in agreement with a 3: 1 ratio [χ^2 = 0.165]. In the F3:
3 plants gave158 progeny true breeding for variegated.
5 plants segregated into 236 variegated and 76 variegated-reduced progeny in agreement with the 3: 1 ratio [χ^2 = 0.068]
2 variegated-reduced plants bred true and gave 88 variegated-reduced progeny. Clearly the trait for variegated foliage was dominant and the trait for reduced variegation was recessive; the gene for variegated-reduced was symbolized as R/r.

How is it that variegation is recessive in the first set of crosses and dominant in the second set? Either there are triple alleles or two genes. The evidence that two genes, and not triple alleles of one gene controlled variegation came from the cross between a true-breeding green and a variegated-reduced plant. The F1 was green, and the F2 segregated into 491 green, 120 variegated, and 34 variegated-reduced progeny, which showed a good fit with the 12: 3: 1 modified dihybrid ratio exhibiting dominant epistasis [χ^2 = 1.104, df. 2].

$$\chi^2 = \Sigma(o_i)^2 / e_i - n = \Sigma 491^2/483.75 + 120^2/120.9375 + 34^2/40.3125 - 645 = 1.104$$

In the F3, the F2 were shown to consist of four classes of green plants:
Green alone, green plus variegated, green plus variegated-reduced,
and green plus variegated plus variegated-reduced.
Two classes of variegated plants:
Variegated alone, and variegated plus variegated-reduced.
One class of variegated-reduced alone.
We may take this opportunity to explain how the two degrees of freedom
may be split into two orthogonal contrasts each with one degree
of freedom. The first division is the contrast between the 12 green: 4
variegated plus variegated-reduced (Table 16.11).

$$\chi^2 = [(a) - 3(b+c)]^2 / 3n \qquad\qquad \chi^2 = 0.4346$$

The second is the contrast between the 3 variegated: 1 variegated-
reduced.

$$\chi^2 = [(b) - 3(c)]^2 / 0.75n \qquad\qquad \chi^2 = 0.6697$$

Letter used in the χ^2 equations	a	b	c	Products
Genotypes	12 V-,--	3 vv,R-	1 vv,rr	
Weight, w	12	3	1	16
	Orthogonal Contrasts **12 V-,--: 4 vv,R- + vv,rr**			
Coefficient, c	1	-3	-3	
Product, wc	12x1	3x-3	1x-3	Σwc = 0
Σwc^2	12x1^2	3x-3^2	1x-3^2	Σwc^2 = 48/16n = 3n
	$\chi^2 = [(a) - 3(b+c)]^2 / 3n$			
	Orthogonal Contrasts **3 vv,R-: 1 vv,rr**			
Coefficient, c	-	1	-3	
Product, wc	-	3x1	1x-3	Σwc = 0
Σwc^2	-	3x1^2	1x-3^2	Σwc^2 = 12/16n = 0.75n
	$\chi^2 = [(b) - 3(c)]^2 / 0.75n$			

Table 16.11. The chi-square for two genes with dominant epistasis is partitioned
into two separate degrees of freedom; the two new chi-square equations are
given.

These two χ^2 values sum to the original value. Additionally, when certain
green plants were crossed with particular variegated plants, the F1 were
all green, and the F2 segregated into 634 green, 158 variegated, and 50
variegated-reduced progeny, showing a good fit with the 12:3:1 ratio [χ^2
= 0.141].

The double homozygous dominant is crossed with a double homozygous
recessive to produce the green F1.
Green × Variegated-reduced   F1   Green
VV,RR × vv,rr   F1   Vv,Rr

The same green F1 is achieved by crossing parents that are homozygous dominant for one gene and homozygous recessive for the other.

Green × Variegated   F1   Green
VV,rr × vv,RR   F1   Vv,Rr

The expected F2 segregation is the same irrespective of the F1 lineage:

9	V-,R-	Green
3	V-,rr	Green
3	vv,R-	Variegated
1	vv,rr	Variegated-reduced

The variegated gene V/v is epistatic to the variegated-reduced gene R/r because the dominant allele V totally inhibits the expression of the R/r. Only in the absence of V, in vv genotypes, does the dominant allele R permit the expression of variegation, whereas in its absence this potential is modified by the recessive genotype rr to produce the variegated-reduced phenotype. This may be illustrated diagrammatically:

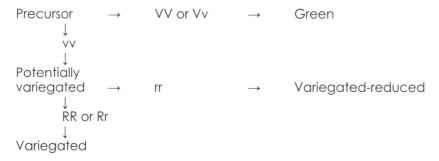

Precursor   →   VV or Vv   →   Green
      ↓
      vv
      ↓
Potentially
variegated   →   rr   →   Variegated-reduced
      ↓
      RR or Rr
      ↓
Variegated

Essentially, epistasis occurs when in a sequence of events, as in a biochemical pathway, the expression or not of a gene acting later in the pathway is entirely dependent on what had occurred earlier in the pathway. It is dominant epistasis when the action of the later gene is blocked by the dominant allele of the earlier gene.

Distinguishing alternative segregation ratios

We are sometimes unsure as to whether a segregating progeny fits one ratio or another, this is especially likely when the progeny are few and chance events can easily bias the data. As progeny size increases, the pattern of the segregation gradually becomes clearer and the true ratio more apparent. When the alternative ratios are very unlike, we would expect this to happen after scoring quite a small number of progeny, whereas when the ratios are similar we would expect to have to score many more. In order to be reasonably certain of avoiding this problem, we need to decide what ratios we might expect, and then to be sure to grow enough progeny. Let us look at a common example of the problem.

Suppose we wish to decide whether one or both of two complementary genes segregate in an F2 generation. If the genotype is A1a1,A2A2 one gene segregates and we obtain a 3: 1 ratio. If the genotype is A1a1,A2a2 both genes segregate, and we obtain a 9: 7 ratio. In practice, sample populations exhibit normal distributions around each ratio, so that some ratios are > 3: 1 and others < 3: 1 and, similarly, some ratios are > 9: 7 and others < 9: 7. Hence, the variance on the side of the ratio < 3: 1 overlaps the variance on the side of the ratio > 9: 7. Whenever an observed segregation falls in the region of overlap, the wrong conclusion might be drawn. As the sample size increases, the chance of overlap decreases, so what is the size of the sample that reduces the chance of overlap to an acceptable level? If we let 'n' be the size of the F2 progeny necessary, there will be some number 'r' of recessives, which if occurring in a family of size 'n' will make both hypotheses equally likely; the situation may be illustrated in the following way:

$$3/4 \ (A1\text{-},A2A2): 1/4 \ (a1a1,A2A2)$$
$$+ \ r$$
$$\text{Deviation at Meeting Point: } 7/16(n\text{-}r) = r\text{-} (1/4n)$$
$$- \ r$$
$$9/16 \ (A1\text{-},A2\text{-}): 7/16 \ (A1\text{-},a2a2 + a1a1,A2\text{-} + a1a1,a2a2)$$

If > r recessives occur, the 9: 7 ratio is more likely.
If < r recessives occur, the 3: 1 ratio is more likely.
In order to solve the problem, the family has to be of a size to ensure that 'r' recessives show a deviation from expectation on either hypothesis only with the probability chosen as the maximum for misclassification. Most of the time the number of recessives is other than 'r', so that one or other hypothesis is less likely than the maximum misclassification allowed, and so may be judged incorrect.
The standard error of the number of recessives expected with a 3: 1 ratio is:

$$\sqrt{pqn} = \sqrt{[3/4 \times 1/4]n} = \sqrt{[3/16]n}$$

The standard error of the number of recessives expected with a 9: 7 ratio is:

$$\sqrt{pqn} = \sqrt{[9/16 \times 7/16]n} = \sqrt{[63/256]n}$$

Now, if we allow 0.05 as the maximum allowable misclassification, we actually utilize the deviate corresponding to 0.10, because we are only interested in the deviation on one side of the ratio. We find from a table of normal deviates, that the deviation of 'r' from the expected number of recessives must not be less than 1.644854 times the standard error.

Then, for the 9: 7 expectations:
$7/16(n-r) = 1.644854 \times \sqrt{[63/256]}n$
For the 3: 1 expectations:
$r-(1/4)n = 1.644854 \times \sqrt{[3/16]}n$
By addition:

$(7/16 - 1/4)n$	$= 1.644854 \times \sqrt{n} \times \sqrt{[63/256]} + \sqrt{[3/16]}$
$(3/16)n$	$= 1.644854 \times \sqrt{n} \times [0.496078 + 0.433013]$
$n/\sqrt{n}$	$= [16/3 \qquad \times 1.644854 \times 0.929091]$
n	$= [8.150501]^2$
n	$= 66.430676$

Hence, we would need a progeny size of 67. The progeny requirement for other comparisons and other probabilities may be calculated in a similar way. Some of the more common comparisons are shown in table 16.12. In this table, I have given four ratios after selfing and three after backcrosses. The most extreme example is the requirement for 688 progeny to separate the 9: 7 ratios from the 1: 1 backcross ratio. As a rule, the breeder knows whether the observed segregation follows selfing or crossing, which reduces the possibilities that need to be considered.

Ratios Compared	Selfs			Backcrosses		
	13:3	3:1	9: 7	5: 3	1: 1	1: 3
Selfs						
15: 1	70	36	11	15	8	3
13: 3	-	470	35	59	221	6
3: 1	-	-	67	136	38	9
9: 7	-	-	-	666	688	24
Backcrosses						
5: 3	-	-	-	-	168	17
1: 1	-	-	-	-	-	38
1: 3	-	-	-	-	-	-

Table 16.12. The numbers of progeny required to being 95% certain of distinguishing between alternative segregation ratios.

What size family do we require?

A frequent difficulty associated with dominance is that we are unable to distinguish visually between individuals that are homozygous dominant from those that are heterozygous. Genetically, we separate the alternatives by back crossing with the homozygous recessive. When the dominant trait is homozygous, the progeny are all heterozygous and so will not segregate; when the dominant trait is heterozygous, the progeny segregate into about half that are heterozygous for the dominant trait and about half that are homozygous for the recessive trait - the 1:1 testcross ratio.

First alternative: AA x aa gives all Aa.

Second alternative: Aa x aa segregates in a ratio of 1 Aa: 1 aa.

The average segregation depends on chance, and on occasions may deviate considerably from expectation. Just by chance, we sometimes obtain a run of one type of progeny. So we need to estimate how many progeny we should score in order to be reasonably sure that no mistake is made. In the case of the testcross, we need to estimate how many plants with the dominant trait we should cross in order to be reasonably sure of obtaining at least one recessive individual among the progeny if the dominant plant really is heterozygous.

Let us decide that failure to segregate in the progeny of the heterozygote should not occur more frequently than one per cent on average. In the progeny of the heterozygote, each individual has a chance of 1/2 of being a dominant, so the chance that n individuals will all be dominant is $(½)^n$. This is the misleading result that we are unwilling to accept more often than 1 per cent of cases. Then the minimum value of n is given by the solution of the following equation:

$$(½)^n = 1/100$$

In logarithms this becomes

$$n \log (½) = \log (1/100)$$
$$-0.3010n = -2.0000$$
$$n = 2/0.301$$
$$n = 6.6$$

So the minimum size of the progeny is 7.

The equation can also be written as

$$(0.5)^n = 0.01$$

Enter 0.5 on a hand calculator, and then press the x^y button.

Now, by iteration, enter values of y = 6, 7 until the answer falls either side of 0.01, when the higher value of y is the value required.

Another problem is to determine how many plants to grow in order to be reasonably sure of obtaining at least one true-breeding double homozygous dominant among the progeny of the F2 dihybrid segregation. In other words, we must work out what is the chance of finding AA,BB in the progeny of the cross Aa,Bb × Aa,Bb, assuming independent assortment of the two genes. We know that 9/16 of the progeny express the dominant trait for both characters. Of these, 1/9 have the required AA,BB genotype, and the remaining 8/9 have another genotype as they are heterozygous for either one or both genes. Suppose we choose the maximum frequency of failure to be 1/500, or 0.002.

$$(8/9)^n = 0.002$$

Enter 8/9, press x^y, enter 52 = 0.0021. This is > 0.002.
Enter 8/9, press x^y, enter 53 = 0.0019. This in < 0.002.
Hence, by iteration, n falls between 52 and 53, so 53 individuals are required.

In table 16.13 we have given the numbers of plants required from a given fraction at a known probability. Suppose we self a plant heterozygous for one gene Aa. We want to raise a family sufficiently large to contain at least one recessive aa in 99 cases out of 100. As recessives are expected in one quarter of the progeny, we look along the second row [1/4] until we reach the fourth column [0.990], where we find that 16 plants are needed. Where the number of individuals is not a whole number, we take the next higher number.

Frequently we want to recover two, three or more plants. In table 16.14 I have given a range of possible requirements at two probability levels as calculated by Sedcole (1977).

If the number of plants is wanted for different values, there are three quick methods of determination that can be used. They differ in complexity and accuracy and are described in Sedcole's paper.

Fraction Expected	Probability Levels						
	0.900 1:10	0.950 1:20	0.980 1:50	0.990 1:100	0.995 1:200	0.998 1:500	0.999 1:1000
1/2	4	5	6	7	8	9	10
1/4	8	11	14	16	19	22	24
1/8	18	23	30	35	40	47	52
1/16	36	46	61	72	83	97	107
1/32	73	95	124	146	167	196	218
1/64	147	191	249	293	337	395	439
1/3	6	8	10	12	14	16	17
1/9	20	26	34	40	45	53	59
1/27	61	80	104	122	141	165	183

Table 16.13. The numbers of individuals required in a progeny in order that a particular fraction should occur at least once depending on the probability level.

We note only that the numbers are not simple multiples of the occurrence once, but are progressively smaller than this.

Number of plants to be recovered r at P = 0.95									
Fraction expected	1	2	3	4	5	6	8	10	15
1/2	5	8	11	13	16	18	23	28	40
1/3	8	13	17	21	25	29	37	44	62
1/4	11	18	23	29	34	40	50	60	84
1/8	23	37	49	60	71	82	103	123	172
1/16	47	75	99	122	144	166	208	248	347
1/32	95	150	200	246	291	334	418	508	697
1/64	191	302	401	494	584	671	839	1002	1397

Number of plants to be recovered r at P = 0.99									
Fraction expected	1	2	3	4	5	6	8	10	15
1/2	7	11	14	17	19	22	27	32	45
1/3	12	17	22	27	31	35	44	52	71
1/4	17	24	31	37	43	49	60	70	96
1/8	35	51	64	77	89	101	124	146	198
1/16	72	104	132	158	182	206	252	296	402
1/32	146	210	266	218	268	416	508	597	809
1/64	293	423	535	640	739	835	1020	1198	1623

Table 16.14. The number of plants necessary in a progeny in order to recover the required number (r = 1-15) with the trait; at two probability levels. Adapted from Sedcole (1977).

Partitioning chi-square for segregation data

One of the backcrosses made by Gregory et al. (1923) in *Primula sinensis* was between plants with flowers homozygous recessive for red stigmas and short styles slsl, and plants with flowers heterozygous for green stigmas and long styles SL/sl. If the two genes are independently assorting, we expect to find four kinds of progeny segregating in a 1: 1: 1: 1 testcross ratio. If the genes are linked, we expect to find the parental classes significantly more frequent than the recombinant classes. In this particular instance, the following data were obtained:

Green stigmas, long styles	459	Parental type
Red stigmas, short styles	489	Parental type
Green stigmas, short styles	321	Recombinant type
Red stigmas, long styles	330	Recombinant type

The parental types are more frequent than the recombinant types, but are these differences significant? We use the chi-square test, with 3 degrees of freedom, for the goodness of fit with a 1: 1: 1: 1 ratio.

$$\chi^2 = \Sigma(o_i)2 / e_i - n \qquad e_i = 1599 / 4 \quad = 399.75$$
$$\chi^2 = [459^2 + 489^2 + 321^2 + 330^2] / 399.75 - 1599$$
$$\chi^2 = 56.3921 \quad df. = 3, \qquad P < 0.001$$

As the probability of the data fitting the 1: 1: 1: 1 ratio is much less that one in a 1000, we reject the hypothesis of independent assortment. The likely alternative is that the two genes are linked. It would be unwise always to make this assumption. Sometimes the deviation from the expected ratio is caused by the reduced viability of some genotypes, or reduced viability is a contributing factor. In order to investigate these possibilities, we partition the χ^2 into three orthogonal contrasts. In each case we determine what is the probability of the contrast, or difference between pairs of data, not being significantly different from zero.

$$
\begin{array}{ccc}
\text{Ratio} & \text{1 Green stigma:} & \text{1 Red stigma} \\
& (459 + 321) & (489 + 330) \\
& 780 & 819
\end{array}
$$

$\chi_2^2 = [780\text{-}819]^2 / 1599$
$\chi^2 = 0.9512 \qquad \text{df.} = 1, \qquad P = 0.5 - 0.1$

A good fit, the chi-square value is not significantly different from zero, so there is no evidence for differential viability between plants with green or red stigmas.

$$
\begin{array}{ccc}
\text{Ratio} & \text{1 Long style:} & \text{1 Short style} \\
& (459 + 330) & (489 + 321) \\
& 789 & 810
\end{array}
$$

$\chi_2^2 = [789\text{-}810]^2 / 1599$
$\chi^2 = 0.2758 \qquad \text{df.} = 1, \qquad P = 0.9 - 0.5$

An excellent fit, the chi-square value is not significantly different from zero, so again there is no evidence for differential viability between plants.

$$
\begin{array}{ccc}
\text{Ratio} & \text{1 Parental:} & \text{1 Recombinant} \\
& (459 + 489) & (330 + 321) \\
& 948 & 651
\end{array}
$$

$\chi^2 = [948\text{-}651]2 / 1599$
$\chi^2 = 55.1651 \qquad \text{df.} = 1, \qquad P < 0.001$

An extremely poor fit with a 1: 1 ratio; the recombinants are much less frequent than the parents clearly indicating linkage.

The partitioning of the original chi-square value into the three orthogonal contrasts shows that the deviation from the 1: 1: 1: 1 ratio is almost entirely attributable to the linkage of the two genes, and not to any significant differences in viability between dominant and recessive traits.

The chi-square values may be summarized as follows:

Green stigmas: red stigmas	0.9512
Long styles: short styles	0.2758
Parental: recombinant	55.1651
Total χ^2 value	56.3921

The summation of the chi-square values for the three orthogonal contrasts, each with one degree of freedom, agrees exactly with the original chi-square value with three degrees of freedom.

This set of three orthogonal contrasts is useful because each answers a well-defined question, and because of their additivity. Occasionally, other contrasts might be of interest. For example, if the two recombinant frequencies were rather different from each other, one could test whether this was significant. It would not be an orthogonal contrast, and so would not carry as much weight as the others. Moreover, if such a difference were related to viability, this would probably have been revealed by the orthogonal contrasts. Hence, such a non-orthogonal contrast is rarely worthwhile.

As the chi-square value for linkage is highly significant, we can measure the map distance between the two genes; the map distance is the recombination frequency expressed as a percentage. The expectation in the absence of linkage is in the ratio of 1 parental: 1 recombinant, so the recombination frequency is calculated without any further adjustment as the frequency of recombinants divided by the total sample size.

$$\% \text{ Recombination} = [651/1599] \times 100 = 40.71$$
Therefore Map Distance between S/s and L/l = 40.71%

It is often useful to calculate the confidence intervals around each measure of linkage. We first calculate the standard deviation s, and then multiply this by t as read from the table of Student's t at infinite degrees of freedom and 95% probability level. With a sample size of 120 or less, the value of t increases. Likewise, one may choose other values of the probability level. At the 99% probability level t = 2.576, which has the effect of enlarging the confidence interval. The standard deviation is the square root of the product of the recombination frequency by the non-recombinant frequency and divided by the sample size.

$s = \sqrt{[p \times q / n]} = \sqrt{[.4071 \times .5929 / 1599]} = 0.012286 \quad p = 0.4071, q = 1 - p$

$t = 1.960$ at 95% probability. Therefore $ts = 1.96 \times 0.012286 = 0.024080$

Confidence Intervals $= p \pm ts = .4071 \pm 0.0241 = 0.3830 - 0.4312$

Therefore the 95% confidence intervals = 38.30 – 43.12 for recombination between the genes S/s and L/l, and the 99% confidence intervals = 37.54 – 43.87.

The three point test cross

Altenburg (1916) studied three linked characters in *Primula sinensis*, each with an alternate pair of traits:

L/l	Flowers with long versus short style.
R/r	Magenta flowers versus red flowers.
S/s	Flowers with green versus red stigma.

He constructed an F1 by crossing the three homozygous dominant traits with their homozygous recessives. The F1 triple heterozygote was then backcrossed to the triple homozygous recessive.

P1 and P2 → LL,RR,SS × ll,rr,ss → F1 Ll,Rr,Ss × ll,rr,ss → Backcross generation

There were eight kinds of progeny in the backcross generation. These were scored and sorted into four pairs of progeny according to their similar frequencies, and the phenotypes and genotypes included alongside (Table 16.15). The most frequent pair is the two phenotypes corresponding to the two parental types. The next most frequent pair has the same first two genes, but the third gene has exchanged places; this is a recombinant event. The third pair has the same last two genes, but the first gene has exchanged places; this is another recombinant event. The last pair, with the fewest progeny, has the middle gene switched around; this is a double recombination event. In this case the genes are placed in their correct order, with R/r in the middle. When the order is unknown beforehand, there are three possible orders – with R/r in the middle, with L/l in the middle, and with S/s in the middle. The correct order is the one that gives the double recombination in the middle.

Phenotypes	Genotypes	Frequency	Total Progeny	Recombination Frequency %
Short, magenta, green	Ll,Rr,Ss	1063		
Long, red, red	ll,rr,ss	1032	2095	56.87 Parental
Short, magenta, red	Ll,Rr,ss	634		
Long, red, green	ll,rr,Ss	526	1160	31.49 Single
Long, magenta, green	ll,Rr,Ss	180		
Short, red, red	Ll,rr,ss	156	336	9.12 Single
Short, red, green	Ll,rr,Ss	39		
Long, magenta, red	ll,Rr,ss	54	93	2.32 Double

Table 16.15. The recombination frequency between three linked genes is determined with the three-point test cross between a triple heterozygote and a triple homozygous recessive in *Primula sinensis*.

The frequency of recombination is calculated as the total number of progeny divided by the total scored. There are two regions and therefore two recombination frequencies. The double recombination is the result of both singles occurring at the same time. The frequency of the doubles is then added to both singles. Each frequency is recorded as a percentage, which is the map distance between two linked genes (Table 16.15).

Recombination region 1 = [1160/3684] × 100 = 31.49%

Recombination region 2 = [336/3684] × 100 = 9.12%

Double recombination = [93/3684] × 100 = 2.52%

Map distance R/r – S/s = 31.49 + 2.52 = 34.01 map units

Map distance L/l – R/r = 9.12 + 2.52 = 11.64 map units.

One would expect the frequency of the double recombination to occur with the combined frequency of the two singles. In practise the actual frequency is somewhat less owing to the interference between the two. In order to assess this interference the coefficient of coincidence is the ratio of the observed to the expected double recombination event. A figure approaching one shows that there is little interference, whereas a much smaller figure shows that the interference is greater. This gives rise to the coefficient of interference, which is one minus the coefficient of coincidence. This multiplied by one hundred gives the percentage interference.

Expected double recombination = region 1 × region 2 = .3401 × .1164 = 0.0396

Coefficient of coincidence = Observed / Expected = 0.0252/0.0396 = 0.6364.

Coefficient of interference = [1 – 0.6364] × 100 = 36.36% interference.

In the present experiment there is a large number of progeny and so we have obtained all eight of the expected classes. With a much smaller progeny size, or with a much higher interference, the classes may be reduced to six. The double recombinant pair will therefore be reduced to zero.

The mechanism of recombination is too complicated to discuss here. We will just say that it occurs at the four-strand stage during the first prophase division of meiosis. It is the result of a crossover between two of the four strands derived from the two parents. Each of the four stands are divided between the four cells that are the product of meiosis, so that two cells receive the crossovers and two cells receive the non-crossovers, that is the parental strands.

The 95% confidence intervals for the greater map distance is calculated as follows:

$s = \sqrt{[p \times q / n]} = \sqrt{[(.3401 \times .6599)/3684]} = 0.007805$ $p = 0.3401, q = 1 - p$

$t = 1.960$ at 95% probability. Therefore ts = 1.96 × 0.007805 = 0.0153

Confidence Intervals = p ± ts = .3401 ± 0.0153 = 0.3248 - 0.3554

Therefore the 95% confidence intervals = 32.48 to 35.54 for recombination between the genes R/r and S/s. The 95% confidence intervals between the genes L/l and R/r is calculated as 10.60 –12.68.

Linkage with incomplete dominance

The two characters, leaf shape and leaf surface, both express traits in which the heterozygotes are intermediate between the alternative homozygotes. The grasped trait also affects the flower turning it into a sterile monstrous form called shishi. A common form of shishi simply carries the rolled leaf; whereas the grasped leaf found in this shishi strain is attributed to the additional effect of a punched factor, u (Miyake and Imai 1926). The behaviour of the F2 segregating families indicated that the F1s are derived from coupling crosses HSi/hsi:

Leaf shape:		Leaf surface:		Flower type:
Normal	HH	Punched	SiSi	Single
Rounded	Hh	Rolled	Sisi	Single
Heart	hh	Grasped	sisi	"Shishi"

F1	Rounded, rolled, single		Hh,Sisi	156
F2	1 Normal, punched, single		HH,SiSi	806
	2 Normal, rolled, single		HH,Sisi	19
	2 Rounded, punched, single		Hh,SiSi	18
	4 Rounded, rolled, single		Hh,Sisi	1698
	1 Normal, grasped, shishi		HH,sisi	0
	2 Rounded, grasped, shishi		Hh,sisi	8
	1 Heart, punched, single		hh,SiSi	0
	2 Heart, rolled, single		hh,Sisi	29
	1 Heart, grasped, shishi		hh,sisi	557

Genotype	Progeny	Parental gametes		Recombinant gametes		Total gametes
		H,Si	**h,si**	**H,si**	**h,Si**	
HH,SiSi	806	1612	-	-	-	1612
HH,Sisi	19	19	-	19	-	38
Hh,SiSi	18	18	-	-	18	36
Hh,Sisi	1698	1698	1698	-	-	3396
HH,sisi	0	-	-	-	-	0
Hh,sisi	8	-	8	8	-	16
hh,SiSi	0	-	-	-	-	0
hh,Sisi	29	-	29	-	29	58
hh,sisi	557	-	1114	-	-	1114
Total	**3135**	**3347**	**2849**	**27**	**47**	**6270**

Table 16.16. Partitioning the data for the nine genotypes according to whether they originated from no recombinant gametes, or one recombinant, or the other recombinant gamete.

As there are two genes segregating, nine F2 phenotypes are expected from the combination (1HH: 2Hh: 1hh)(1SiSi: 2Sisi: 1sisi). With independent assortment, the overall expected ratio is 1: 2: 2: 4: 1: 2: 1: 2: 1. The data clearly show that this expectation was not realised. Instead, the parental phenotypes were much more frequent than the recombinant ones indicative of the linkage of the two genes. As the heterozygotes can be separated from the homozygotes, it is possible to score all the parental gametes and all the recombinant gametes (Table 16.16) and so determine the recombination frequency directly.

Recombination frequency   =   Number recombinant gametes / Total gametes

                             = $[74 / 6270] \times 100$

                             =   1.18%

Evidently, the two genes are closely linked on the same chromosome.

We may partition the data to reveal the two chi-square values, ignoring the third:

    H: h   = 2549:586; $\chi^2 = 66.5264$, df. = 1, P < 0.001

    Si: si   = 2570: 565; $\chi^2 = 81.4062$, df. = 1, P < 0.001

In both cases, the homozygous recessive trait is less frequent than expected. Hence, there is a significant deficit of the parental double homozygous recessive hh,sisi, which means that the frequency of the parental gametes is underestimated and so the linkage value is higher than it ought to be. Only to a limited extent would this be counteracted by the deficit of the smaller recombinant classes containing hh or sisi. The 95% confidence intervals may be calculated as follows:

    $s = \sqrt{[p \times q]/n} = \sqrt{[0.0118 \times 0.9882]/3135}$ t = 1.96 at 95%.

    ts = 0.0000675

    p = 0.0118 ± 0.0000675

    p = 0.011867 – 0.011732

    95% Confidence intervals = 1.17 and 1.19 between genes H/h and Si/si.

Linkage with unequal segregation

Gregory *et al.* (1923) identified two genes in *Primula sinensis* for flat leaves versus crimped leaves F/f, and sinensis-shaped corolla and calyx with many teeth, usually 10, versus stellata or star-shaped corolla, and calyx 5-toothed Ch/ch. The authors backcrossed the double heterozygote in coupling with the double homozygous recessive, and they selfed the double heterozygote in coupling and in repulsion. The table 16.17 shows the chi-square values for the goodness of fit of the segregation with the expected mono- and dihybrid ratios, and the estimates for the recombination frequency between the two genes.

Crosses	Ratios tested	F Ch	F ch	f Ch	f ch	Total	χ^2 values	P	Rec. %
FCh/fch × fch/fch	-	762	86	72	606	1526	991.588	-	10.35
Coupling	1F-: 1 ff		-	848	678	1526	18.938	<0.001	-
	1Ch-: 1chch		-	834	692	1526	13.214	<0.001	-
	Linkage		-	1368	158	1526	959.436	<0.001	-
FCh/fch	-	1404	90	83	383	1960	1066.199	-	9.41
Coupling	3F-: 1ff		-	1494	1398	5880	1.567	0.5-0.1	-
	3Ch-: 1chch		-	1487	1419	5880	0.786	0.5-0.1	-
	Linkage		-	4851	519	17640	1063.845	<0.001	-
Fch/fCh	-	514	268	187	6	975	91.483	-	16.92
Repulsion	3F-: 1ff		-	782	579	2925	14.089	<0.001	-
	3Ch-: 1chch		-	701	822	2925	5.006	0.05-.01	-
	Linkage		-	568	1365	8775	72.388	<0.001	-

The six model equations for calculating the χ^2 values are:

1F-: 1ff	$\chi^2 = [(a+b)-(c+d)]^2 / n$	3F-: 1ff	$\chi^2 = [(a+b)-3(c+d)]^2 / 3n$
1Ch: 1chch	$\chi^2 = [(a+c)-(b+d)]^2 / n$	3Ch-: 1chch	$\chi^2 = [(a+c)-3(b+d)]^2 / 3n$
Linkage	$\chi^2 = [(a+d)-(b+c)]^2 / n$	Linkage	$\chi^2 = [(a+9d)-3(b+c)]^2 / 9n$

Table 16.17. For each cross or self, the top row shows the numbers of progeny obtained, the total, the chi-square value for the goodness of fit assuming independent assortment, and the percent recombination between the two genes. The second, third and fourth rows show the segregation, with numbers adapted for the chi-square models, for one gene at a time, or for the parental versus recombinant classes, followed by the corresponding chi-squared values and the probability of fit on the assumption of equal frequencies.

The backcross, and the selfing with the parental genes in repulsion, both exhibit significant to highly significant deficits of the homozygous recessive classes, yet the alternative self with the parental genes in coupling exhibits only a non-significant deficiency. As the deficiency of the recessives is not large, and not consistent, and as the morphological traits seem to be ones unlikely to affect the viability of developing embryos or germinating seedlings, it is probable that there has been some misclassification. This can easily happen if there is not always a sharp division separating the traits. For example, if occasionally the calyx teeth are less than ten but more than five, to which trait does the flower belong? Or, likewise, is it not likely that there is overlap between slightly crimped flat leaves and slightly flat crimped leaves? In these circumstances it is often the homozygous recessive that shows up as a deficiency owing to the recessive trait failing to be fully expressed, or becoming expressed late in development, after the counting is over. The observer is reluctant to recognize the recessive trait unless it is well expressed, and so takes the side of caution towards the normal.

Once the deficiency is identified through the goodness of fit test, the experimenter ought to look again at the criteria for scoring the alternative traits to see if any adjustment is appropriate. If there is no room for adjustment, then perhaps the problem really is one of total failure of expression by some individuals, or an unknown problem that requires investigating.

The selfing of the double heterozygote in repulsion means that the double homozygous recessive, that is the smallest class with independent assortment, is extra small because it occurs only as a recombinant. The result is almost a hundred-fold difference in frequency between the two recombinant classes. When the genes are in coupling the two recombinant classes are expected to be the same frequency and almost are. Hence, the coupling self is preferable to the repulsion self, and, indeed, the recombination frequency from the coupling self turns out to be much closer to the value determined from the backcross progeny.

In the case of the backcross, the linkage is simply the ratio of the recombinants to the total. In the case of the two selfs the estimation of the linkage is determined by using two formulae. P = ad/bc where a and d are the parental frequencies and b and c the recombinant frequencies, or the other way round. The value of P is then entered into an equation for p2, from which the value of p, or 1-p is calculated. This value, when multiplied by 100, is the map distance. These formulae are the result of a fairly complicated set of algebra, and so I will do no more than demonstrate their use here.
In the case of the coupling self:

$a = 1404, b = 90, c = 83, d = 383$ and $n = 1960$

$P = ad / bc \quad = 1404 \times 383 / 90 \times 83 = 71.98554$

$p^2 = [(P + 1) - \{\sqrt{(3P + 1)}\}] / (P - 1)$

$p^2 = [(71.98554 + 1) - \{\sqrt{(3 \times 71.98554 + 1)}\}] / (71.98554 - 1)$

$p^2 = 58.25609 / 70.98554$
$p^2 = 0.82067$

$p = 0.9059$ and $1 - p = 0.0941$

Hence Recombination Frequency = 9.41%

In the case of the repulsion self:

$a = 514, b = 268, c = 187, d = 6$ and $n = 975$

$P = ad / bc \quad = 515 \times 6 / 268 \times 187 \quad = 0.06154$

$$p^2 = [(P + 1) - \{\sqrt{(3P + 1)}\}] / (P - 1)$$

$$p^2 = [(1.06154) - \sqrt{1.18461}] / 0.93846$$

$$p^2 = -0.02688 / -0.93846$$

$$p^2 = 0.02864$$

$$p = 0.1692 \text{ and } 1 - p = 0.8308$$
Hence Recombination Frequency = 16.92%

We will not calculate the confidence intervals in this case, although you may do so.

Mapping the position of linked genes

The characters and alternative traits of a linkage group in *Primula sinensis* (Gregory *et al.*, 1923) are:

Style length - Gene S/s: S short style as opposed to s long style.

Petal colour - Gene B/b: B blue as opposed to b not blue but slaty. In the blues [really more purple] the anthocyanin of the petal epidermis appears diffuse through the cells, whereas in most of the cells of the epidermis of slaty flowers the anthocyanin pigment is concentrated in a spot. The authors refer to the difference as the anthocyanin being in solution versus being in a solid form.

Stigma colour - Gene G/g: G green as opposed to g red stigma.

Stem and leaf back colour -Gene L/l: L light reddish stems and leaf backs as opposed to l parts a deep claret red

These genes all belonged to the same linkage group. They were assembled together in six pairs, and as far as possible, the heterozygote in coupling and in repulsion was selfed and backcrossed to the homozygous recessive. The map distance between the two genes was estimated for all the four crosses, and for all the six pairs. I took the average of the four estimates as the map distance, and used the average recombination frequencies to create a map of the four linked genes along the corresponding chromosome on which they are located. This is achieved through a few logical steps:
1.   The gene pair with the highest recombination frequency has its two genes the furthest apart; this pair is S-L, 38.56%.
2.   The two other genes are in between.
3.   The nearest to S is B as S-B is 9.33%
4.   The nearest to L is G as G-L is 2.57%
5.   Hence, the order is S/s – B/b – G/g – L/l.
6.   The linear map may be written out as approximately:

S/s-------9.33-------B/b----------------------------35.48------------------------G/g-2.57-L/l
B/b-----------------------------37.16----------------------------------L/l
S/s--37.98---G/g
S/s--38.56---------------------------------------L/l

The estimates of map distance are approximately additive and they fit the proposed order well without contradiction.

One estimate that was not used was for selfing Gl/gL because there was no data for the frequency of the double homozygote. This illustrates the disadvantage of selfing over the backcrosses. After selfing, with independent assortment, the double homozygous recessive would have an expected frequency of 1/16, but if, owing to linkage, it is expected in the recombinant class, then its frequency will be much lower. In this case, the two genes were closely linked and this rare trait never appeared, although a few might have been expected in such a large progeny.

References

Altenburg, E. (1916).
Linkage in *Primula sinensis.* Genetics 1, 354-66.

Almouslem, A.B. (1988).
Qualitative and quantitative genetical studies in *Pelargoniums* x *Hortorum*
Bailey. Ph.D. Thesis, University of Swansea, Wales.

Baur, E. (1907).
Untersuchungen über die Erblichkeitsverhältnisse einer nur in Bastardform
lebenfähigen Sippe von *Antirrhinum majus.* Ber. Dtsch. Bot. Ges. 25, 442-454.

Gregory, R.P., de Winton, D. and Bateson, W. (1923). Genetics of *Primula
sinensis.* Journal of Genetics 13, 219-253.

Grieve, P. (1869).
A history of ornamental-foliage pelargoniums. 2nd ed. The British Pelargonium
and Geranium Society 1977.

Mather, K. (1951).
The measurement of linkage in heredity. Methuen and Co. Ltd., London.

Miyake, K. and Imai, Y. (1926).
On a monstrous flower and its linkage in the Japanese morning glory. Journal
of Genetics 16, 63-76.

Miyake, K. and Imai, Y. (1934).
Chlorophyll deficiencies in the Japanese morning glory. Journal of the College
of Agriculture, Tokyo 13, 27-44.

Punnett, R.C. (1932).
Further studies of linkage in the sweet pea. Journal of Genetics 24, 97-112.

Sedcole, J.R. (1977).
Number of plants necessary to recover a trait. Crop Science 17, 667-668.

Stern, C. and Sherwood, E.R. Eds. (1966).
The origin of genetics. A Mendel source book. W .H. Freeman and Company,
San Francisco and London.

Index to Authors

Index to Cultivars

Subject Index